T5-AXE-285
extending mathematical power

Everyday Number Sense

Mental Math and Visual Models

TEACHER BOOK

 TERC

Donna Curry, Mary Jane Schmitt, Tricia Donovan, Myriam Steinback, and Martha Merson

Mc Graw Hill Education

Bothell, WA • Chicago, IL • Columbus, OH • New York, NY

TERC
2067 Massachusetts Avenue
Cambridge, Massachusetts 02140

Cover
Science Photo Library — IAN HOOTON/Getty Images

***EMPower* Authors**
Donna Curry, Mary Jane Schmitt, Tricia Donovan, Myriam Steinback, and Martha Merson

Contributors and Reviewers
Melissa Braaten, Beverly Cory, Marlene Kliman, Donna Parrish, Cathy Suarez, and Susan Swinford

Technical Team
Production and Design Team: Valerie Martin, and Sherry Soares

Photos/Images
Valerie Martin, Martha Merson, Myriam Steinback, and Rini Templeton

EMPower™ was developed at TERC in Cambridge, Massachusetts. This material is based upon work supported by the National Science Foundation under award number ESI-9911410 and by the Education Research Collaborative at TERC. Any opinions, findings, and conclusions or recommendations expressed in this publication are those of the authors and do not necessarily reflect the views of the National Science Foundation.

TERC is a not-for-profit education research and development organization dedicated to improving mathematics, science, and technology teaching and learning.

All other registered trademarks and trademarks in this book are the property of their respective holders.

http://empower.terc.edu

Printed in the United States of America

2 3 4 5 6 7 8 9 LHS 23 22 21 20 19 18 17

ISBN 978-0-07-672144-3
MHID 0-07-672144-2

© 2016 TERC. All rights reserved.

Limited Reproduction Permission
The publisher grants the teacher who purchases *Everyday Number Sense: Mental Math and Visual Models* and who adopts the student version of the book for his or her class the right to reproduce material for use in his or her own classroom, as many as 25 copies annually. Similarly, a learning center that purchases a copy or copies of the *EMPower* teacher books has the right to make as many as 25 copies of the student version of the book annually. Unauthorized copying of *Everyday Number Sense: Mental Math and Visual Models* constitutes copyright infringement and is a violation of federal law. Reproduction or distribution in any form or by any means of the *EMPower* teacher books without prior written consent of McGraw-Hill Education is strictly prohibited.

Send all inquiries to:

McGraw-Hill Education
8787 Orion Place
Columbus, Ohio 43240

Dedication

We dedicate this revision to Mary Jane Schmitt and Tricia Donovan, outstanding educators, with gratitude for their vision and commitment.

Acknowledgments

Many friends and family members supported teachers' and *EMPower*'s efforts. Thank you all who made timely and substantive contributions to the first and second editions. We appreciate the encouragement and advice from our many colleagues. In addition, we thank the National Science Foundation, MetLife Foundation, and Fund for Public Schools, as well as TERC and the Education Research Collaborative at TERC for its support.

We are indebted to every adult student who participated in the piloting of *EMPower*. *EMPower* authors thank the teachers who were part of original pilot testing in AZ, ME, MA, NJ, NY, PA, RI, and TN in 2001-2004, as well as NYC teachers who participated in the pilot of the revisions in 2012-2013. The honest feedback and suggestions for what worked and what did not work were invaluable.

Contents

Getting Started with *EMPower Plus*

Background on *EMPower*

Extending Mathematical Power (EMPower) was the first math series that integrated mathematics education reform for educators, adult learners, and out-of-school youth. *EMPower* was designed especially for those students who return for a second chance at education by enrolling in remedial and adult basic education programs, high school equivalency programs, and developmental programs at community colleges. However, the curriculum is appropriate for a variety of other settings as well, such as high schools, workplaces, and parent and paraprofessional education programs. *EMPower* builds interest and competency in mathematical problem solving and communication. The series serves as a model for a cohesive mathematics curriculum that offers content consistent with research and standards, including but not limited to the College and Career Readiness Standards and the Common Core Standards for Mathematical Practice. The curriculum fosters a pedagogy of learning for understanding; it embeds teacher support and is transformative yet realistic for multi-level classrooms.

New in *EMPower Plus*

This edition includes three fully updated books for students and teachers. Although *EMPower* users will recognize many of the activities from the first edition, we have also added new lessons and several opportunities for students to examine notation and algorithms (or methods) for solving problems with the four basic operations. In response to the increased mathematical rigor of the College and Career Readiness Standards for Adult Education and the new high school equivalency tests, the three updated *EMPower Plus* books—*Everyday Number Sense*, *Using Benchmarks*, and *Split It Up*—help students build a foundation of number and operation sense for algebraic thinking. The work of cognitive psychologists and mathematics education researchers is starting to show what adult math educators have long suspected: attention to conceptual understanding with opportunities to notice and talk about patterns and strategies increases students' flexibility with numbers and problem solving. In these updated *EMPower Plus* books, users will notice more opportunities for students to predict the results of operations and to see the connections between operations and their inverses (multiplying undoes division; square roots undo the effect of squaring). The excitement of learning math is in finding the meaning behind problem-solving steps that once seemed random. Recognizing mathematical properties at work has multiple benefits. Properties like the commutative property of addition and multiplication or the multiplicative identity make it possible for students to solve problems with understanding and with fewer errors. Recognizing the properties can lead students to value the strategies they use on a daily basis. Through *EMPower Plus* lessons, educators who have never thought much about operations, mental math, visual models, or benchmark numbers have opportunities to identify and encourage sturdy and reliable methods.

The Point of *EMPower*

EMPower consistently challenges students and teachers to extend their ideas of what it means to do math. The goal of *EMPower* is to help learners manage the mathematical demands of life by connecting situations and problems to mathematical principles. Situations include not only managing finance and commerce, but also interpreting news stories, applying health information, and facilitating family learning. *EMPower* is meant to be foundational, targeted to adults and young adults who test in the 4th-7th grade range and who often have both areas of strength and gaps in their understanding. *EMPower* lessons introduce important mathematical ideas. They invite learners to identify patterns and to make connections. The lessons offer opportunities for students to explain their thinking and to justify their reasoning. Rather than focus on extensive, rote practice, *EMPower*'s main focus is to build learners' conceptual understanding, a critical platform from which they can explore more advanced concepts needed for future educational and career success.

In the following sections, you will read how *EMPower* shifts the culture of the classroom and how the lessons embody the College and Career Readiness Standards as well as the Common Core Standards for Mathematical Practice. The introduction provides an overview of the *EMPower* series as well as Frequently Asked Questions and Answers on both facilitation and the math content focus (number and operation sense with fractions) of the lessons within this book.

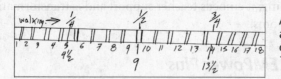

A student uses benchmark fractions as labels. The sketch shows evidence of reasoning about division of an 18-block walk into equal parts.

A Focus on Pedagogy and the Culture of the Classroom

Mathematics is meaningful within a social context. While mathematical truths are universal, the meaning and relevance of numbers change according to the setting and culture. *EMPower* classrooms become places where math ideas, strategies, hunches, and solutions are shared and discussed. The *EMPower* materials ask students to:

Work collaboratively with others on open-ended investigations;

Share strategies orally and in writing;

Justify answers in multiple ways;

Enter into and solve problems in various ways.

Key features of curriculum activities provide teachers with:

Clear mathematical goals related to essential mathematics;

Contexts that are engaging, challenging, and useful for adolescents and adults;

Opportunities to strengthen learners' mathematical language and communication skills through productive struggle; and

Puzzling dilemmas and problems that spark students' interest and motivate them to seek solutions.

These features make *EMPower* a resource for preparing students for tests of high school equivalency and community college coursework.

Students and teachers who experienced a traditional math education may find the expectations of *EMPower* take some getting used to. The chart highlights the contrast.

A rule-based approach emphasizes	*EMPower*'s approach emphasizes
Computation, usually calculations by hand, with paper and pencil.	Mental math, visual models, and estimation using benchmark numbers, supported by a calculator when the numbers get unwieldy.
Procedures, often with limited attention to understanding; students practice following a given set of steps and then applying them to problems.	Conceptual understanding, sense-making, building on what students know, identifying patterns, and solving problems based on real or realistic contexts, all strengthened by connecting words, symbols, and visual models.
Completing the computational procedure correctly as evidence of understanding.	Being able to view the problem in a variety of ways, being able to communicate what the problem means or provide an example, and knowing what to expect as a sensible answer.
Applying the "correct" computational procedure to a problem.	Explaining and justifying their thinking, using strategies that illustrate flexibility and creativity when solving problems.

The Mathematical Practices and *EMPower*

EMPower's math background sections and unit introductions reference research in both K-12 and adult learning. In implementing *EMPower* lessons, teachers will foster the eight practices described in the Common Core and Career and College Readiness Standards for Mathematical Practice:

1. Make sense of problems and persevere in solving them.
2. Reason abstractly and quantitatively.
3. Construct viable arguments and critique the reasoning of others.
4. Model with mathematics.
5. Use appropriate tools strategically.
6. Attend to precision.
7. Look for and make use of structure.
8. Look for and express regularity in repeated reasoning.

The Mathematical Practices describe independent, proficient mathematical thinkers. The essence of the practices is visible and audible in *EMPower* classes as students:

- generalize, to explain their reasoning;
- use tools such as number lines, arrays, fraction strips, pattern blocks, and calculators;
- work with estimates, rounding, and place value;
- use the structure of numbers (e.g., breaking numbers into 10's and 1's), to solve problems;
- examine algorithms, generalize from patterns to form rules, and justify their thinking;
- make observations about notation and operations that help them solve problems more efficiently.

Overview of EMPower Units
Features of the Teacher Book

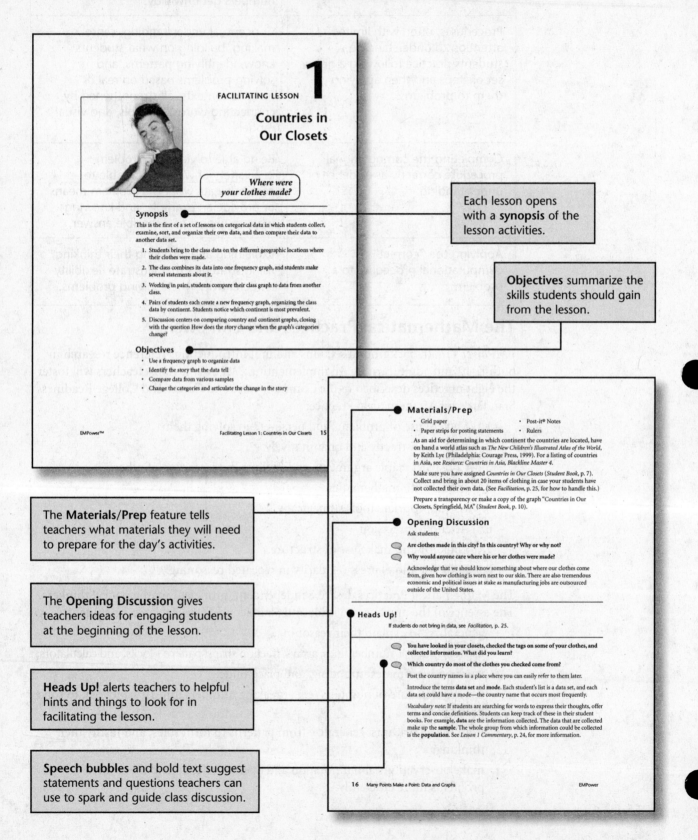

FACILITATING LESSON 1

Countries in Our Closets

Where were your clothes made?

Synopsis

This is the first of a set of lessons on categorical data in which students collect, examine, sort, and organize their own data, and then compare their data to another data set.

1. Students bring to the class data on the different geographic locations where their clothes were made.

2. The class combines its data into one frequency graph, and students make several statements about it.

3. Working in pairs, students compare their class graph to data from another class.

4. Pairs of students each create a new frequency graph, organizing the class data by continent. Students notice which continent is most prevalent.

5. Discussion centers on comparing country and continent graphs, closing with the question How does the story change when the graph's categories change?

Objectives

- Use a frequency graph to organize data
- Identify the story that the data tell
- Compare data from various samples
- Change the categories and articulate the change in the story

EMPower™   Facilitating Lesson 1: Countries in Our Closets   15

> Each lesson opens with a **synopsis** of the lesson activities.

> **Objectives** summarize the skills students should gain from the lesson.

Materials/Prep

- Grid paper
- Paper strips for posting statements
- Post-it® Notes
- Rulers

As an aid for determining in which continent the countries are located, have on hand a world atlas such as *The New Children's Illustrated Atlas of the World*, by Keith Lye (Philadelphia: Courage Press, 1999). For a listing of countries in Asia, see *Resource: Countries in Asia, Blackline Master 4*.

Make sure you have assigned *Countries in Our Closets* (*Student Book*, p. 7). Collect and bring in about 20 items of clothing in case your students have not collected their own data. (See *Facilitation*, p. 25, for how to handle this.)

Prepare a transparency or make a copy of the graph "Countries in Our Closets, Springfield, MA" (*Student Book*, p. 10).

Opening Discussion

Ask students:

💬 **Are clothes made in this city? In this country? Why or why not?**

💬 **Why would anyone care where his or her clothes were made?**

Acknowledge that we should know something about where our clothes come from, given how clothing is worn next to our skin. There are also tremendous economic and political issues at stake as manufacturing jobs are outsourced outside of the United States.

Heads Up!

If students do not bring in data, see *Facilitation*, p. 25.

💬 **You have looked in your closets, checked the tags on some of your clothes, and collected information. What did you learn?**

💬 **Which country do most of the clothes you checked come from?**

Post the country names in a place where you can easily refer to them later.

Introduce the terms **data set** and **mode**. Each student's list is a data set, and each data set could have a mode—the country name that occurs most frequently.

Vocabulary note: If students are searching for words to express their thoughts, offer terms and concise definitions. Students can keep track of these in their student books. For example, **data** are the information collected. The data that are collected make up the **sample**. The whole group from which information could be collected is the **population**. See *Lesson 1 Commentary*, p. 24, for more information.

16   Many Points Make a Point: Data and Graphs   EMPower

> The **Materials/Prep** feature tells teachers what materials they will need to prepare for the day's activities.

> The **Opening Discussion** gives teachers ideas for engaging students at the beginning of the lesson.

> **Heads Up!** alerts teachers to helpful hints and things to look for in facilitating the lesson.

> **Speech bubbles** and bold text suggest statements and questions teachers can use to spark and guide class discussion.

A **Summary Discussion** guides the conclusion of the lesson.

Practice, Extension, and **Test Practice** sections list and describe choices for additional work.

Math Inspections are an opportunity to examine a notation or structure, to name a pattern, or to test an idea.

Looking Closely draws the teacher's attention to the objectives and suggests teaching strategies.

Math Background helps teachers deepen their understanding of mathematical concepts.

Summary Discussion

Finish the lesson by posing the following questions. (Students may not have ready answers at this point, but the questions will be a thread through the rest of the lessons.)

What stories can be told from this set of data (or what questions can be asked and answered)?

How does organizing the information into different categories impact how the data may be interpreted?

Who would be curious about what the people in this class eat?

Direct student to the *Reflections* questions (*Student Book*, p. 145).

DATA

- Collect
- Sort
- Describe
- Graph
- Predict

Practice

Take a Sample, p. 24
For practice choosing a representative sample.

Thirsty and *Ouch!,* pp. 26 and 28
For practice organizing information and making statements.

Extension

Friends and Family Drink Too, p. 30

Data Collection, p. 31
Students begin recording what they eat for a project they will do in a later lesson. For now, they just write down all the foods they eat throughout the day.

Test Practice

Test Practice, p. 32

Looking Closely

Observe whether students are able to

Organize data into consistent categories

Do students group similar foods together? Make sure students are moving index cards around and that they are writing down the category names. If students seem stuck, have them ask you specific questions.

If you see foods categorized incorrectly, ask a question such as "Do all group members agree with the categories?" Encourage students to think, question, and defend their reasoning. If students use overlapping categories such as "cereal" and "grain," present an example close to their own experience. Say, for instance, "It is

LESSON 1 COMMENTARY

Rationale

The lesson takes students through the first steps of displaying data: collecting and organizing the information. As you work through this lesson, you and your students will notice that each time you categorize and recategorize the data set, you tell a different story.

Math Background

Data are information. This information may be numerical—e.g., salaries, test scores, heights, age, weight—as well as categorical—e.g., countries, foods we eat, types of product defects.

Most data are reported using statistics based on fractions and percents—one-third of pregnant mothers, half of native plants, etc. Commonly used, or benchmark, fractions and percents are often invoked to influence others to make decisions. When the headlines shout, "One-half of all pregnant women …," readers tend to form opinions based on the data. What readers often neglect to consider is the size of the sample, where the data were collected, and how the data were organized.

The media generally report data that are based on a sample. It is rare for any group to have the time or resources to ask every person in the population to contribute information. The idea of sampling is to study a part in order to gain information about the whole. The sample—its size and characteristics—influences the data and the conclusions of the study.

A representative sample by definition includes representation across the population being surveyed. For example, a representative sample of the community would include individuals from across town, not just one neighborhood. Likewise, a representative sample across America would include individuals from many different states and regions, not just one or two. The size of the sample is important when inferences are made. For example, 30 samples could be sufficient for a population of several hundreds. The deciding factor for determining sample size is how confident you want to be about the inference.

It is not the concern of this unit to determine appropriate sample size, but it is important to note that statisticians use formulas derived from repeated surveys to decide sample size. Regardless, small samples are used in many studies. Factors such as availability of subjects or scarcity of time or financial resources might lead researchers to use a small sample and to base policy or claims upon the outcome.

Throughout this unit, it will be important to help students begin to think critically about data, whether the data are grouped into categories of information or into graphs. They will need to understand that a random sample will often yield different results from one that is not random. This topic resurfaces in *Lesson 2*.

> The authors offer ideas for **Making the Lesson Easier** and **Making the Lesson Harder**.

Context

Some students may know about *maquiladoras* in Mexican border towns, where women make clothes for very little money and with no benefits or environmental Occupational Safety and Health Administration (OSHA) workplace protections. CorpWatch (www.corpwatch.org) is one source for information on *maquiladoras*.

Facilitation

If students do not bring in data, or if their sample is too small, skip the second part of the *Opening Discussion*. Have available a pile of 20 clothing articles with labels. First, ask students to predict where the clothes were made. Post the list of their guesses. Note that it will be hard for them to answer this question unless they organize the information on the labels. Then divide up the 20 articles of clothing. Have students write the name of the country for each piece of clothing on a Post-it Note, one country name per note. Ask: "Where are most of our clothes made?" Then continue with the activity.

Making the Lesson Easier

Frequency graphs lend themselves to comparisons among categories. If students have little fluency stating comparisons, you may choose only to compare size, using terms like "greater," "fewest," or "less than." For students who are encountering data formally for the first time, the notion that collapsing data yields different stories may be difficult. Treat this lightly in the activity, and revisit such questions after students have more experience categorizing and recategorizing data in the homework and in *Lesson 2*.

Making the Lesson Harder

If your students can handle benchmark fractions and percents, get them to look critically at the data, including the source and sample size. You might ask:

💬 If we asked another class what countries are in their closets, what do you think would happen to the categories? What if we asked the entire community?

💬 How do you think your data would compare to data from another class of adult students in another community?

If students struggle with the idea of sample, you might try this: Have them each write their favorite color on a Post-it Note. If you have a small class, ask them to write the color on two Post-it Notes. Place all of the notes in a container. Have someone randomly (eyes closed) choose a few notes from the container and place them across a line to form a frequency graph. Ask the students how they think this sample compares to the actual total number of colors on notes in the container. You can have them do another frequency graph to compare the sample to the actual total.

LESSON 1 IN ACTION

Alice articulates the mathematical principle behind compressed data.

> I asked, "How did the change in categories affect what we noticed about the data?"
>
> Alice answered, "Well, we keep losing information."
>
> "How so?"
>
> Patiently, Alice explained that when we started our work, every bit of data was visible. She added that we had lost details initially recorded. "At first, we knew every country in every person's closet and how many pieces of clothing came from that country. Then we combined the data, and we lost track of who had which countries. Then we did it by continent, and we lost track of all the countries."
>
> Alice's realization quickly gained agreement from the rest of the class. After all, just the previous week a classmate had noted, "When you change the amount of data you look at, you find different things."
>
> Sonia added her comment with increased conviction: "It is like politics. Politicians use a graph and tell you this is true, but you look at the graph, and it does not tell you everything."
>
> *Tricia Donovan*
> *Pioneer Valley Adult Education Center, Northampton, MA*

> In **Lesson in Action**, *EMPower* teachers share their classroom experiences.

Overview of EMPower Units
Features of the Student Book

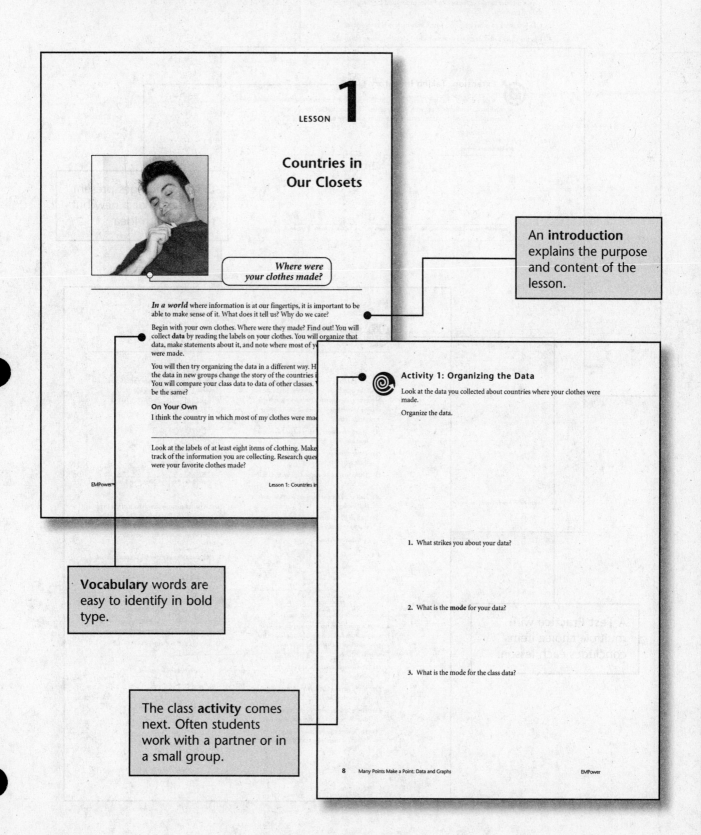

LESSON **1**

Countries in Our Closets

Where were your clothes made?

In a world where information is at our fingertips, it is important to be able to make sense of it. What does it tell us? Why do we care?

Begin with your own clothes. Where were they made? Find out! You will collect **data** by reading the labels on your clothes. You will organize that data, make statements about it, and note where most of y[...] were made.

You will then try organizing the data in a different way. H[...] the data in new groups change the story of the countries i[...] You will compare your class data to data of other classes. [...] be the same?

On Your Own
I think the country in which most of my clothes were ma[...]

Look at the labels of at least eight items of clothing. Make [...] track of the information you are collecting. Research ques[...] were your favorite clothes made?

EMPower™   Lesson 1: Countries i[...]

An **introduction** explains the purpose and content of the lesson.

Vocabulary words are easy to identify in bold type.

The class **activity** comes next. Often students work with a partner or in a small group.

Activity 1: Organizing the Data

Look at the data you collected about countries where your clothes were made.

Organize the data.

1. What strikes you about your data?

2. What is the **mode** for your data?

3. What is the mode for the class data?

8   Many Points Make a Point: Data and Graphs   EMPower

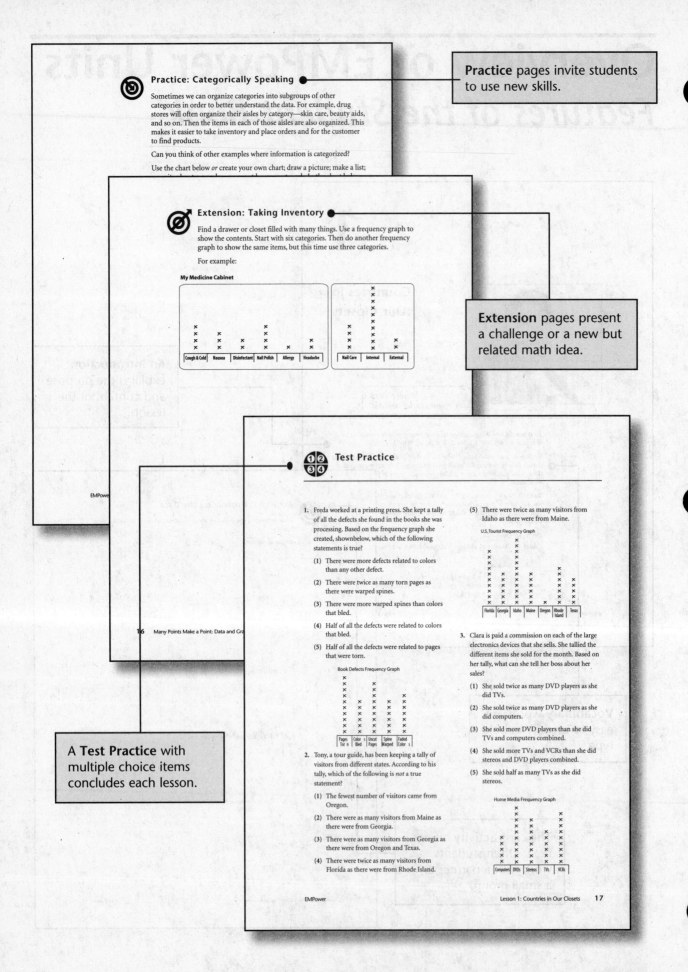

Practice pages invite students to use new skills.

Practice: Categorically Speaking

Sometimes we can organize categories into subgroups of other categories in order to better understand the data. For example, drug stores will often organize their aisles by category—skin care, beauty aids, and so on. Then the items in each of those aisles are also organized. This makes it easier to take inventory and place orders and for the customer to find products.

Can you think of other examples where information is categorized?

Use the chart below *or* create your own chart; draw a picture; make a list;

EMPower

Extension: Taking Inventory

Find a drawer or closet filled with many things. Use a frequency graph to show the contents. Start with six categories. Then do another frequency graph to show the same items, but this time use three categories.

For example:

My Medicine Cabinet

Cough & Cold	Nausea	Disinfectant	Nail Polish	Allergy	Headache

Nail Care	Internal	External

Extension pages present a challenge or a new but related math idea.

A Test Practice with multiple choice items concludes each lesson.

Test Practice

1. Freda worked at a printing press. She kept a tally of all the defects she found in the books she was processing. Based on the frequency graph she created, shownbelow, which of the following statements is true?

   (1) There were more defects related to colors than any other defect.

   (2) There were twice as many torn pages as there were warped spines.

   (3) There were more warped spines than colors that bled.

   (4) Half of all the defects were related to colors that bled.

   (5) Half of all the defects were related to pages that were torn.

   Book Defects Frequency Graph

Pages Tor n	Color s Bled	Uncut Pages	Spine Warped	Faded Color s

2. Tony, a tour guide, has been keeping a tally of visitors from different states. According to his tally, which of the following is *not* a true statement?

   (1) The fewest number of visitors came from Oregon.

   (2) There were as many visitors from Maine as there were from Georgia.

   (3) There were as many visitors from Georgia as there were from Oregon and Texas.

   (4) There were twice as many visitors from Florida as there were from Rhode Island.

   (5) There were twice as many visitors from Idaho as there were from Maine.

   U.S. Tourist Frequency Graph

Florida	Georgia	Idaho	Maine	Oregon	Rhode Island	Texas

3. Clara is paid a commission on each of the large electronics devices that she sells. She tallied the different items she sold for the month. Based on her tally, what can she tell her boss about her sales?

   (1) She sold twice as many DVD players as she did TVs.

   (2) She sold twice as many DVD players as she did computers.

   (3) She sold more DVD players than she did TVs and computers combined.

   (4) She sold more TVs and VCRs than she did stereos and DVD players combined.

   (5) She sold half as many TVs as she did stereos.

   Home Media Frequency Graph

Computers	DVDs	Stereos	TVs	VCRs

16 Many Points Make a Point: Data and Gra

EMPower   Lesson 1: Countries in Our Closets   17

Changing the Culture

Teachers who use *EMPower* often face the challenge of transforming the prevailing culture of their math classrooms. *EMPower* teachers have offered these ideas for facilitating this transition:

- **Set the stage.** Engage students in drafting and agreeing to ground rules. Explicitly state that this is a space for everyone to learn. As one teacher said, "We are in this together. Share, even if you do not think you are right. Whatever you add will be helpful. It lets us see how you are looking at things."

- **Group your students.** Match students whose learning styles and background knowledge complement each other. Ask questions such as, "How did it go to work together? How did everyone contribute?

- **Allow wait time.** Studies have shown that teachers often wait less than three seconds before asking another question. Students need time to think.

- **Sit down.** Watch students and allow them to struggle a bit before interrupting to help them. Listen for logic and evidence of understanding. Follow the thread of students' thinking to uncover unconventional approaches. During discussions with the whole group, hand over the markers. Let students draw and make notes on the board.

- **Review written work.** Look beyond right and wrong answers to learn everything you can about what a student knows. Determine what seems solid and easy, as well as patterns in errors. If students are scattered, suggest ways they can organize their work. This is likely to lead to more efficient problem-solving and clearer communication.

Sequences and Connections

Any one of the *EMPower* books can stand alone, yet there are clear connections among them.

Some *EMPower* teachers alternate the books that focus on numbers with the books on geometry, data, and algebra. Particularly in mixed classes with some students at National Reporting System (NRS) Beginning Basic level or with older learners with minimal formal education, *Over, Around, and Within: Geometry and Measurement* works well as a starting point. The activities are concrete. Lessons introduce concepts like perimeter, area, and volume of two-dimensional shapes while keeping the computation focused on small whole numbers. Ratio and proportion unfold with scaffolding to insure that students can reason about rates and proportional relationships.

For teachers and students determined to become powerful problem-solvers with algebraic reasoning, begin with whole numbers and follow with fractions, decimals, and percents; ratio and proportion; and algebra. For this sequence, *Everyday Number Sense: Mental Math and Visual Models* is a starting point to develop whole number mental math skills and operation sense. *Using Benchmarks: Fractions and Operations* grounds students in part-whole relationships and operation sense with fractions. And *Split It Up: More Fractions, Decimals, and Percents* continues to expand students' repertoire with part-whole ratios in fractions, decimals, and percents. *Seeking Patterns, Building Rules: Algebraic Thinking* builds upon the tools and relationships used in *Keeping Things in Proportion: Reasoning with Ratios*. The work with fractions and decimals is useful in describing approximate relationships between data sets in *Many Points Make a Point: Data and Graphs*.

Book Descriptions

Over, Around, and Within: Geometry and Measurement
Students explore the features and measures of basic shapes. Perimeter and area of two-dimensional shapes and volume of rectangular solids provide the focus.

EMPower Plus *Everyday Number Sense: Mental Math and Visual Models*
Students solve problems and compute with whole numbers using mental math strategies with benchmarks of 1, 10, 100, and 1,000. Number lines, arrays, and diagrams support their conceptual understanding of number relationships and the four operations.

EMPower Plus *Using Benchmarks: Fractions and Operations*
Students use the fractions 1/2, 1/4, 3/4, and 1/10; the decimals 0.1, 0.5, 0.25, and 0.75; and the percents 50%, 25%, 75%, and 100% as benchmarks to describe and compare all part-whole relationships. Students extend their understanding of the four operations with whole numbers to fractions. They decide upon reliable procedures for the four operations with fractions.

EMPower Plus *Split It Up: More Fractions, Decimals, and Percents*
Building on their command of common benchmark fractions, students build fluency finding tenths, 10%, and 1%. They work with decimals to the thousandths place. In analyzing the impact of the four operations on decimal numbers, they expand their repertoire and competence with part-whole relationships.

Seeking Patterns, Building Rules: Algebraic Thinking
Students use a variety of representational tools—diagrams, words, tables, graphs, and equations—to understand linear patterns and functions. They connect the rate of change with the slope of a line and compare linear with nonlinear relationships. They also gain facility with and comprehension of basic algebraic notation.

Keeping Things in Proportion: Reasoning with Ratios
Students use various tools—objects, diagrams, tables, graphs, and equations—to understand proportional and nonproportional relationships.

Many Points Make a Point: Data and Graphs
Students collect, organize, and represent data using frequency, bar, and circle graphs. They use line graphs to describe change over time. They use benchmark fractions and the measures of central tendency—mode, median, and mean—to describe data sets.

Frequently Asked Questions about Facilitation

Q: Is there an ideal level for the EMPower *series?*

A: The *EMPower Student Book* pages include situations and instructions that require some proficiency in written English. Students who test at NRS low and high intermediate levels or grades 4–7 grade level equivalency in mathematics are the best candidates for *EMPower*. Such students may have some familiarity with basic operations and know some number facts but might be unable to retain some procedures or perform them accurately and reliably—for instance, in the case of long division or of fraction operations. See the prerequisites for more information. Students who are higher level can benefit from *EMPower* if they have trouble getting started on a problem on their own, or if they are anxious and shut down when they see equations that look complicated. *EMPower* sets them up to be more independent, to test multiple solution paths, and to feel more confident in being flexible with numbers.

Q: *I have classes that are widely multi-level. Can this work?*

A: Many teachers see a wide range of levels within the group as an obstacle. Turn the range of levels to your advantage. Focus on students' representations (words, graphs, equations, sketches). This gives everyone the chance to see that answers emerge in several ways. Slowing down deepens understanding and avoids facile responses. Having calculators available can even the playing field. Implement the suggestions in *Making the Lesson Easier* and *Making the Lesson Harder* in the *Lesson Commentary* sections.

Q: *How do I deal with erratic attendance patterns?*

A: Uneven attendance can be disruptive. Students who miss class may feel disoriented; however, the lessons spiral back to the most important concepts. When the curriculum circles back, students will have a chance to revisit concepts and get a toehold.

Q: *What do I do if I run out of time, and there is no way to finish a lesson?*

A: Each activity is important, but reviewing it is equally important. It is better to cut the activity short so there is time to talk with students about what they noticed. Maximize the time by selecting a student or group whose work you feel will add to the class's understanding to report their findings. Be conscious of when you are letting an activity go on too long because the energy is high. Fun is good, but be sure important learning is happening. If you like to give time in class to reviewing homework, and you want to hear from everyone in discussions, you will run out of time. Schedule a catch-up session every three or four lessons.

Q: *How do I respond to comments such as "Can't we go back to the old way?"*

A: Change is unsettling, especially for students who are accustomed to math classes where their job is to work silently on a worksheet solving problems by following a straightforward example. Be clear about the reasons why you have chosen to de-emphasize some of the traditional ways of teaching in favor of this approach. Ultimately, you may need to agree to some changes to accommodate students' input. Meanwhile, reiterate for students what they have accomplished. When there is an "Aha!" moment, point it out.

Q: *My students don't have the time to go through a full curriculum. How can I convince students the value of using this program, even when their goal is to "get in and get out" as quickly as possible? Shouldn't I spend whatever time they have on a program designed to prepare them for college placement or high school equivalency tests?*

A: The National Center for Education and the Economy launched an intense study of the mathematics students need to be college and career ready. They determined that middle school math is vital for success in nine different programs offered at community colleges. They based their assessment on texts and exams from programs including nursing, accounting, and criminal justice. Though middle school math—fractions, decimals, percents, ratio, and proportion—are taught, they are not learned well. Teaching these concepts so that learners have a true foundation rather than a shaky, passing familiarity with a number of topics and procedures will enable students to meet their long-term goals.

Q: My own math background is not strong. Will I be able to teach this curriculum?

A: Yes! Most teachers tend to teach the way they were taught. Adopting a different stance requires support, and the more types of support, the better. This curriculum offers support in a few ways. The *Teacher Book* for each unit lists open-ended questions designed to keep the math on track. In the *Lesson Commentary* sections, the *Math Background* helps teachers deepen their understanding of a concept. In addition, the *Lesson in Action* sections provide examples of student work with comments that illuminate the underlying mathematics.

Expand your network of supportive colleagues by joining the Professional Learning Environment for EMPower. Post questions to the discussion board. Consider joining the Adult Numeracy Network, http://adultnumeracynetwork.org, and attend your regional NCTM conference. You can find face-to-face and on-line course offerings through the Adult Numeracy Center at TERC, http://adultnumeracy.terc.edu.

Everyday Number Sense
Introduction

Overview

EMPower strives to make the most of strategies adults bring to the table and makes explicit the understandings adults hold about numbers so that new ideas can be built on this foundation. Highly numerate adults use flexible, accurate, and efficient strategies for manipulating numbers and quantities in real-world problem-solving.

Learning the relationship between operations is key to building strong operation sense, and this unit emphasizes that by connecting addition and subtraction, addition and multiplication, subtraction and division, and multiplication and division. Order of operations and the commutative property (for addition and multiplication) are stressed.

The lessons encourage multiple ways to perform calculations. Students are encouraged to attend to the structure of number and equations. They visualize and decompose numbers (to see 14 as 10 + 4, for instance) and look for patterns in order to facilitate multi-digit operations and lay the groundwork for algebra (Star et al, 2015). The unit clues students into the simplicity and elegance of the base-10 number system (by applying the pattern of multiplying by powers of 10 or adding and subtracting by multiples of 10's and 1's, for instance). The emphasis is on observing and understanding patterns rather than learning short-cuts by rote.

Goals

By the end of this book, students should be able to

- Solve problems mentally with estimates and exact answers;

- Represent operations (×, ÷, +, −) using objects, pictures, arrays, number lines, and mathematical notation to explain and support reasoning;

- Choose operation(s) that match problem situations (e.g., know when to multiply and when to divide) and represent situations using mathematical notation;

- Explain and develop strategies for rounding, adjusting, and using benchmark numbers (10's and 100's) to solve problems;

- Demonstrate a command of basic number properties that form the basis for algebra;

- Use the scientific calculator.

Major Themes

The importance of students bringing their understanding into the classroom

Many students have invented or amassed a set of strategies that circumvent the procedures (the methods or algorithms) historically taught in school, yet may think those are not the school-approved or "real" ways. Observations of adults at work and in consumer situations uncover a surprising assortment of methods. It is important that students be encouraged to bring their own good math sense to bear in various situations for managing the mathematical demands of school and everyday life. Strategies and methods may include a mix of finger counting, mental math, estimation, calculator use, and paper-and-pencil methods. Such strategies can support insight into higher mathematics.

Developing number sense

To have sense about numbers means both to understand how numerical quantities are constructed and how they relate to one another.

Numerate adults can be flexible with numbers. They are able to break apart numbers in different ways. For example, they might see 36 as six more than 30, four less than 40, or more than half of 50. They use numbers such as 10, 100, and 1,000 as benchmarks with which to reason. Moreover, they can compare numbers to one another in an absolute way (how much more is 3,000 than 200?) as well as in a relative way (3,000 is how many times as great as 200?).

To support the development of this useable and supple appreciation of numbers, the lessons in the unit encourage students to look for patterns and generalizations. For example, mental math practices require students to generalize about patterns of multiplying by powers of 10 or to examine a multiplication table for patterns. Students are repeatedly asked to decompose numbers in various ways, such as in the activity "Number of the Day," in which they express the number 48 in as many ways as they can.

Recognizing operation sense

Most of the lessons in *Everyday Number Sense: Mental Math and Visual Models* are not about teaching or even reviewing the usual algorithms for the four operations. Rather, learners share and strengthen their own trustworthy strategies, which may include sequential doubling, halving, multiplying by multiples of 10, and using the commutative, associative, and distributive properties.

A common question in any math class is, "What should I do: add, subtract, multiply or divide?" This puzzle may stem from several factors: difficulty moving between text and print; a fragile understanding of place value and weak mental math or estimating skills (so that they are not sure of the magnitude of the answer); or lack of a true understanding of addition, subtraction, multiplication, and division. Learners need to "understand meanings of operations and how they relate to one another" (National Council of Teachers of Mathematics (NCTM), 2000, p. 34).

Deep understanding comes when a person has a sense for the various models for an operation. It is not enough, for example, to conceive of subtraction as taking away one amount from another. The "take away" model works for having an amount of money, spending some, and figuring out what you have left. However, nothing is taken away when you compare the amount of money you have in the bank with the amount you wish you had. A concept of subtraction as difference or comparison is helpful in such a case. Knowing how operations relate to one another gives a person a wider range of ways to approach solving a problem.

The importance of mental math

When a group of adults was asked to keep track of how they used math in a 24-hour period, most of the math (85%) they did was in their heads or by arriving at good estimations (Ginsburg, Manly, and Schmitt, 2006; Northcote & McIntosh, 1999). The researchers also found that estimates were sufficient for approximately 60% of all calculations, and exact answers necessary only 40% of the time.

In this unit, mental math is consistently a focus of practice and discussion. Students are encouraged to solve problems by grouping, visualizing, and decomposing numbers. Estimation is treated as a first step in problem-solving. Precision or accuracy can be as easily achieved by rounding and adjusting as it can by calculations on paper. Furthermore, students recognize that estimating or rounding (and adjusting) can help them determine a solution that is accurate enough for many circumstances. Estimations are particularly useful for gauging the accuracy of calculator-generated solutions, and it is vital for students to know how and when to use a calculator. A numerate person has all of these strategies at his or her disposal.

The importance of visual models

To ably communicate mathematically and to flexibly approach problems, adults need visualization and expressive skills. They need to "see" the problem, and they need to know how to express the problem and their solution processes not only in words and with notation, but with visual representations as well.

A recurring question for students here is "How do you know?" To answer this question and to make the workings of mathematics visible, we count on visual representations, such as number lines, arrays (where objects are arranged in rows and columns), diagrams, words, and equations. In this way, the lessons extend opportunities to develop multiple ways to solve problems. Only by perceiving more than one way can the problem-solver then choose the most efficient method.

Prerequisites

Students beginning this unit are assumed to have some math background, including the ability to:

- compare whole numbers, that is to recognize which of two numbers is larger

- distinguish even and odd numbers

- count by 2's, 5's, 10's

- label a number line, recognize sequence of numbers (e.g., 28 falls between 20 and 30, closer to 30)

- understand place value in whole numbers: ones, tens, hundreds, thousands, (e.g., the 3 in 1,386 represents 3 hundreds or 300, the 8 represents 8 tens or 80, etc.)

- double a number

- add, subtract, multiply, and divide with single digit numbers

- recognize at least one model for the meaning of operations, e.g., 3×8 is the same as $8 + 8 + 8$; 5 shirts at \$18 per shirt cannot be solved by adding $5 + 18$

- find half and halfway

Be aware that students will increase their competence in all of these areas. If they start out shaky, the lessons will take longer and some ideas will need to be pre-taught.

The Flow of the Unit

This unit contains

- Facilitation notes for *Opening the Unit* and *Closing the Unit*

- 14 lessons

There are fourteen lessons with embedded ongoing assessments as well as separate assessment sessions in the opening and closing sessions. Each lesson has one or more activities or investigations. Most include a math inspection. Math inspections call attention to the structure of mathematics, for example, inverse operations and the function of the equal sign. Encouraging students to identify and generalize patterns offers another way for them to master material. Instead of relying on memorizing certain procedures, students can re-construct their reasoning. Allowing time for opening and summary discussions (including time for student reflections), reviewing practice pages, and assuming a thoughtful pace, most lessons will span multiple class meetings. Students' literacy levels will also affect how long each lesson takes.

In *Lessons 1* and *2*, students

- Use mental math strategies to estimate totals;

- Calculate answers mentally by rounding and adjusting;

- Use mathematics notation to describe mental math process.

In *Lessons 3–7*, students

- Use the number line as a thinking tool;

- Locate numbers on the number line and determine the distance (difference) between the numbers. In *Lesson 5*, the number line is extended to include negative numbers;

- Record mental math and number line actions with equations;

- Examine different models of subtraction.

In *Lessons 8* and *9*, students

- Examine and identify the composition of numbers in terms of 10's, 100's and 1,000's;

- Use mathematical notation, including parentheses, to show how they solve a problem;

- Identify and use patterns when multiplying and dividing by 10, 100, and 1,000.

In *Lessons 10* and *11*, students

- Represent expressions using arrays and/or groups arranged to correspond with numbers and operations;

- Identify and find equivalent expressions;
- Record problem-solving strategies using equations and pictures.

In *Lessons 12–14*, students

- Focus on two models of division and making sense of remainders;
- Solve division problems involving splitting an amount into equal parts;
- Work with direct measurements and scale to find the number of groups of a given size in a total;
- Establish the relation between division and multiplication;
- Identify factors of numbers;
- Find remainders and express them using fractions, decimals, and whole numbers.

Assessments and Pacing

Initial and Final Assessments

Everyday Number Sense: Mental Math and Visual Models opens and closes with assessment. In both cases, the *Teacher Book* provides multiple ways to gauge what students know. Teachers may spread the tasks out over multiple days or delay the written tasks of the pre-assessment, particularly if students have just completed a school-administered placement test.

Ongoing Assessment

Much of the work students do will take place in small groups or pairs. This work must be evaluated to determine the extent to which students are comfortable with the main ideas and to diagnose difficulties, as well as to determine when to provide more challenging work. The *Looking Closely* section of each lesson focuses teachers' attention on the lesson's objectives and the corresponding observable behavior. Look for evidence of understanding and when a majority of students grasps concepts, move on. The material is spiraled so that students have multiple chances to take command of the material. As students gain skills, teachers will want to track their progress and communicate observations to them.

Frequently Asked Questions

Q: Why focus on meaning-making?

A: When meaning is lost, it is difficult to leverage the intuitive or to make common sense we can bring to problem solving, to recognize patterns, to generalize, and make connections.

The National Research Council summarizes the research on the development of children's mathematical proficiency. Their conclusion about teaching rational numbers is that instructional programs that use "approaches that build on students' intuitive understanding and use of objects or contexts that help students make sense of the operations offer more promise than rule-based approaches" (NRC, 2002).

Students' work in math class should involve connecting "symbolic representations and operations with physical or pictorial representations, as well as translating between various symbolic representations" (NRC, 2002).

In *EMPower* books, students are encouaraged to build upon what they know about operations and also to expand their repertoires. They justify reasoning with objects, diagrams, real-life situations, and their own number sense, which is grounded by the benchmark fractions, decimals, and percents.

Q: Why the emphasis on developing number sense through mental math?

A: There are at least three reasons for the emphasis on developing mental math skills with whole numbers, everyday fractions, decimals, and percents: (1) good mental math skills are a basis by which to judge the reasonableness of estimates; (2) good mental math skills are a basis by which to judge the reasonableness of error-prone rule-based calculations and electronic entries; and (3) mental math strategies accentuate the structure of the number system—an important foundation for measurement as well as algebraic problem solving.

Q: What role does operation sense play?

A: Many people confront math problems and find themselves uncertain which operation to use: addition, subtractraction, multiplication or division. Operation sense includes understanding the relationships among the operations, and the effect an operation will have on a pair of numbers (Huinker, 2002).

Operation sense also includes understanding the meanings and models of operations, the real-world situations they connect with, and the symbols that represent them. Limited understanding of operations with whole numbers often leads to confusion about which operation to use.

Q: Why does having different models for operations matter?

A: Different models cover different situations. Teachers and students become more conversant with different models and begin to anticipate how multiplication, addition, subtraction, and division affect whole numbers, fractions, and decimals.

Recognizing problem types and testing or matching them to different models ultimately gives a person a wider range of ways to approach any problem. It strengthens strategic competence. Consider, for example, this problem: "How much do 2 1/2 pounds of meat cost at $3.00/lb?" Some people see it in terms of addition ($3.00 + $3.00 + $1.50). Some see it in terms of multiplication (2.5 × $3.00). The relationship between multiplication and repeated addition is why both approaches work.

Researchers argue that a focus of the behavior of operations allows students to start in familiar territory of number and computation to progress to true engagement in the discipline of mathematics (Russell, Bastable, & Schifter, 2011).

Q: What happens if some people don't know their multiplication facts? Shouldn't those be taught first?

A: In most classes, teachers will detect a wide range of automaticity with one-digit addition, subtraction, and multiplication facts. Some students have never learned to recite their tables automatically. But adults who have never memorized 6 × 7 = 42, or even 6 + 7 = 13, buy things, earn money, and pay bills, and in doing so, do a lot of math. You do not have to know your multiplication tables to do some interesting math, but it certainly helps. Memorization is one strategy; however, for learners late to memorizing the tables, this is not always the most effective strategy. Noticing patterns and using known facts may be more advantageous.

Look for and assign *Mental Math Practice* sheets that focus on using patterns to get a good grasp on number facts. These practice pages are designed to build number fact facility.

Q: *Shouldn't calculators come later?*

A: Knowing how to use a calculator well is a basic skill. The calculator will even the playing field among class members. Students with strong conceptual skills will be able to punch in numbers, arrive at answers more quickly, and therefore participate more actively in class. The calculator should free students from some computation and allow for more attention to problem-solving and communicating their reasoning. For some students, using a calculator, particularly the scientific calculator, will be a first. Simply using a calculator is not a substitute for having strong mathematical thinking and computation skills; a calculator is a tool, and to use it well, good mental math and estimation skills are essential. To ensure the accuracy, efficiency, and flexibility that are the basis for strong number sense, the unit stresses mental math and visualization, supported by the calculator.

Q: *Why are the traditional algorithms de-emphasized?*

A: Numeracy requires making sense with numbers, and that good sense is often suspended when a person loses his or her inner compass and applies school-taught algorithms that were never quite understood.

So most of the lessons in *Everyday Number Sense* are directed toward learners sharing and strengthening their own trustworthy strategies with the goal that their methods or procedures are reliable and their calculations are accurate.

Q: *What is the hallmark of a numerate adult?*

A: One of the goals for adults revisiting arithmetic is to become computationally fluent with whole numbers. The notion of computational fluency, as discussed by Susan Jo Russell (1999), entails making error-free calculations (accuracy); approaching the calculation in a variety of ways (flexibility); and selecting a less tedious method from among the variety of possibilities (efficiency).

Competency in reaching these objectives is a process, and abilities to do so lie along a continuum. The more numerate a person is, the richer the host of skills and understandings he or she brings to problem-solving. Take, for instance, the simple "naked number" problem: 23×13. A numerate adult has the following options:

- Enter the numbers into a calculator and achieve precise results.

- Use a pencil-and-paper procedure to achieve precise results.

- Decompose the numbers mentally to achieve precise results ($23 \times 10 = 230 + 23 \times 3 = 230 + 69 = 299$).

- Round quantities to estimate an answer ($20 \times 10 = 200$; the answer must be greater than 200).

- Picture 23 on a number line with that interval repeated 13 times.

- Picture an array with 23 rows and 13 columns.

- Picture 13 groups of 23 objects.

- Envision a situation represented by the numbers, such as, "I have to make 13 payments of \$23 each, so that is a year plus one month or $23 \times 12 + 23$."

- Recognize the inverse situation; for example, in a division problem, take the total of 299 and divide it by 23 to yield an answer of 13.

Q: *Why focus on algorithms and properties of arithmetic?*

A: Though an algorithm is any method that works, some methods undermine students' mathematical understanding because they short-cut meaning-making opportunities. Some algorithms conflict with a method learned early on. The emphasis here is examining sturdy methods that can be connected to a visual representation, so the meaning is kept intact.

"How much do two and one-half pounds of meat cost at $3.00/lb?"

Some people see it in
terms of addition:
$3.00 + $3.00 + $1.50

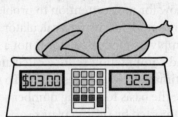

Some see it in terms
of multiplication:
2.5 × $3.00.

In the 21st century, the reasons for reviewing arithmetic have less to do with teaching computation (shopkeeper math) and more to do with laying the foundation for understanding the structure of mathematics. Too often students manipulate elements in an algebraic equation without understanding why some moves are allowable and others are not. They become increasingly frustrated when equations and models become more complex. They have no foundation in the properties (e.g., commutativity, associativity, distributivity, identity, and inverse relationships) on which to build. The point is for learners to understand why what they are doing works. They will need to apply the skills they are learning broadly as we help them prepare for college and careers.

Every Number Sense Materials List

Lesson	Recommended materials to have on hand	
Opening	Copies of *Blackline Masters 1-3* to display	*Initial Assessment Checklist* (*Appendices*, p. 200), 1 copy per student
	Markers Easel paper	*Initial Assessment* (*Appendices*, pp. 195-199), 1 copy per student
1	Copies of a catalog (e.g., Sears, LL Bean, JC Penney), 1 per student pair	Post-It™ Notes (a few for each student or student pair)
	Markers Easel paper	*Blackline Master 4* for *Activity 1*
2	Colored markers Easel paper	
3	A book with more than 1,000 pages such as a dictionary Colored markers Meter stick	Adding machine tape or receipt tape Post-it Notes Large U.S. wall map (optional)
4	Colored markers Easel paper Rulers Adding or receipt tape or strips of easel paper for number line	Assorted items that have number lines—a thermometer, rulers, yardsticks, meter sticks, pictures of gauges, etc. for the *Opening Discussion* Copies of *Blackline Master 5*, 1 per each group of 2-3 students
5	Markers Easel paper Number lines for reference	Manipulatives that make it possible to distinguish 10's and 1's, such as Base 10 Blocks or two color counting chips
6	Calculators 8.5" X 14" paper or strips made from easel paper Colored pencils (including red and black) or markers	Rulers Non-digital outdoor thermometer(s) Several large, blank number lines World map
7	Metric rulers or meter sticks *Blackline Master 6*, 1 per pair *Blackline Master 7*, optional resource for *More Practice*, 1 per student pair *Blackline Master 8*, 5 of the same cards from the full set per pair, cut apart *Blackline Master 9*, optional resource for *More Practice*	Two-color chips, or two colors of paper squares, several per student, or red and black markers along with paper squares Material for large number lines (masking tape, strips of paper, Post-it Notes) Play money for *Activity 2*

8	Calculators Play money or slips of paper marked in denominations of $1, $10, $100, and $1,000	*Blackline Master 9* and *10*, 1 copy per student pair
9	Scientific calculators, 1 per student; make sure they follow order of operations	*Blackline Master 12*, to display
10	Colored markers Easel paper *Blackline Master 13*, to display	Uniform objects for counting, such as paper clips, pennies or counting chips, enough so that each student or pair can have between 30 and 60
11	Grid paper Uniform objects for counting such as paper clips, chips, small plastic or wood tiles, or pennies, 25 per student	*Blackline Master 14*, several copies if students need a clean multiplication table
12	Calculators *Blackline Master 15*, 1 set per 4-6 students	Manipulatives, countable objects that are convenient to give to students in sets of 100, such as paper clips, pennies, tiles or cubes, playing cards, or Post-It Notes
13	Measuring containers: 2-oz. jigger (or 1/4-cup measure), 8-oz. paper or measuring cup, and a half-gallon jug or bottle full of some liquid String (approximately 5 yards per group of 3 students; 3 colors is ideal but not absolutely necessary)	Envelopes, 2 per every group of three students Tape An atlas or a variety of road maps or maps of the United States
14	Packs of gum (six pieces per pack) and Lifesavers™ or a similar type of candy that comes in rolls	Small manipulatives, such as paper clips or chips Rope, string, or wire (something that comes in lengths that can be divided)
Closing	Calculators Markers Easel paper Scrap paper (if doing optional *Activity 2*)	*Blackline Master 16* and *17*, 1 copy per student pair *Final Assessment* (*Appendices*, pp. 201-205), 1 copy per student *Final Assessment Checklist* (*Appendices* p. 206), 1 copy per student

Facilitating
Opening the Unit:
Everyday Numbers

> *Where is math in your everyday life?*

Synopsis

This session is designed to welcome students to the unit by asking them to reflect upon and share their uses of math in daily life. It is also an opportunity to assess how fluently and flexibly they work with whole numbers, including how they use **mental math** and connect **mathematical notation** with **visual models** and problem situations.

1. Students reflect upon occasions when they have used math recently, how they did the math (in their heads, with calculators, or with paper and pencils), and whether the answer was exact or an estimate.

2. The class works on "Number of the Day," writing numerical **expressions** for "360."

3. Students complete an *Initial Assessment* of mental math and ways they connect symbolic expressions, situations, and visual models.

Objectives

- Share personal experiences using math
- Demonstrate mental math skills
- Demonstrate fluency with visual models and symbolic expressions
- Demonstrate understanding of number properties such as the commutative and distributive properties

Materials/Prep

- Markers
- Easel paper
- *Initial Assessment* (*Appendices*, pp. 195–199), one copy per student
- *Initial Assessment Checklist* (*Appendices*, p. 200), one copy per student

Prepare to display or project the Number of the Day and *Blackline Masters 1–3: Mental Math Challenges*. The *Blackline Masters* are located in the *Appendices*.

Opening Discussion

Tell students that you are interested in gathering information about where and how they use math in their everyday lives. You also want to know how they do calculations and how they make connections between situations, math notation, and visual models like pictures, diagrams, and sketches. This is a day to show how many ways they know to work with numbers.

Activity 1: Where Is the Math in Your Life?

Refer students to *Activity 1: Where Is the Math in Your Life?* (*Student Book*, p. 2).

Say:

 How do you use math in your daily lives? Take a few minutes to think of all the times during the past month or so that you used numbers and did some math. Make a list, filling in the first column with at least five examples. Do not count the math you do in school. List the math you do in your everyday life.

After everyone has made his or her list, begin a class list on the board with students' reported uses. For each reported use, ask:

 How did you do the math? Did you do it in your head? Did you use a paper and pencil? Did you use a calculator?

 Did you find an exact answer or did you get an estimate?

The board might look something like this as you record offerings:

Where We Used Math	Head/Paper/ Calculator?	Exact/ Estimate
Figuring a 25% discount	H	Estimate
Figured out how many hours I worked	P	Exact
Saw if I had enough money for shopping	H	Estimate
Figured my bank balance	C	Exact
Paid bills	H	Exact
Made a cake	H	Exact

Ask students to mark each of their own entries in their books with "H," "P," or "C" and to note whether they got an exact or estimated answer.

Then ask:

 What do you notice about our list?

Students might say

> "We did a lot of the math in our heads."
> "We didn't always need the exact answer."
> "It's about money and time."

Conclude the opening by saying that this unit, *Everyday Number Sense: Mental Math and Visual Models,* is designed to give everyone a chance to work with numbers in a variety of ways. It should help everyone get better at using math in daily life, and that will include improving mental math skills. Sometimes students will estimate; sometimes they will be asked to calculate an exact answer.

 ## Activity 2: Number of the Day

Refer students to *Activity 2: Number of the Day* (*Student Book*, p. 3). Start with an example, saying,"if the Number of the Day is 12, think of two numbers that when added together give you 12, or two numbers that multiplied together give you 12." If nobody says anything, say 6 + 6 or 3 x 4. Explain that each of these is an **expression**. An expression is numbers, symbols, and operators (such as + and –) grouped together. They are another way to name or show the value of something.

Say:

 Today's number is 360. Let's see how many different numerical expressions you can write that have the answer 360.

When everyone is clear about the directions, allow about 10 minutes to generate expressions. Encourage students to use each of the four operations at least once, as well as any other **mathematical notation** they know. Notation is the numbers and symbols used to convey mathematical ideas about patterns, shape, quantities, and change. Examples include: numerals, exponents, and different ways to write division and multiplication.

Introduce the vocabulary section in the *Student Book*, p. 253.

 As we work together on math, you might come across some words that are new to you. Relax about that and recognize it as part of the process of exploring new ideas. As you encounter a new word or term, you can write it down on your vocabulary sheet (*Student Book*, p. 253) and look it up later.

Pull the class together and ask for suggestions, writing responses on the board or on easel paper where all can see them.

The responses might include

$100 + 100 + 100 + 60$	$400 - 40$
$3(100) + 60$	$4 \times 100 - 40$
$12(30)$	$40(10) - 40$
$36(10)$	$720 \div 2$

When several expressions have been offered, ask whether there are any that are questionable. You want to see whether students detect any incorrect expressions. It is not necessary to point them out yourself, but take note of any incorrect responses.

Save the work for comparison with the one created in the final lesson. You will want to see whether students become more flexible in the ways they break up numbers.

 # Activity 3: Initial Assessment

Distribute a copy of the *Initial Assessment* to everyone.

Explain that there are five tasks:

> Task 1: Mental Math Challenge
>
> Task 2: Picturing the Math
>
> Task 3: Four Operations
>
> Task 4: Is It Always True?
>
> Task 5: Four Problems

This is another place to let students know that they might see new vocabulary. Advise them not to panic. They can write the words down on *Student Book,* p. 253, and look them up or ask about them later.

Facilitating Task 1

Tell students:

 I am going to show and read some problems. Your challenge is to do the math in your head and then write down the answer. Do not use paper and pencils or calculators!

Starting with *Blackline Master 1: Mental Math Challenge,* display the problems. Reveal each problem one at a time and read it aloud. For each problem, allow a few moments for students to think about and write the answer. This is not a timed test, but move along at a good pace. You are trying to see how fluent students are with the numbers. Continue with the next two *Mental Math Challenges* (*Blackline Masters 2* and *3*).

Facilitating Tasks 2–5

Before students attempt the problems in Tasks 2–5, read through the problems together.

The *Initial Assessment* is a flexible tool. Some teachers proceed either to assign the problems students feel most confident about or to ask students to try them all. Establish a time limit, and collect the packets to analyze later. Students' work on the problems will provide a point of comparison for assessing progress with the *Final Assessment*.

See the *Initial Assessment Checklist* (*Appendices,* p. 200) for instructional decisions.

Summary Discussion

Ask students to comment on the assessment session by writing in the *Reflections* section (*Student Book,* p. 257). Students record definitions in *Vocabulary* (*Student Book,* p. 253).

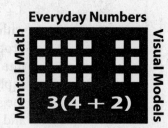

 What did you find out about your strong points?

 What challenged you?

Explain that the goal of this unit is to prepare students so they can solve any of these problems and others. They will use the methods they already know and explore new ways to look at problems.

Introduce the unit goals by reading together *Everyday Number Sense: Goals* (*Student Book,* p. 4). Ask students to add their own goals.

 ## Looking Closely

Observe whether students are able to

Share personal experiences using math

Do students come up with examples of their math use? Don't be surprised if an initial reaction is, "I never use math!" There are studies documenting adults' under-reporting of math in their lives. Probe if necessary. Ask students whether they shopped or paid bills, made any decisions with numbers, or figured out anything to do with time, such as how much longer it would be until the bus came or work was over. Did they ever have to measure anything?

Demonstrate mental math skills

To what extent are students able to handle the mental math challenge? Do they exhibit some automaticity with basic facts? Do they have strategies or tricks that they count on? The amounts in the *Mental Math Challenge* are presented in dollars and cents to make the numbers very real. If the *Mental Math Challenge* is a struggle, that is a good indication that the unit will be quite appropriate. As you complete each lesson, make sure to assign the *Mental Math Practices,* which are designed to develop skills at doing math in one's head.

Demonstrate fluency with visual models and symbolic expressions

Are students able to create or interpret visual models for the word problem? Are they able to use a number line to show their mathematical thinking? Notice who will need support to accomplish this type of task. Notice how complex the symbolic expressions are that students create for *Activity 2: Number of the Day* (*Student Book*, p. 3). The expressions each student writes will reveal which operations he or she is comfortable doing. As you proceed through the unit, challenge students to generate more complex expressions.

Demonstrate understanding of number properties

Are students able to recognize the equivalence of expressions such as 2 + 4 and 4 + 2? If they do, this indicates that students are not automatically calculating without looking at the relationships in the equation. They are taking in the problem as a whole and thinking about the relationships. Students might have an intuitive sense of number properties or they might have learned the properties explicitly. At this point, you want to see that students are paying attention to the structure of a problem (the order of numbers, how they are configured with and around the operations). If problem solvers identify a pattern or recognize equivalent expressions, or other similarities that can save them time calculating, this is positive. Extensive calculations open one up to errors. Prompt students to look for related problems, to extrapolate from one problem to the next or from one side of an equation to the other. These problem-solving moves can be save time *and* increase accuracy as well.

Rationale

By knowing students' strengths and weaknesses before starting a unit of study, you can make wise instructional decisions. You can help students recognize they need to learn some things and affirm what they already know.

Math Background

The mathematics in these assessment activities involves whole numbers (or dollars and cents) and the four basic operations. Students are asked to apply representational skills and use basic number facts. The decision to emphasize mental math is based on two premises. First, many of the calculations numerate adults perform in their everyday lives tend to be done with mental math, either to arrive at good estimations or to check the reasonableness of electronically computed results. For example, when paying for a $2.59 coffee and a 79¢ donut with a $10 bill, one might estimate the change to be a little more than $6 because, if one starts with $2.59, the 79¢ brings the total to somewhere just short of $3.50. The customer would expect to get six dollars and coins back from the cashier.

There is another reason why mental math is a focus of this unit on whole number and dollar and cents calculations. By stressing the need to be thoughtful about the many ways to break up or combine numbers, the underlying algebraic properties of arithmetic are brought to the fore. The distributive, commutative, and associative properties come into play as one reasons more precisely that
$$\$2.59 + \$0.79 = \$[(2.60 - 0.01) + (0.80 - 0.01)] = \$[(2.60 + 0.80) - (0.01 + 0.01)]$$
$$= \$3.40 - \$0.02. = \$3.38.$$

Context

The session is launched from students' everyday math use. As they report on meeting the mathematical demands of daily life, they share strategies.

Facilitation

Note who has mental math skills and visualization skills. Be aware that some students will require more time than others. Also, note who is relying on algorithms (applied correctly or incorrectly), as these students will be challenged in the unit to learn new ways of seeing problems. They may need to be reminded of the purposes of visualizing math problems: to represent them in a variety of ways that are helpful when problems are confusing and to solve them mentally when pencil and paper or calculator are not handy.

Making the Lesson Easier

Work through the problems as a class. If individuals struggle to participate, give students smaller numbers to see if they are able to mentally solve the problems.

Making the Lesson Harder

Try some larger or "messier" numbers in the various problems.

1

Close Enough with Mental Math

> *When do you do math in your head?*

Synopsis

Students draw upon their prior knowledge from everyday shopping experiences as they estimate the total cost of several items. Then they apply rounding to several situations, relying upon mental math to arrive at reasonable answers.

1. The class practices **rounding** when finding **approximate,** or ballpark totals.

2. Student pairs create wish lists of items for a community center area or for themselves, using mental math as they round to make estimates.

3. Student pairs review each other's work, and the class hears about strategies used.

4. The class summarizes strategies used to estimate totals.

Objectives

- Use mental math strategies to estimate totals
- Informally consider the role of commutativity in addition of whole numbers

Materials/Prep

- Copies of a catalog (e.g., Sears, LL Bean, JC Penney), one per student pair
- Markers
- Easel paper
- Post-it Notes (a few for each student or student pair)

Prepare to display or project *Blackline Master 4: Six Problems* for *Activity 1*, (e.g., on easel paper or a smart board). You will show only one problem at a time.

Opening Discussion

Get students thinking about a familiar situation involving some mental math estimation by posing the following scenario:

 A friend and I go out for a night on the town. We see a movie and have dinner. The movie costs $9.50 per ticket. Dinner for the two of us is $43.50. About how much will our evening out cost each of us?

Ask students to make their estimates in their heads without using pencils and paper.

When students share estimates, ask them how they arrived at their answers, recording what they say in writing on the board or on an overhead transparency. Expect some students to raise the idea of rounding numbers. If the following points do not come up, bring them up yourself:

- $9.50 is about $10.
- $43.50 is about $44; half of $44 is $22.
- $22 and $10 is $32.
- It will cost each of us about $32.

Or

- $9.50 is about $10.
- Two tickets are about $20.
- Dinner is almost $44.
- $44 and $20 is $64, and half of that is $32.

Stress estimation:

 Rather than getting exact answers, today we will make estimates that are close enough, or, as they say, "in the ballpark."

 ## Activity 1: About How Much?

Explain that for each of the six problems you will show, students will select the closest answer from among three choices (*Student Book*, p. 6).

Show the first problem in *Blackline Master 4: Six Problems*, giving students only a short time to find the closest answer; they should not have enough time to find the exact answer.

Ask for volunteers to explain how they found the closest answer. Record students' strategies.

If the following issues are not shared, raise them yourself:

- Round up each number.
- $1.95 is close to $2, and $3.95 is close to $4.
- $2 + $4 is $6.
- Add the dollars ($1 + $3 is $4), and then round the cents up to $1, and add another $2.

Repeat the process for the rest of the problems.

End the activity by saying:

 How do the ballpark estimates you made in these six problems relate to estimates you make in your daily life?

Ask for specific examples. Then proceed to *Activity 2*.

Activity 2: Wish List

Refer students to *Activity 2: Wish List* (*Student Book*, p. 7).

Review the directions:

- Using a catalog and working in pairs, students shop for items for a community center, themselves, or their families.
- They are responsible for buying at least five different items from the catalog.
- Each pair has a spending limit of $500 (or another limit that makes sense in relation to the prices in the catalog).
- Student pairs will report an estimate of the total cost of their items and then find the actual total cost.

Distribute the catalog.

Decide spending limits and assignments (e.g., library, garden, after-school program, themselves, their children's new rooms, etc.).

Spending limits will depend on the cost of the items in each catalog. To maintain students' focus on estimation and rounding, choose a spending limit that enables them to purchase five or more different items.

Emphasize mental math—although pairs should try to stay within their budget, they do not need to count every penny but should instead make close estimates.

Once student pairs have chosen and recorded their items, they write about how they made their estimates, using what you recorded in *Activity 1* as a model for the process.

As students finish up, they share their lists and strategies with another pair of students. If many students finish up at about the same time, distribute easel paper for posting lists. Students read each other's wish lists. They place Post-it Notes on one another's work with any questions or comments they have. Finally, they figure out if their partner pair was a bit over or under the spending limit—and by how much.

Ask each student pair:

 How did you keep track of all the prices to make sure you were close to your spending limit?

 Once you made your choices, how did you find out whether you were over or under your spending limit? Are you satisfied with your estimate?

Listen to students' descriptions and name strategies you recognize—rounding, grouping by 10's, grouping by 100's, etc.

Math Inspection: Agree or Disagree?

This is the first of many opportunities for students to begin to think critically about algorithms, or procedures. Students have a chance to think about their own procedures and then judge the reasoning of others.

Ask students to work in pairs to discuss each method used by the four friends. In the examples, Lianne, Peter, and Ana are demonstrating the commutative property of addition, which states that the sum is always the same regardless of the order of the addends. Chen's method relies on the associative property of addition, since he is grouping the addends while adding—a method that will also result in the same sum. Thus students explore the commutative and associative properties of addition. They see that order doesn't matter in addition and that numbers can be grouped in various ways.

As a class, have them share their responses to the question, "What is the best advice about the order in which numbers can be added?" Listen to and record several suggestions in students' exact words on the board, then seek a class consensus on the clearest way to say that the order in addition does not matter.

You might hear and record ideas such as:

> It is OK to order the numbers from smallest to largest, but this isn't a procedure that must be followed.
>
> When you have a list of numbers to add, you can take them two at a time.
>
> When you add, the order doesn't matter. You get the same answer either way.
>
> $a + b = b + a$

Summary Discussion

Ask students to share how they made their estimates in this lesson's activities:

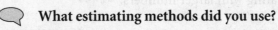 **What estimating methods did you use?**

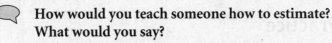 **How would you teach someone how to estimate? What would you say?**

Then summarize with some general statements that you have heard students make about estimates and mental math. For example:

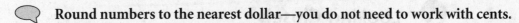 **Round numbers to the nearest dollar—you do not need to work with cents.**

 Tens are easy to work with, so it is helpful to combine numbers to make 10's or to round to a multiple of $10.

 It can be easy to find the answers in your head, but it helps to use a pencil and paper to keep track of the subtotals.

Refer students to *Reflections* (*Student Book*, p. 257), where they describe their favorite way of estimating a total for a number of items or explain what is difficult for them when trying to estimate a total. Remind students to write their definitions and examples of the vocabulary words in this lesson in *Vocabulary* (*Student Book*, p. 253).

Practice

Nearest Dollar, p. 9
For practice rounding to the nearest dollar.

Nearest 10, p. 10
For practice rounding to the nearest $10.

Closest Answer, p. 11
For practice estimating answers to addition and subtraction problems.

It's About ... , p. 12
For estimating totals by rounding and using mental math strategies.

Getting Close, p. 13
For estimating readings on gauges and scales (number lines).

Digital Read-out, p. 15
For converting estimated analog reading to digital reading and practice reading the number line.

Mental Math Practice

How Much Money Is in the Jar? p. 17
For practice finding friendly combinations that make $1.

Bigger Jars of Money, p. 18
Further practice finding friendly combinations that make $10.

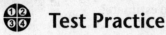

Extension

Big Bucks Estimates, p. 19
For work on estimating with larger numbers.

Test Practice

Test Practice, p. 20

Looking Closely

Observe whether students are able to

Use mental math strategies to estimate totals

Can students round money amounts to the nearest dollar? Students struggling with this would benefit from working on *Practice: Nearest Dollar* (*Student Book,* p. 9) and *Practice: Nearest 10* (*Student Book*, p. 10).

Ask students to write down all number combinations that equal 10 if they are not familiar with them. As they do this, encourage them to organize their number pairs so they can keep track of which they have already done and which are missing. *Mental Math Practices: How Money Much Is in the Jar?* (*Student Book,* p. 17) and *Bigger Jars of Money* (*Student Book*, p. 18) provide practice.

What strategies do students use for estimating? Help students find an approach that makes sense given the numbers they are working with. For instance, if prices end with $0.99, they should round up to the nearest dollar. If they are working with larger amounts, they might round to the nearest $10.

When choosing items from a catalog, are students able to get started and keep track of their selections? Help them organize with one of these first steps:

- Start with one item. If needed, round its price to the nearest dollar or $10. Then subtract the cost of the item from the spending limit. How much is left to spend?

- Start with two items. Round their prices and find out about how much they cost together. Are you past the spending limit yet? If so, exchange at least one item for a cheaper one. If not, choose another item.

Informally consider the role of commutativity in addition of whole numbers

Do students recognize that the order in which they add two numbers does not change the sum? If not, probe for that with a specific question: how are 23 + 17 and 17 + 32 related? If they do recognize that, then when adding for example, $17 + $95, they can start with $95, and add $17 to it, which they may do mentally by breaking the $17 into $5 + $12, to get $95 + 5 = $100, $100 + 12 =$112.

Rationale

Numeracy skills in day-to-day life often do not require exact answers. Those who can estimate using mental math to come up with an answer that is "close enough" or "in the ballpark" will feel more at ease in the grocery store, on job sites, taking tests, and in other such situations. Making ballpark estimates requires an understanding of rounding. For example, if something costs $1.29, do you round to $2 or to $1? By asking students to make estimates in their heads, you enable them to think through the numbers and develop a practical real-life skill that numerate adults need.

Math Background

Estimation skills are among the most important skills in arithmetic. The commutative and associative properties support mental math and estimation as they allow problem-solvers to change the order for addition and multiplication problems and to re-group quantities, for example, grouping numbers that add to 10 or other friendly numbers. Knowing when an answer is in the ballpark involves having a good idea of what the numbers are individually, combined, separated, or grouped. So, for example, seeing 29 as 1 less than 30 or 4 more than 25 is important for different reasons and different problems (e.g., $29 + 17 \approx 30 + 20$; $29 + 74 \approx 25 + 75$). By practicing estimation, students will gain flexibility in their thinking and problem solving, both of which are aspects critical to attaining fluency with computation.

Context

Money is often the everyday context in which people estimate. This lesson has several scenarios that enable students to think through and arrive at ballpark estimates in familiar situations involving money.

Facilitation

Making the Lesson Easier

To solidify the idea of ballpark estimates, pose problems such as these:

- The real cost is $19.74. Jamal estimates the cost to be $20. Is he in the ballpark? Karen estimates it will be about $15. Is she in the ballpark?

- The real cost is $1,100. Jamal estimates the cost to be $1,500. Is he in the ballpark? Karen estimates the total to be $1,000. Is she in the ballpark? When would Jamal's estimate be better to use than Karen's?

Explain that estimates are context dependent, for example, how high the actual cost is and how tight money is are factors.

For *Activity 2*, set a low spending limit and select catalogs with prices that are easy to round. Where appropriate, suggest students select no more than three or four items for their wish lists.

Mental Math Practices: How Much Money Is in the Jar? (Student Book, p. 17) and
Bigger Jars of Money (Student Book, p. 18) will help students with combinations,
and *Nearest Dollar (Student Book*, p. 9) will give them practice rounding.

Making the Lesson Harder

Set a high spending limit for each group and ask students to mentally calculate the
exact amount of their planned purchases. Tell them to explain in writing how they
know they are within the limit.

Introduce estimation with units of measure other than dollars and cents, such as
lengths in inches and feet or weights in pounds and ounces.

In this class, the teacher found a way to help her students think about why mental math may be useful.

Students continuously stated, "Why would I do this in my head? It's much easier if I write it down"; "This seems more complicated to me than just writing it down"; or, "I don't do it this way." Only two out of seven students said they used estimation when they shopped. Someone said, "I just throw the stuff in, and if I don't have enough money, then I don't." Another student said, "I just get what I need, and if I don't have enough money—oh well. 'I'm poor', I tell them, 'so just put these items back.'"

At the end of class, I shared a problem I had done in my head recently while driving: The Festival bought 75 bales of hay for $1.50 each. Five were destroyed during the event, leaving 70 bales. We planned on selling those to someone for 75¢ each. How much money would we get?

Students asked me why I didn't use a pencil and paper to figure out the answer. I said, "I really couldn't do that while I was driving."

"Well, why didn't you just wait?" one student wondered.

I replied, "Sometimes you get to thinking about a problem, and you want to solve it right then and there. That's what's so great about mental math: You can!"

Tricia Donovan
Pioneer Valley Adult Education Center, Northampton, MA

One student, who took and failed the math GED, has said more than ten times that this is worth the time and effort spent in class. Another student made the connection between the concept of "friendly numbers" and the *Math Inspection*. Students seem challenged but excited with the work.

Students found answers in a variety of ways and, as the lesson progressed, were more likely to use <u>mental</u> math over paper and pencil. Understanding increased from weak to solid, but few are strong at this point. [It's a] challenge encouraging students to "think outside of the box"—add in any order and to be comfortable with an estimate that doesn't follow "rounding rules."

Teacher
New York City

Mental Math in the Checkout Line

> **Do you have enough money to cover the cost of your purchases?**

Synopsis

Students first estimate grocery prices by rounding amounts and then adjust the estimated totals using mental math to find exact totals.

1. The class shares strategies for determining totals in a few scenarios you pose. You model a way to record the steps in reasoning.

2. Student pairs work on four problems and share strategies.

3. The class focuses on using notation to describe strategies.

4. The class considers the equal sign and its role in showing that two sides of an equation are equal.

Objectives

- Mentally compute by rounding and then adjusting
- Use mathematical notation to describe mental math process
- Make generalizations about equations

Materials/Prep

- Markers
- Easel paper

Prepare to display student work.

Heads Up!

Flexiblility with numbers builds a solid foundation for algebraic thinking. However, it is important to keep moving through the lessons to build operation sense as well as number sense. If students struggle, move on to *Lesson 3*. Circle back to the activities and practice pages in *Lesson 2* as students build their operation sense in later lessons.

Opening Discussion

Write the following items in no particular order on the board:

4 cans of tomato paste @ $0.49 each

1 box of spaghetti for $1.59

1 jar of sauce for $3.74

1 loaf of bread for $2.29

Set the scenario:

💬 **Suppose you were in a grocery store and had $10 to pay for seven items. Would you have enough money? Answer the question using mental math instead of a calculator or pencil and paper.**

Ask:

💬 **How did you come up with an estimate?**

💬 **How did you come up with an exact answer?**

If no one has an exact answer, present strategies for rounding and adjusting. (See *Lesson Commentary*, p. 28, for ways students might either estimate or mentally calculate an exact answer.)

Ask who uses mental math and how they do it.

💬 **Who does this sort of mental math at the store? Why?**

💬 **On what other occasions is mental math useful?**

For each example students give, inquire:

💬 **How close does your estimate need to be?**

Ask for specifics. For instance, if you have only $10 to spend at the grocery store, you need to make sure your purchases do not exceed that amount, so you might round all the items up to avoid going over your limit. On the other hand, if you want just a ballpark figure for the cost of gas for a trip, you might only need to know whether it would be *about* $10, $50, or $100.

Heads Up!

Students might insist that using paper and pencil and the traditional algorithm is easier. Remind them that mental math can be useful in real life as well as test situations and that with practice they will find it more efficient than using pencil and paper. Encourage them to look for opportunities to use mental math in the next week.

Discuss with the class when and why it would be useful to be able to figure out the cost of items using mental math. If the following ideas do not arise, raise them yourself:

- Knowing whether you are being charged correctly

- Figuring out whether you have enough money to buy something additional

- Knowing whether you are being given the correct amount of change

- Knowing whether your department at work can afford a purchase

Tell the class that they will work on honing their mental math skills so they will be able to figure out exact totals in their heads.

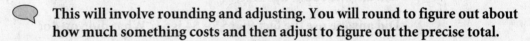 **This will involve rounding and adjusting. You will round to figure out about how much something costs and then adjust to figure out the precise total.**

Post the words "rounding" and "adjusting" with definitions and examples.

Activity 1: Math in Line

Allow time for students to practice rounding and adjusting amounts to find precise answers.

Refer students to *Activity 1: Math in Line* (*Student Book*, p. 22) and read the story in the first problem together:

On the way home from work yesterday, I stopped at the store and bought two items. One cost $1.89 and the other cost $3.15. While I was waiting at the checkout line, I reached into my wallet and realized I only had a five-dollar bill. Did I have enough money for my purchases? How do you know?

Do the math in your heads—no pencils and paper!

One possible response is: "$1.89 is a bit under $2, and $3.15 is a bit more than $3, so I might have enough, but I'm not sure and I need to check."

Record and display students' approaches, using a combination of words and numbers and following students' language:

- $1.89 is 11¢ less than $2 ($2 is rounded amount).

- $3.15 is 15¢ more than $3 ($3 is rounded amount).

- $2 + $3 = $5 (estimated total).
- That's 11¢ less than $2.00 and 15¢ more than $3.00, so that's 15¢ − 11¢ = 4¢ more than $5.00 (now adjusting).
- You did not have enough money! You are 4¢ short.

Summarize by recording:

$1.89 + $3.15 = ($2 + $3) + (15¢ − 11¢) = $5 + 4¢ = $5.04

Then ask:

💬 **If the cost of one of the items remained the same, what could the cost of the other item be so that $5 would be enough money to pay for both?**

Expect many possible responses. For example, $1.89 and $1.00, $1.89 and $3.11, $3.15 and $1.50, or $3.15 and $1.85. Ask a few students to explain their reasoning.

Next, mention a price just over a whole dollar amount; such prices often include tax (base prices often being just under a whole dollar amount). Ask :

💬 **Suppose you are buying two rolls of tape that cost $2.05 each, including tax, and you give the cashier a $5 bill. How much change would you get back?**

Share solutions for finding the change due. Prompt for a variety of responses, including counting up and subtracting from a dollar:

💬 **Did anyone count up? How?**

💬 **Did anyone use the fact that $5 − $4 is $1? What did you do?**

Pair students. Refer them to Problems 2–5, *Activity 1: Math in Line* (*Student Book*, pp. 22-23). Partners take turns explaining their strategies and answers, as you did on the posted newsprint.

Tell students:

💬 **Work with a partner. Solve the problems and compare your strategies.**

Remind students that they can record intermediate steps.

When everyone has completed the activity, call the group together to share various solution strategies. Prompt for those that involve rounding, adjusting, and breaking apart dollars and cents. If someone mentions multiplying (likely with Problem 4), connect it with addition strategies.

Heads Up!

Keep the focus on students' strategies.

As a final step, you might have a volunteer "cashier" use the calculator to confirm the other solution methods, but only if students are able to stay focused on the mental math.

Process problems with questions such as these:

💬 **To find the exact cost, did anyone round up? How did you adjust the price?**

💬 **Did anyone figure out the dollars and cents separately? How? When?**

💬 **To find how much change was owed, did anyone count up from the total cost? What did you do?**

💬 **How could you find the change by counting down from the total cash available? What would you do?**

💬 **Did anyone find the answer a different way? If so, how did you do it?**

⊛ Activity 2: Rounding and Adjusting

To prepare for the activity, check students' rounding skills. Write on the board:

$1.95 $0.39 $18.99 $5.10 $6.75

Ask volunteers, one at a time:

💬 **How would you round each of these amounts?**

Record answers and look for consensus on the rounded figures.

Ask:

💬 **By how much did you change each amount to round it?**

Probable answers respective to the amounts listed above are by 5¢, 1¢, 1¢, 10¢, and 25¢.

Pose one more question before starting the activity:

💬 **So, if you bought two (or three or four) items at $1.95, about how much would the total cost be?**

💬 **By how much would your estimate differ from the real cost?**

Students should see that if the estimate differs from the actual cost by 5¢ for one item, then it will differ by 10¢ for two items, 15¢ for three items, and so on.

Pair up students. Review directions for *Activity 2: Rounding and Adjusting* (*Student Book*, p. 25). To model the activity, do the first problem together as a class.

Allow about 15 minutes for students to work on these problems. Then ask:

💬 **How did you round the amounts?**

💬 **How did you figure out how much to adjust by to find the exact amounts?**

Strategies that involve separating dollars and cents to see the difference between the actual and the rounded amount and adding or multiplying that difference for the number of items should be shared.

Math Inspection: Make It True

This is an opportunity for students to think about the equal sign and its role in showing that two sides of an equation are equal. The activity positions the equal sign in places other than at the end of a series of operations. Typically the equal sign indicates: "Here comes the answer," such as in this problem

$$2 + 3 - 4 + 5 = \underline{\qquad}.$$

In these problems, the unfamiliar set-up is meant to trigger critical thinking about the value of the numbers. Students need to think critically about the value of the numbers in order to create a balanced equation.

Give students time to notice patterns and justify their reasoning.

Ask students to work individually or in pairs to determine the solution to each problem. Then, as a class, have volunteers share their reasoning about how they determined where to place addition signs and the equal sign. Be sure that students can articulate that the equal sign is a signal, not to "do" something, but rather to show that the values on each side of the equal sign are equivalent. This will build understanding of the mathematically important concept of *equality*.

 # Math Inspection: Check Both Sides of the Equal Sign

This inspection is designed to encourage students to understand why a simple mental math trick works when adding numbers. Addends can be adjusted to make it easier to add numbers in your head. For example, **79 + 7** is easier to compute if you think of it as **(79 + 1) + (7 − 1)**, or **80 + 6**. This works because by adding and subtracting the same amount you are only adding 0. This Inspection can highlight the additive inverse ($a + -a = 0$) and additive identity ($a + 0 = a$) principles.

In this math inspection, begin by asking students to articulate what the equal sign means (that the value on the left is equivalent to the value on the right). Ask them to verify that this is true for each of the three equations.

Now write **9 + 7** on the board.

Then write **10 + 6**.

Ask:

 Are these amounts equal? (Yes)

Then ask:

 How do you know?

People may have varied responses (e.g., because I know my facts—they are both 16; because 10 is 1 more than 9 and 6 is one less than 7). Record responses on the board for all to see.

For students who struggle to see the pattern, offer additional examples using small numbers and allow them to use manipulatives to see how the numbers change from one side of the equation to the other. For example, the first equation could be modeled using a pile of 9 chips and another pile of 7 chips. By shifting one chip from the second pile to the first, students can see why adding one to the first pile necessitates subtracting one from the second. Give struggling students more problems with small numbers to work out with chips until they are clear why the amount added and subtracted must be the same.

Focus on the idea that we haven't taken anything away nor added anything, just rearranged the numbers: 10 is 1 more than 9 and 6 is one less than 7, so we still have the same amount.

Ask pairs to work together on parts 1-4, using this idea. Bring the class together to share what they have noticed.

Then have them discuss their reasoning used in mentally determining each of the answers in part 5. Listen for a solid base for understanding what important concepts such as *identity* and *equality* mean.

Summary Discussion

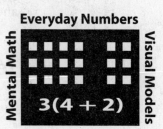

Ask students to share ideas on what they learned or practiced in this lesson that will be helpful in everyday life.

Then pose a final everyday shopping problem (involving nontaxable items) designed to engage everyone in reflecting on the strategies they learned in the lesson:

 You are on the way to a friend's house for dinner, and you want to buy some flowers. You have $10 to spend. You see some beautiful sunflowers for $2.97 each. How many could you buy and still have enough left over for a drink that costs 89¢?

As students share their strategies for finding the solution, make sure these ideas are raised:

- You can round $2.97 to $3 to help you find the answer.
- The total amount you can spend on flowers will be about $9, because you need about $1 for the drink.
- You will be able to buy three flowers because they will cost a little under $9, leaving enough money for the drink.

Invite students to take a few moments to capture their thoughts about this lesson in *Reflections* (*Student Book*, p. 258), and in *Vocabulary* (*Student Book*, p. 253)

Practice

Using Math Notation, p. 29
For practice using parentheses and other appropriate mathematical notation.

More Adjustments, p. 30
For practice rounding and adjusting using money.

Closer to $50 or $60? p. 31
For practice estimating using rounding and adjusting.

Mental Math Practice

Fast Actions with 10 or 100, p. 32
For practice adding or subtracting 10 or 100 mentally.

Fast Actions with 9 or 90, p. 33
For practice adding or subtracting 9 or 90 mentally.

Extension

Weekly Totals, p. 34
For practice rounding and adjusting in different contexts: hours and minutes, and miles.

Test Practice

Test Practice, p. 36

Looking Closely

Observe whether students are able to

Mentally compute by rounding and then adjusting

Can students keep track of the difference between rounded and actual amounts? Students might jot down intermediate steps to help them keep track. If the actual price is $1.95 and they round to $2, they can note that they need to account for the 5¢ difference.

Do students know when to adjust by adding and when to adjust by subtracting? Work through this concept with them by referring to everyday shopping situations: If your total purchase is $3.97, how much less than $4 is it? How can you figure out your change?

Do students rely on number sense and knowledge of basic facts? Help students relate problems to everyday shopping situations they face, adjusting numbers to simplify if needed. Try to engage students in using their own number sense to solve computation problems; even if they choose to use traditional paper-and-pencil strategies, they should have some exposure to other approaches. Over time, as they build number sense, they may come to value and rely more upon mental strategies. *Mental Math Practices* are designed to give practice with building number sense.

Use mathematical notation to describe mental math processes

In addition to spoken explanations, can students describe their solution process using appropriate notation? As they explain their strategies, model these using notation, as shown in the examples in the *Opening Discussion* and in *Activity 1*.

Be explicit about an actual amount being more or less than an estimated amount to help students see how to make adjustments. For example, in *Activity 2*, to figure out the cost of five items at $6.98 each, $6.98 is rounded to $7, and then a 2¢ adjustment must be made for each item:

$7 × 5 = $35

2¢ × 5 = 10¢ (and this is 10¢ too much)

So,

$35 − 10¢ = $34.90

More formally, this might be recorded as follows:

$5(\$6.98) = 5(\$7) - 5(\$0.02) = \$35.00 - \$0.10 = \$34.90$

Make generalizations about equations

The math inspections offer opportunities to make generalizations about equality. Are students able to think critically about the value of the numbers in order to write a balanced equation?

Students should see that the expressions on each side of the equation are equal to one another but different. Look to see if students can articulate, in their own words, that one addend increases and one addend decreases by the same amount. When two numbers are added, if you increase one addend by an amount and decrease the other addend by the same amount, the sum remains the same. In symbols, this generalization is $a + b = (a + c) + (b − c)$, where c is the amount by which the addends are increased or decreased. In each equation the expression on the right has values that have become easier to add because there is a multiple of 10 or 100, and these "rounded" values were created by regrouping the addends on the left hand side. For instance, $9 + 7 = 9 + (1 + 6) = (9 + 1) + 6 = 10 + 6$. This regrouping is possible based on the associative property of addition.

Students might recognize that they have used regrouping, but perhaps thought of it as a trick to make adding simpler. If they have ever regrouped in clumps of 10, i.e. $2 + 4 + 7 + 8 = (2 + 8) + 4 + 7$, or applied the same principle to larger numbers, e.g., : $38 + $56 + $12 = $38 + $12 + $56, they have used the associative property of addition.

Rationale

When making estimates of sums, the ability to round and adjust numbers is critical. Often you only need an estimate, for example, to make sure that the amount of money you have is enough to cover the items you want to purchase. However, at times it is necessary to find an exact amount. Students have opportunities to do both of these in this lesson.

Math Background

The difference between an estimate and an exact amount is such that an adjustment is necessary. If $10.11 is rounded to $10, and $19.99 is rounded to $20, $30 would be a good estimate of their sum. To figure out the exact amount, however, an adjustment is needed: 11¢ short (rounding $10.11 to $10) and 1¢ over (rounding $19.99 to $20), so 10¢ short, total. The exact amount, then, is $30.10. To use this process implies that we know that $19.99 + 1¢ = $20 *and* that $20 − 1¢ = $19.99, and $20 − $19.99 = 1¢.

More generally, one of the big ideas in mathematics is that if $a + b = c$, then $c - b = a$ or $c - a = b$.

One way to keep track of the adjustments is to notate as follows:

Rounded	Adjusted by
$20 ...	−1¢
$10 ...	+11¢
$30 ...	−1¢ + 11¢ = 10¢

Context Background

Most people are familiar with various prices that end in 90-something cents. When this topic arises in the lesson, it may be worth digressing to talk about why items are priced this way—sometimes to keep a price under a whole dollar amount, for example, so it seems less expensive.

Facilitation

Bear in mind that this lesson works on listening skills as well as problem-solvers' skills. In order to record problem-solvers' steps, it is necessary to listen carefully and ask clarifying questions. Model using notation where needed.

If necessary, ask students whether they know how to write "a dollar and two cents." If some students confuse $1.02 and $1.20, give them a couple of other dollars-and-cents amounts to write, such as $5.01 and $5.10, $7.05 and $7.50, and $0.03 and $0.30.

To support the development of faster mental math, assign *Mental Math Practices: Fast Actions with 10 or 100* (*Student Book*, p. 32) and *Fast Actions with 9 or 90* (*Student Book*, p. 33).

Making the Lesson Easier

Ask students to find the total of only two items.

Use labeled diagrams, real objects, or coins to help those students who struggle to understand what is meant by rounding and adjusting.

Making the Lesson Harder

Solve problems involving amounts *not* close to a whole dollar, such as $3.79 and $15.44. Ask students to use appropriate mathematical notation to describe their solution processes.

Ask students to work on *Extension: Weekly Totals (Student Book,* p. 34), in which the units involve hours and minutes, and miles in decimals.

Suggest that students pose their own problems. Their partners could solve these, and then pairs could verify the answer together.

One teacher found a way to bring students' math reasoning outside of the classroom into the class.

I asked a group of my GED math students to tell me how much it would cost if I bought four shirts for $7.98 each. They were told they could figure it out any way they wanted, except they could not use paper and pencil. I watched as they used their fingers in the air or "wrote" on the desk. Most were able to multiply and get the right answer. When I asked *how* they got their answers, all agreed that they needed to multiply $7.98 by four.

I then asked whether when they were in a store and had to figure out the same problem, they would have done it the same way. All agreed they probably would *not* solve it the same way in "real life." Some said they would have multiplied four by seven and four by one, added the products, and then subtracted eight cents from that total. Others said they would have rounded $7.98 to $8.00, multiplied that number by four, and then subtracted $0.08 from the product. I then asked why no one admitted to solving the problem that way in class. The response was that this was math class so they needed to "do it out."

Marilyn Moses
Brockton Adult Learning Center, Brockton, MA

Traveling with Numbers

> *Have you ever driven across the United States?*

Synopsis

Students work together to locate numbers on a **number line** and begin to use the number line as a thinking tool.

1. The class estimates the number of pages in a large book. Students place their estimates on a number line and compare their estimates to the actual number of pages.

2. Student pairs track an imaginary trip across the United States along Interstate 90 (I-90) using a number line.

3. Pairs round the distances to the nearest 10 or 100, add them, and use a calculator or mental math to check the totals.

4. The class summarizes by stating how they know one number is bigger than another and listing what they consider when comparing numbers.

Objectives

- Locate, order, and operate with numbers on a number line
- Round numbers to the nearest 10 and 100

Materials/Prep

- A book with more than 1,000 pages such as a dictionary
- Adding machine tape or receipt tape
- Colored markers
- Meter stick
- Post-it Notes
- Large U.S. wall map (optional)

Make a three-meter-long number line marked from 0 to 3,000 in increments of 100 and labeled at the 0, 1,000, 2,000, and 3,000 marks. Adding machine tape works well for this. Use the meter stick markings as a guide. Each meter will stand for 1,000, each decimeter for 100.

Opening Discussion

Display a large book with more than 1,000 pages for all to see.

Ask:

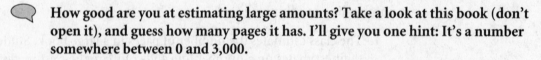 **How good are you at estimating large amounts? Take a look at this book (don't open it), and guess how many pages it has. I'll give you one hint: It's a number somewhere between 0 and 3,000.**

Ask each student to write a best estimate on a Post-it Note. You want to have 10–20 numbers to use. If the class is small, ask each person to write down two or three guesses.

When everyone has made one or more estimates, draw attention to the 0–3,000 number line, posted for all to see.

Ask:

What do you notice about this number line?

Then ask more specific questions:

If this mark stands for 0 and this one for 1,000, what is the value of each of these smaller parts? (100)

How many 100's make up 1,000? 2,000?

Ask for volunteers to carefully place their Post-it Notes on the number line. You might organize the postings by asking:

Who guessed 500 or less? (Establish where the 500 mark is.)

Where is a number that is more than 500, but less than 1,000 indicated on the line? (Continue in groupings of 500.)

Encourage students to consult with and help each other. Then ask:

💬 **What is the highest estimate? The lowest?**

💬 **Whose estimates are almost the same?**

Post the actual number of pages in the book on the number line, distinguishing this number from the estimates. Ask:

💬 **Which estimate was the closest to the actual number of pages? How far off was it? How can you show that difference using the number line?**

💬 **How can you figure out how far off your estimate was?**

Ask for a few examples of how people figured this out, and point out that the distance between any two numbers is the **difference**.

Summarize by asking:

💬 **What helped you place your estimate on the number line?** (For example, "First, I look at the largest part of the number and then decide whether it is more than half of the number line.")

Keep the number line posted.

◉ Activity 1: How Many Miles to Boston?

Display the U.S. map on the wall, if possible.

💬 **Have you ever driven across the United States? How far do you think that is?**

💬 **Look at the map in your Student Book on p. 39, that shows Interstate Highway 90. If you started in the west and traveled east, in which cities would you start and end?**

💬 **What are some states you would pass through?**

After students offer guesses, refer pairs to *Activity 1: How Many Miles to Boston?* (*Student Book,* p. 38). After they have worked on the activity, draw the class together to share responses.

First, concentrate on the questions which have to do with the map (Problems 1–3). If there is disagreement about the longest and shortest distances across states or the midpoint, allow discussion.

Second, focus on the number line (Problem 4). Ask for a demonstration of the 300-mile jumps on the posted number line.

To emphasize the jumps of 300 on the number line (in Problem 1, 300 miles each day), ask:

💬 **How far have you traveled by day 2? By day 4?**

Activity 2: Planning Where to Stay

Refer students to *Activity 2: Planning Where to Stay* (*Student Book*, p. 40).

To decide on places to stay, students should be mentally counting up by 300. They might count by 3's to get the first digit of each new number (300, 600, 900, 1,200, and so on).

There are various plans that are reasonable because none of the cities or towns are exactly 300 miles apart.

Ask students to find a partner to share plans. How were their plans the same? How were they different?

 ## Activity 3: Rounding Distances

Refer students to *Activity 3: Rounding Distances* (*Student Book*, p. 43).

Note that the distances across each state (in miles) are listed in the chart. Students must round those distances to friendlier numbers.

First, they will round to the nearest 10. Do the first few problems together, always asking:

 Between which two 10's is the number?

 To which 10 is it closer?

Ask students to use the number line as a tool to demonstrate or test proximity.

Do the same for rounding to 100's, asking:

 Between which two 100's is the number?

 To which 100 is it closer?

Finally, compare the sums of the different roundings. Direct students to *Tips on Rounding* (*Student Book,* p. 45), for a reminder of how to round to the nearest hundred.

Summary Discussion

Ask students:

 How did you know that one number was bigger than another?

 What do you look at when you are comparing numbers?

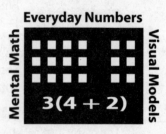

If the following ideas do not arise, prompt for them:

- More digits means a bigger number (unless there is a decimal point in the number, as with money).
- To compare numbers, look at the number of places and the digits.

- Compare digits starting with the number with the largest value—for example, 100's first, then 10's, then 1's.

Focus on the number line. Ask:

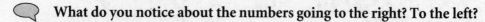 **What do you notice about the numbers going to the right? To the left?**

What do you notice about the spaces between the numbers?

Where else do you see number lines in everyday life?

End by asking students to write in the *Reflections* section (*Student Book*, p. 258), and to add their definitions and examples of the vocabulary words in this lesson in *Vocabulary* (*Student Book*, p. 254).

Practice

Trip Investigation, p. 46
For practice using the number line to show how many days it would take to travel across country at various average daily mileages.

High and Not So High Peaks, p. 48
For practice ordering large numbers.

Checks—Say It in Words, p. 50
For practice going from words to numbers.

More Check Writing, p. 52
For practice going from numbers to words.

Filing, p. 53
For practice ordering numbers.

More Filing, p. 54
For more practice ordering numbers.

How Close Is Close Enough? p. 55
For practice considering the purpose of estimating—which influences how exact one needs to be and the strategies one chooses.

For additional practice using number lines, reading gauges, and scales, revisit *Lesson 1, Practice: Getting Close* (*Student Book*, p. 13). Ask students to label all lettered points this time.

Mental Math Practice

Doubles, p. 57
For practice seeing patterns multiplying by two.

Triples, p. 58
For practice seeing patterns multiplying by three.

Rolling in Money, p. 59
For practice looking for patterns when doubling and tripling.

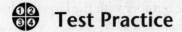 **Test Practice**

Test Practice, p. 61

 Looking Closely

Observe whether students are able to

Locate, order, and operate with numbers on a number line

How well are students able to use the number line as a thinking tool? Are they able to determine the value of unlabeled markings? To deepen their facility with number lines, ask students to create number lines of their own.

Do students accurately locate and order their estimates on the number line, using cues from the markings? If not, labeling the markings with their number values could be helpful.

For students having trouble ordering numbers, assign the three practices pages which present other contexts: *High and Not So High Peaks* (*Student Book*, p. 48); *Filing* (*Student Book*, p. 53); and *More Filing* (*Student Book*, p. 54).

Do students connect mathematical operations to the work on the number line? For example, when asked how far off from the actual number their estimates were, do they connect the distance between any two numbers to the difference, the result of subtraction? Or do they see how traveling up by 300 in consecutive jumps is analogous to both repeated addition and multiplication? Do they see the connection to division? In other words, do students understand that finding the number of 300-mile jumps across the country (3,112 miles) is the same as dividing 3,112 by 300?

Round numbers to the nearest 10 and 100

The activities in this lesson call upon a sense of estimation. At this point, how solid are students' rounding skills?

Emphasize rounding as an activity on the number line, rather than a rote procedure (e.g., if the number ends in five or more …). When rounding to 10 ask, "Between which two 10's is the number? To which is it closer?" Do the same when rounding to the nearest 100.

Do students consider the context when they are rounding? Can they explain why they chose to round up or down possibly in spite of rounding "rules" because it might be preferable for an estimate to be high or low (for example, to make sure you don't overspend)? Do students have a sense of how rounding to different place values affects the accuracy or exactness of the estimate, and do they take that into consideration? Do they round to benchmarks that will simplify the mental math? The goal is for students to realize that rounding is governed by certain conventions and also a tool at their disposal.

Rationale

Both elements of the subtitle, *Mental Math and Visual Models*, become the foci of this lesson. The visual model of the number line can support the development of mental math ability by providing a different way to see the relationships among numbers.

Math Background

The number line is a visual model that can be used as a thinking tool. Connecting numbers to points is a powerful idea and grounds understanding of graphs and like instruments (thermometers and rulers). A number line allows one to see the relative values of numbers and also illuminates operations on numbers. Adding and subtracting can be viewed as jumping up and down the number line. Differences between numbers connect to the distance between points. Multiplication is visually represented by jumps of equivalent size (repeated addition), and division can be seen as counting the number of times a particular distance can be found in another distance.

Rounding draws attention to the markings on a number line. For example, students are asked to consider the placement of 1,170 on a number line extending from 0–3,000, marked in increments of 100. The corresponding point should be closer to 1,200 than to 1,100.

Lesson 4 will further develop the number line as a time line, and *Lesson 6* will ask students to extend their thinking to numbers below zero.

Context

Lessons 1 and *2* rely on students' familiarity with dollars and cents. This lesson focuses on other contexts, such as distances traveling across the United States. The main activities create a social studies context for students as they examine the states from west to east across the country.

Facilitation

Students who already have a handle on paper-and-pencil methods may not see the value of using number lines. If this is the case, emphasize applications of the number line, such as graphs and measurement tools.

Making the Lesson Easier

Work together as a class and check students' work often if using the U.S. map is too much of a challenge.

Making the Lesson Harder

Incorporate numbers with fractions or decimals when rounding or working with the number line. For example, ask where the number 297.6 would fall on the 0–3,000 number line and what 297.6 rounded to the nearest 100 would be.

Teachers commented on their students' engagement with the lesson and offered her own adaptations.

We are using the number lines. The students totally understand the concept and are thrilled to be using it. However, when it came time to solve the problems, they wanted to do it the "old way"(with paper and pencil). I encouraged them to keep on showing their thinking on the number line. Then they had a substitute teacher who tried to show them another traditional algorithm. The students held firm and told her I wouldn't let that happen.

In *Practice: High and Not So High Peaks,* I added the task of rounding off to the nearest hundred. It was interesting because the first mountain's height was 48 feet. I had those who finished early figure the average height of the mountain peaks; their own goals were to learn more about averages.

The students loved doing the practices with file drawers. They saw real-life applications—not only for filing, but also for putting other things in order, for example, nuts and bolts in a hardware store.

Michelle Brown
Read, Write, Now, Springfield, MA

Students were engaged throughout the entire class. They worked independently or in pairs, and made gains in both modalities. They discussed their methodologies to estimating distances among themselves. Students liked the activity with the map. [They] enjoyed counting by 300 and seeing names of other places. We were estimating distances across a map. Some of the students were able to count by 300 as prescribed in the lesson. They also were able to identify the 11 towns where they were supposed to make stops on their 3,200 mile trip, figuring out an effective strategy by themselves. In *Activity 3: Rounding Distances*, students seemed to have a strong understanding that a number can be rounded to the nearest 10 and nearest 100 and have the same result.

My biggest challenge was trying to get the students to slow down and read the directions carefully.

Teacher
New York City, NY

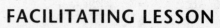

Traveling in Time

How long ago was that?

Synopsis

Students place dates of birth and historical events on number lines. Using the number lines and mental math, they add and subtract using 10's and 1's to calculate people's ages and calculate how long ago their birthdays occurred. Students record their strategies both on the number line, a tool that makes mental math strategies visible, and by writing **equations**.

1. Working as a group and then in pairs, students figure out different time spans and explain their strategies. They use the number line as a tool for computing and for showing their problem-solving methods and record their strategies using equations.

2. Students share what they learned about using number lines in order to solve problems.

3. Students examine quantities on both sides of the equal sign.

Objectives

• Use a number line to compute and to explain mental math strategies

• Use counting up and down by 10's and 1's to solve addition and subtraction problems

• Record mental math and number-line actions using equations

• Make generalizations about how addition and subtraction behave in equations

Materials/Prep

- Adding or receipt tape or strips of easel paper for number lines
- Colored markers
- Easel Pad
- Rulers
- Assorted items that have number lines—a thermometer, rulers, yardsticks, meter sticks, pictures of gauges, etc. for the *Opening Discussion*.

Make a current timeline from adding machine tape or long strips of paper, marked from 1850–2020, to post in the front of the classroom for *Activity 1*.

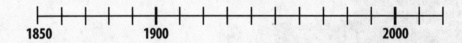

Make one copy of *Blackline Master 5: U.S. Historical Events* for each group of three students with each copy cut into a set of six cards and placed in an envelope for *Activity 2*.

Opening Discussion

Review what students remember about the number lines used in *Lesson 3*. Distribute items that use number lines (thermometers, barometers, tape measures, yard sticks, rulers, meter sticks, beakers, timelines, etc.) to pairs of students.

Say to students:

Describe the number line in your object. What does it measure?

Compare the objects, highlighting what they are designed to measure, the numbers listed, and the values of the marked intervals.

Conclude by saying:

Today we will use number lines to explain how we use mental math to find the difference between two numbers.

Activity 1: Birthday Numbers

Start with the following scenario to introduce the first problem in *Activity 1: Birthday Numbers* (*Student Book*, p. 64)

A friend of mine just celebrated her 46th birthday. I was trying to figure out in my head when she was born. In what year was my friend born? How do you know?

Invite students to share their strategies for solving the problem. Someone may be 46 years old and know the answer immediately. However, try to bring out the mental calculations students used.

Heads Up!

The following examples are written for the year 2015. Adjust the lesson to the current year and follow the same method.

Starting with the first volunteer, write on the board the mental steps he or she used to determine the birth year for the 36-year-old. Use the number line to demonstrate the steps, explaining the student's process as you write. For instance:

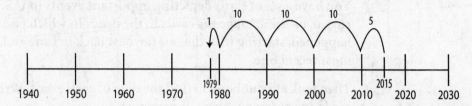

💬 **You started at this year (2015 or the current year, 20XX). You went back 5 years (or X years) to the year 2010, a round number. Then you went back 30 years to 1970, and then you went back one more year to 1969. Adding 5 and 30 and 1, you get 36 years.**

💬 **Did anyone solve the problem a different way?**

Listen to examples, tracking students' reasoning on the number line. If student examples are not forthcoming, offer one of your own.

Once you record the number-line jumps and written steps for a few strategies on the timeline, begin to describe the steps, using mathematical notation. For instance, for the example above, you might write and talk through the problem as follows:

$$2015 - 15 = 2000$$
$$2000 - 30 = 1970$$
$$1970 - 1 = 1969$$
$$2005 - 15 - 30 - 1 = 1969$$

Ask students to write both the number-line jumps and an equation in their books as they complete the problems on the page.

Take time for students to share number-line strategies and equations for each problem.

Name the methods you see students using—counting back by 10's, or multiples of 10's; adding on by 1's and 10's; or finding a benchmark date, such as 2000, and working from there. Summarize briefly:

💬 **All these strategies help us find the difference between two dates and how far apart different birth dates are from the current year, 2015 (or 20XX).**

💬 **The equations show—in writing—how we add and subtract mentally. Though it might take more steps to calculate in our heads than with paper and pencil, what are some of the advantages of calculating mentally?**

Allow time for learners to complete *Activity 1* and briefly discuss strategies used.

⊚ Activity 2: How Long Ago?

Distribute one envelope of cards cut from *Blackline Master 5: U.S. Historical Events* to each group. Tell students:

💬 **History sometimes seems like a jumble of dates and events. We often wonder, "When did that war happen?" or "How long ago was that?"**

💬 **You have a set of cards depicting important events in U.S. history. With books closed, please arrange the cards in the order in which you think the events happened, starting with the one farthest back in time and working up to the most recent one.**

💬 **Then look at your book to find the date of each event. Write the dates on your cards and rearrange them, if necessary.**

After students have arranged the cards, review the directions for *Activity 2: How Long Ago?* (*Student Book,* p. 66). Clarify the term "difference," then ask students to answer the questions, and as you circulate, notice who is working with 10's and 1's comfortably. Always ask:

💬 **How would you find the answer in your head without using pencil and paper?**

💬 **What is another way you could do the problem?**

Notice how students determine missing numbers. Do they count spaces accurately? Do they see the patterns of increments? Notice how they use the number line. Do they mark off 10's and 1's accurately? Do they use multiples of 10? The more fluent the students become, the more likely they will be able to work with larger increments of numbers, preferring to go down by 50 rather than 10, for instance. Encourage this efficiency and connect it with five 10's jumps on the number line when sharing strategies with the class.

If no one chunks time into larger intervals, ask them how they could do that.

Ask students to share their methods by putting their number lines and equations on easel paper. Post these for the class to see.

Choose some examples and ask:

💬 **How did you know what the missing numbers were here?**

💬 **What other numbers did you put on the number line? How did you decide where to place them?**

Compare methods students used. Then focus on their solutions, asking:

💬 **Did you do the problem first in your head or on the number line?**

💬 **Did counting with 10's (or multiples of 10) help you? How so?**

Then focus on their solutions, asking:

💬 **How did you know how many years ago this event happened? How do you know that the event happened more or less than 100 years ago?**

If students subtract in some other way (traditional algorithm, for example), make sure they also show what they did on the number line.

Because student pairs will only choose two or three events, you may want to assign them the rest for homework as extra practice.

Math Inspection: Make It True

This math inspection extends the work with the equal sign by including the subtraction sign along with the equal sign and addition sign. As they explore the relationship between the numbers, students should begin to realize that addition and subtraction are related; in fact, they are inverses of one another. Two of the final equations will illustrate the idea of additive inverse (**40 + 20 − 40 = 20** and **40 = 20 + 40 − 20**). Students should check to see that their strategies work for any pair of numbers, *a* and *b*. If they are only dealing with positive numbers, they may say that the first number has to be the larger.

This inspection deals with the reflexive property of equality:

$a + b = a + b$ or $a − b = a − b$

Anything is equal to itself.

This idea shows up in algebra: In the equation $a + b − a = b$, on the left side of the equal sign, adding *a* and then subtracting a results in 0, so b is left on both sides of the equation. The same is true if the action happens on the other side of the equal sign: $a = b + a − b$. On the right side of the equal sign, addition and then subtraction of b results in 0, so a is left on both sides of the equation.

Ask students to work individually to determine the solution to each problem.

Then, as pairs, have them share how they determined where to place addition and subtraction signs. Post the different solutions and ask students to articulate the similarities and differences among them. Give students time to decide if this will work with any pair of numbers, and ask for examples. Finally (#4), ask:

 Why will equations patterned like 40 + 20 − 40 = 20 and 40 = 20 + 40 − 20 always work?

You may hear comments like:

> "Because you are adding and subtracting the same amounts."

> "Because adding the 20 cancels subtracting 20."

If no one brings it up, record this in algebraic notation: $a + b − a = b$

This is the moment to have students check to see that their strategies work for any pair of numbers, *a* and *b*. If they are only dealing with positive numbers, they may say that the first number has to be the larger. If students are familiar with negative numbers, volunteers may offer examples such as -25 + -60 − (-25) = -60. Acknowledge that yes, the generalization works for more than just positive whole numbers. If this does not come up, you can raise it at this point or return to this point in *Lesson 6: Extending the Line,* after students have had more experience combining positive and negative numbers.

Math Inspection: Check Both Sides of the Equal Sign

This inspection extends the work with the equal sign and asks students to notice patterns that occur with subtraction. This is a case in which noticing patterns and generalizing from them can lead to important insights about operations and the mathematical concept of equality.

In the equations for students to consider (for example, $9 - 6 = 10 - 7$), they are asked to look at the relationship between the numbers on the left and right of the equal sign. To maintain equality, each number increases by one. The relationship among the numbers remains stable and so the answer does not change. This is different from what we see with addition (for example, $5 + 2 = 6 + 1$). With addition, if one number on one side of the equal sign increases, the other on that same side has to decrease for the sum to remain the same. Students may be confused or surprised by this contrast at first. Use number lines to illustrate what is happening in specific equations. Students may find it helpful if you and they mark off steps down a hall or across the classroom so they can act out sample equations with numbers less than 20. In this way they have a kinesthetic means to experience what changes and what stays the same.

As you prepare, you may notice that in the subtraction problem on the right $(10 - 7)$, the numbers are each 1 more than the subtraction problem on the left $(9 - 6)$, but the difference is the still the same (3). In the second equation, each number is three more. In the third, each number is 25 more. The difference remains the same as the difference between the original numbers. Another observation might be that in each case, the expression on the right side of the equation is easier to simplify since it is subtracting a multiple of 10, and that the right side can be created from the left by adding the same number to each value (for instance adding a 1 to the 9 and to the 6 results in $10 - 7$). In other words, this is a good strategy for making numbers friendlier in order to do mental math calculations or to eliminate the need to borrow.

In mathematical terms, this is the zero identity property at work. For instance, $48 - 13 = (48 + 2) - (13 + 2)$, which can be rewritten as $48 + 2 - 13 - 2$, and $+ 2$ and $- 2$ equal 0.

Begin by asking students to articulate again what the equal sign means (that the value on the left is equivalent to the value on the right). Ask them to verify that this is true for each of the three equations.

Now write **9 – 6** on the board.

Then write **10 – 7**.

Ask:

 Are these amounts equal? (Yes)

Then ask:

 How do you know?

People may have varied responses (for example, because I know my facts—they are both 3). Record responses on the board for all to see.

If no one says that each amount increases by 1, ask:

 How do the amounts on the left change compared to the amounts on the right side?

Focus on the idea that "10 is 1 more than 9 and 7 is one more than 6, yet you still have the same difference."

Ask pairs to work together on problems 1 through 3, using this idea. As you circulate, you might ask students to think about how to show (with chips, pennies, on a number line) why this works with subtraction. Ask them to compare with their generalizations in the *Math Inspection* in *Lesson 2*, where 9 + 6 = 10 + 5.

Bring the class together to share what they have noticed.

Instruct students to put their pencils down. Talk through Problem 4. Ask them to discuss their mental math strategies for determining each of the answers.

You or students may summarize the take-home point, which is: If you are looking for the difference between two numbers, you can add the same amount to both numbers and not change the difference. Make sure everyone is clear, and if not, allow more time to demonstrate and restate this concept.

Summary Discussion

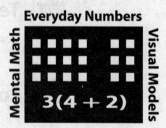

Ask students to turn to a partner and share one new idea they learned in this lesson.

End this conversation by asking students what they learned about comparing two amounts:

 Think about all the problems you worked on in which you found the difference between dates (and times). What did you learn that helped you solve those problems?

If the following points are not raised, bring them up yourself:

- A number line can help you understand and solve problems.
- Counting up or down by 10's can help you solve an addition or subtraction problem more easily.
- There is more than one way to solve problems; sometimes adding on is easier and other times counting back is easier.
- Any time you have two or more quantities that are different in number or size, you can use a number line to compare them.

Suggest that students record vocabulary definitions (*Student Book*, p. 254) and respond to the reflection questions (*Student Book*, p. 259).

◉ Practice

Use Up the Space—Plan Well, p. 75
For practice marking even increments on number lines.

On the Number Line, p. 76
For more practice locating numbers on the number line and using them to solve problems.

✚ Mental Math Practice

Count Up and Down by 10's, p. 77
For skip counting practice.

By What Did I Count? p. 78
For more practice with skip counting.

∅ Extension

Life Line, p. 79
For practice making a number line with personal life events.

▦ Test Practice

Test Practice, p. 80

◉ Looking Closely

Observe whether students are better able to

Use a number line to compute and explain mental math strategies

Emphasize that a number line helps one think about the meaning of the problem, rather than only the question "Do I add or subtract the two numbers?"

Do students understand equal intervals? Make the connection between equal-sized spaces and the number of years each space represents. If students are unsure about how to label amounts between marked intervals, ask where the halfway mark is and what number that would be.

Are students able to set up the number line? Help them move from the smallest number on the left to the largest number on the right; choose a starting point appropriate to the problem; recognize when they need to label each number; label the jumps (for instance, +10, +3); and then use those labels to arrive at the solution of the problem, as well as to write their equations.

Help students get started if they seem confused. For example, for Problem 3 in *Activity 1*, tell students to start with the year 1949. If they add 10, what number do they have? How many more numbers must they add to get to the year 1999? to 2000? to 2015?

If students use the number line but only write the starting and ending numbers and do not indicate any moves other than the jump, ask, "How do you know how many years that is?" Help them by starting the count yourself.

Use counting up and down by 10's and 1's to solve addition and subtraction problems

Are students counting by 10's and multiples of 10? Encourage them by repeatedly asking them to do so in each problem.

Draw students' attention to the year 2000, and ask them why that year is a good reference point. Encourage them to move first to a number that ends in zero, so, for example, if they are finding how many years have passed since President Kennedy's assassination (1963), they can move seven on the number line to reach 1970 and continue to add years from that date.

As needed, simplify numbers so students can easily count up or back by 10's or multiples of 10. If the numbers are too easy, adjust them so students will be challenged, starting with dates such as 1919 or 1957.

Record mental math and number-line actions using equations

Are students writing equations that accurately reflect their mental strategies and movements on the number line? Model writing *number sentences* and equations for the jumps they make on the number line.

How flexible are students with notation? Can they move between an addition statement and a subtraction statement and connect the two? If more than one operation per line is too confusing, advise students to limit their equations to one step and operation at a time.

Are they able to judge the accuracy of an equation? When students write their equations, suggest they check back with the moves on the number line to confirm that what they have written reflects the moves they made.

Make generalizations about how addition and subtraction behave in equations

Are students beginning to notice inverse relationships? If you add and subtract the same amount, the operations cancel each other out. Are students able to explain, in their own words, why adding the same amount to the minuend and the subtrahend preserves the difference between the numbers? Look for students to connect this to a visual model, showing the distance between two numbers on the number line remains stable when the same amount is added to elements of an equation or expression.

If students did not fully grasp this point while completing the *Math Inspection: Make it True*, they will return to inverse relationships later with a discussion of the additive inverse and zero pairs in *Lesson 7*.

Rationale

Time and time intervals play an important role in our lives. Dates provide landmarks that we use as reference points. For example, the number of days, months, or years since we no longer had to wear braces, lived at home, went on our last vacation, or got our first cell phone. There are many ways that people count these time intervals, and some claim they cannot do this without a paper and pencil. Using mental math strategies, accompanied by a visual tool (number line) to show the strategies, people can find these intervals and explain their reasoning to others.

Timelines are used to show the sequence of historical events by displaying the dates of those events as marks on the line. Number lines are sequential; the numbers increase to the right of 0 and decrease to the left of 0. Sometimes the lines include marks for every number; other times, for example, for every 10, 25, 50, or 100 intervals. Sometimes the lines include 0; other times they do not. The better able students are to count by 10's and multiples of 10, the better they will be able to travel along the number line.

The ability to calculate differences or to compare amounts mentally empowers people to make decisions more efficiently. Some may not possess the strategy of counting by 10's or multiples of 10 to reach quick solutions to problems. This lesson encourages students to build up to or down from numbers in increments of 10 or multiples of 10 to develop and refine their number sense and, thereby, their facility with numbers. The use and construction of number lines paves the way for reading and constructing graphs. This topic is developed in EMPower's data and algebra books.

Math Background

These problems about number comparisons call for either subtraction or addition to solve them:

- I'm 54, Rachel is 27, how much older am I?
- Sally lives on 53rd Street and I live on 120th Street; how far apart do we live?
- How long ago did the Wright Brothers fly their first plane?

The problems above represent two models for subtraction: (1) how much larger one number is than another (the age example) and (2) the distance between two numbers (the address and airplane examples). In each one, subtraction solves the problem. So does addition. Traditionally, school books teach these as 54 – 27 or 120 – 53. However, when people solve these mentally, they often use addition. Using the age problem as an example, people may count on:

"27 to 30 is 3, to 54 is 24, and 3 and 24 is 27."

Or they count on and adjust:

"27 to 57 is 30, but I've gone too far, so it's 3 less, or 27."

And when subtracting, people sometimes explain the problem as follows:

"54 minus 4 is 50, minus 20 is 30, minus another 3 is 27, so that's 4 and 20 and 3, or 27."

Or they may picture the traditional vertical algorithm and borrowing:

$$\begin{array}{r} 4^{1} \\ \cancel{5}4 \\ -27 \\ \hline 27 \end{array}$$

Here is another way to notate this:

$$\begin{array}{r} 40 \\ -20 \\ \hline 20 \end{array} \qquad \begin{array}{r} 14 \\ -\ 7 \\ \hline 7 \end{array} \qquad 20 + 7 = 27$$

All of these strategies get to the solution, in this case 27. The focus in this lesson is on counting forward or back and using the number line to help show the moves.

Using groups of 10's, 5's and 1's to count is one of the first efficient methods that students acquire for totaling or comparing numbers. In this lesson, you may notice that some students count only by 1's. The number line can encourage different strategies, such as counting on, adding on, and counting back.

The following is one way you might introduce those categories in class.

💬 **I drew a number line to show when Prohibition started.**

💬 **I went from 1919 to '20, '20 to '30, and then what?**

As students answer, for instance, '30 to '40, and '40 to '50, add these to your number line, and indicate the number above each jump, like this:

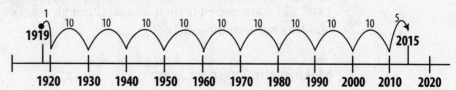

This way is called "count on or add up to a multiple of 10."

 What if you started with the larger number and counted back? I started at '05, then went to '04, '03, '02, '01, '00, then '90 then '80... then what?

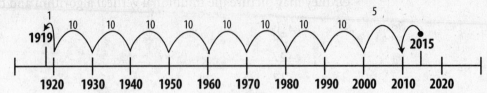

As students tell you the rest (for instance, '70, '60, '50, ... '20, '19), ask them to help you label the numbers, and write

$1 + 1 + 1 + 1 + 1 + 10 + 10 + 10 + 10 + 10 + 10 + 10 + 10 + 10 + 1 = 96$ years

or

$5 + 90 + 1 = 96$ years.

 This way is called "subtract/count down to a multiple of 10."

Working with 10's and 1's reinforces the place value system we use for numbers. As students become more proficient, however, expect that they will count by multiples of 10—by 20's, 50's, or 100's.

Context

Most of the historical dates in this lesson center on 20th century U.S. history. If students in the class are from other countries, ask for important dates in their own countries' histories, locate them on the timeline, and do some math with those dates.

Facilitation

Acknowledge students' interest in, and history with, traditional algorithms but remind them that mental math is extremely useful in daily life and will also strengthen their ability to select the correct answers on tests. Often on tests, they are asked to solve a problem more than one way; they can use their algorithm for their second way.

Some students will need to label the number lines in more detail than others. Encourage them to do that and then move them to bigger intervals. That is, when finding the number of years between 1939 and 2005, some will mark only 1939, 1940, and 2005, and note their jumps, although others will need to mark more numbers between those dates.

Making the Lesson Easier

Together, mark off 1's on at least part of the number line.

Practice counting by 10's , starting at a number between decade numbers—at 1933 or 1987, for example.

Refer students to *Mental Math Practices: Count Up and Down by 10's* (*Student Book*, p. 77) and *What Did I Count By?* (*Student Book*, p. 78), where they practice counting back and subtracting.

Consider working only from events with easy dates such as 1920, women getting the vote; 1935, The Great Depression; or 1945, the end of World War II.

Find historical events that are closer to the current date or, as a jumping-off point for comparing numbers on a number line, have students work from their birth dates (in the 1900's), rather than the current date.

Ask:

 How many years ago were you born?

Making the Lesson Harder

Choose dates farther back in time, thus using 100's as well as 10's and 1's: Simon Bolivar, South America's "George Washington," declares Venezuela's independence from Spain (1810); the United States Declaration of Independence (1776); the Discovery of Photosynthesis (1779); the Discovery of Bacteria (1683); Queen Elizabeth I ascends the throne in England, and Shakespeare is actively writing (1558); Christopher Columbus's arrival in the Western Hemisphere (1492); Joan of Arc leads the French army to victory over the invading English (1429); and the Norman Conquest of Britain (1066).

This teacher opened the session by connecting the context to students' lives. Here are the observer's notes from that session.

The teacher opened by saying, "I know we have some people from Haiti here, so I want to congratulate them on the 200th anniversary of their country's independence. For the rest of you who aren't from Haiti, when was that?"

Silence.

The teacher wrote "2004" on the board and asked again, "If Haiti won it's independence 200 years ago, when was that?"

Mabel, an ESOL student, replied, "Nineteen thousand."

The teacher wrote "19,000" on the board and asked, "Is this what you mean?"

Immediately, Mabel answered, "No, nineteen hundred."

"Hmm. . . Is that exact or an estimate?" asked the teacher, as she wrote "1900" to the right of the two numbers, 2004 and 2000.

"It looks like a pretty good estimate to me," declared Carol, who sat one seat over from Mabel.

"Yes, but what would it be exactly?"

Silence.

The observer asked, "What date would be 100 years ago from the year 2000?"

The students responded with a chorus of "1900."

The teacher drew a line connecting 1900 and 2000, saying, "So, one hundred years ago from the year 2000 would be 1900."

"So, what would be 100 years ago from 2004?" the observer asked.

Finally, Mable announced, "1904."

The teacher wrote "1904" on the board. "That would be exactly 100 years ago from this year. What would be 200 years ago?"

Several students called out, "1804," which the teacher wrote on the board.

The teacher then provided the historical date 1776 and asked how many years ago that had been. When no one replied, she explained, " You need to know this date for citizenship tests and for the GED. The United States won its independence in 1776. How many years ago was that?"

continued on next page

continued from previous page

Students forwarded several guesses, and the teacher posted these as if they were answers for a multiple-choice question. She wrote on the board:

> The United States won its independence in 1776.
> How many years ago was that?
> 1. 300
> 2. 229
> 3. 228
> 4. 3,580
> 5. Not enough information

The teacher asked for a show of hands as to which answer students thought was right. Everyone chose 228.

"How can we check that to see if it's right?" she inquired.

"Add them," came the reply from several students.

The teacher set up the problem, and a student performed the calculations. They were all correct.

Esther Leonelli, observed by Tricia Donovan
Notre Dame Education Center, Boston, MA

[The students] had good understanding of the use of number lines and round numbers to help estimate and calculate exact time periods. I adapted this lesson for higher level students using a Sierra Club leaflet showing how old the giant redwoods are (3,500 years!)

During class I prompted the students to confer with classmates about the way to solve a problem. Comments included, "You could do this (calculating the number of years that have passed since the Vietnam War) a lot of different ways," and, "How can I tell which happened first?" I asked students: "What other 'jumps' could you make on the timeline?" and "When the time period on the timeline is greater, what happens with the 'friendly' or rounded numbers used on the timeline?"

Adam Weiss
Bronx Adult Learning Center, New York City, NY

FACILITATING LESSON **5**

Meanings and Methods for Subtraction

> *What about subtraction makes a lot of sense to you?*

Synopsis

Students focus attention on three models for subtraction: (1) the *take-away* model, (2) the *difference* or *comparison* model, and (3) the *missing-part* model. Then they apply these models to make decisions on how to efficiently do some quick figuring in their heads. Finally, the class examines the mathematical principles behind the algorithms they use to perform paper-and-pencil whole number subtraction, including the U.S. standard algorithm.

1. The class examines three different subtraction problems to determine what is the same and what is different about them.

2. The class shares visual models for subtraction and classifies the type of models created.

3. Then students use these models to do some efficient mental math.

4. The class examines the ways in which the various algorithms they use work and the mathematical principles embedded in their methods.

5. The class summarizes what they have learned.

Objectives

• Identify and use three models (or interpretations) for subtraction

• Examine, understand, and explain why addition and subtraction algorithms work

Materials/Prep

- Markers
- Easel paper
- Manipulatives that make it possible to distinguish 10's and 1's, such as Base 10 Blocks or two color counting chips
- Number lines for reference

Suggested background reading for instructors about algorithms used for subtraction in other countries: *The Answer is Still the Same … It Doesn't Matter How you Got It! A Comparison of U.S. and Other Computation Methods for Math Teachers and Students from Various Backgrounds*

https://www.terc.edu/pages/viewpage.action?pageId=3179325

Suggested background reading for instructors about the different models for subtraction: *Investigations in Number, Data, and Space: Addition and Subtraction and the Number System*

http://investigations.terc.edu/library/curric-math/addsub_2ed.pdf

Opening Discussion

Start by saying:

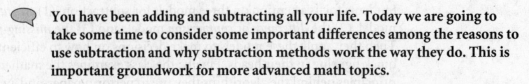 **You have been adding and subtracting all your life. Today we are going to take some time to consider some important differences among the reasons to use subtraction and why subtraction methods work the way they do. This is important groundwork for more advanced math topics.**

Activity 1: Ways to Think About Subtraction

Begin by explaining that subtraction can mean more than take away.

If you understand the different meanings of subtraction, you may find it easier to figure out when a situation requres subtraction.

Refer students to *Activity 1: Ways to Think About Subtraction* (*Student Book*, p. 84).

Walk around the room, noticing whether students are focusing on the subtraction aspect of each story. (Is it looking for a missing part, or the difference between two things, or is it taking an amount away?)

Bring everyone back together and discuss each problem, asking the following questions to get at student definitions of types of subtraction situations:

Is this a situation that involves subtraction?

What is this problem asking you to look for? [missing part for the first problem, difference or comparison for the second problem, and how much is left (take away) for the third]

What strategies did you use to figure out the answer?

Activity 2: How Do You See It?

Part 1

Begin by writing **40 - 27** = _____ on the board.

 If someone asked you what this subtraction problem could mean, how would you show it visually—such as with a picture or diagram? And how would you connect that to a real-world situation?

Refer students to Part 1 of *Activity 2: How Do You See It?* (*Student Book*, p. 85).

Walk around the room, noticing students' interpretations. Look to see if there are

- Take-away interpretations, where someone begins with one amount, removes some part of it, and *the answer is what remains, or is left.* For example, "I had 40 CDs in my collection, then gave 27 to my friend. How many do I have now?"

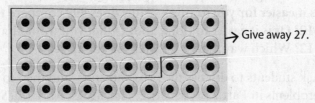

Start out with 40. → Give away 27.

- Comparison interpretations, starting with two amounts, where the *answer tells how much more (or less) one is than the other, or the difference* between them. For example, "I have 40 CDs. My sister has 27. How many more do I have than she does?"

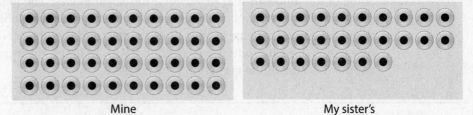

Mine   My sister's

- Missing-part interpretations, where one starts with an amount (the total), is left with a known partial amount, and is trying to find the other part. For example, "This week I want to work a full 40 hours. I know that I still have 27 hours to go. How many hours have I already worked?" The back and forth of part-part-whole of addition and subtraction is the action. For example, 40 - ? = 27 can be thought of as 27 + ? = 40.

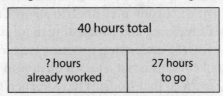

40 hours total	
? hours already worked	27 hours to go

Invite a volunteer to present an interpretation and explicitly label it as a take-away, missing-part, or comparison model.

Who also interpreted subtraction this way, as a take-away, missing-part or comparison model?

 What was your story and picture?

 Did anyone look at it a bit differently?

Ensure that all three models, with pictures and real-life situations, are addressed. Provide examples if all three types are not brought forth by the volunteers.

Part 2

Write on the board:

512 – 499

 Being able to look at a subtraction problem in three ways can help you understand the situation and possibly solve the problem faster. Try this in your head using the comparison interpretation, then the take away interpretation. Is it easier for you to think "How does 499 compare to 512? How much more is 512? Or is it easier to think about what you would have left if you took 499 from 512? Which way makes it faster for you to see?

Ask students to discuss the pros and cons, and then to try the subtraction problems in Part 2 of *Activity 2: How Do You See It?* (*Student Book*, p. 86). After people are done, come back to discuss their reasoning.

Heads Up!

Some of the problems may make sense to see either way. The importance of the discussion is that students end this lesson understanding that subtraction means more than take away. There are at least three models, and that they can think through a problem with each model if they need to do so. At times, one model is easier to use than another because of the numbers in the problem.

Activity 3: Total the Numbers

Activities 3 and *4* are discussion activities (not in the *Student Book*) that provide an opportunity for students to examine the mathematical principles behind the procedures, or algorithms, they regularly use. Many problem solvers follow the steps for *carrying* and *borrow*ing without attaching meaning to those problem solving moves. The discussion may unearth algorithms commonly taught in other countries. Comparing and contrasting those steps with the U.S. standard algorithm can reveal the underlying structure (e.g., of tens and ones) that students may have overlooked. This is not a lesson on *how* to add or subtract with paper and pencil. It is assumed that students have learned to do this. If there are some who do not know how to, this discussion will uncover that, and you may want to provide extra practice.

Part 1: Students share their algorithms for addition

This activity launches from the algorithms that students use. It's important to document these. Post and keep a record that can be referenced later.

Start by saying:

💬 **I know you have been doing basic addition and subtraction all your lives, sometimes in your head, sometimes with a paper and pencil, and sometimes with a calculator or computer. It depends on what the situation is.**

💬 **Right now, we're going to take a look at the paper-and-pencil methods you learned in school, and may still use, and discuss not just *how* they work, but *why* they work.**

Present some numbers where carrying a 1 and a 2 is necessary, such as 946 + 697 + 1,901. (Ask for an estimate, before students calculate.)

💬 **How would you total these using paper and pencil to get an exact answer?**

Ask students to check with another person to see if they did it exactly the same way. Then have volunteers show various methods on the board, explaining how they did it.

Heads Up!

Students from other countries may not have learned the U.S. standard algorithm, but instead use an algorithm that is based on other sound mathematical principles. Please refer to the Materials/Prep section for the background reading *The Answer is Still the Same*.

Part 2: Probing WHY school methods work mathematically

After methods are posted, direct discussion to the mathematical reasoning behind the procedures or algorithms.

Point to any numbers that were carried.

💬 **Hmmm, I see a little 1, and a little 2. What's going on here? Is this really a 1? A 2?**

If students say "carrying," ask:

💬 **How would you explain to a young child what "*carrying*" means? What are you really "carrying"?** (In this case, not 1, but 10)

Look for opportunities to point out the commutative and associative properties in action:

💬 **I see someone added 946 + 697 + 1,901, and another added 697 + 1,901 + 946. Does the order matter when you are adding?**

💬 **Why do teachers usually insist on "lining up the numbers?"**

Make sure expanded notation is demonstrated in the U.S. standard algorithm.

Start with a simpler problem.

💬 **One way to show what carrying means is with expanded notation—where you see the real value of every number.**

$$57 = 50 + 7$$
$$+\,35 = 30 + 5$$
$$80 + 12 = (80 + 10) + 2 = 90 + 2 = 92$$

You will want to make sure students undersand this step. Ask:

💬 **Why did I break the 12 into 10 + 2? Why did I group the 80 and the 10 together?**

Keep the focus on ideas of place value.

$$96 = 90 + 6$$
$$+\,48 = 40 + 8$$
$$130 + 14 = (130 + 10) + 4 = 140 + 4 = 144$$

$$179 = 100 + 70 + 9$$
$$+\,308 = 300 +\ \ 0 + 8$$
$$400 + 70 + 17 = 400 + (70 + 17) = 400 + 87 = 487$$

Ask students:

💬 **What is important to remember about the mathematical idea of carrying?**

🌀 Activity 4: Subtraction Methods

This is a discussion. There are no accompanying pages in the *Student Book*.

Part 1: Students share their algorithms for subtraction

Once again, launch discussion based on the algorithms that students use. Document and post ideas. You might title a page of easel paper: Our Subtraction Methods.

Start by saying:

💬 **Let's take a look at the paper-and-pencil methods you learned in school for subtraction and discuss not just *how* they work, but *why* they work.**

Present a problem with numbers where borrowing is necessary, such as 52 – 35. (Ask for an estimate, before the calculations.)

💬 **How would you do the subtraction by hand (paper and pencil) to get an exact answer?**

Ask students to check with one other person to see if they did the problem the same way. Then have volunteers show various methods on the board, explaining how they work.

Part 2: Probing *why* school methods work mathematically

After a variety of methods are posted, direct discussion to the mathematical reasoning behind the methods. Start with an example that used the U.S. standard algorithm.

Point to any numbers that were borrowed.

$$\begin{array}{r} \overset{4\ \ 1}{52} \\ -35 \\ \hline 17 \end{array}$$

💬 **What's going on here? Where did this 1 come from? What does it mean?**

If students say "borrowing," ask:

💬 **How would you explain to a young child what *borrowing* means?**

💬 **So what are you really borrowing? (In this case, not a 1, but a 10)**

Use expanded notation to demonstrate the *why* of the U.S. standard algorithm:

💬 **One way to show borrowing is with Expanded Notation—where you see the real value of every number by breaking up the number differently.**

$$52 = 50 + 2 = 40 + 10 + 2 = 40 + 12$$
$$- 35 = \qquad\qquad\qquad\quad -(30 + 5)$$
$$\qquad\qquad\qquad\qquad\qquad\ 10 + 7$$

This still means 52.

Parentheses remind us to subtract the whole thing.

If students have a hard time following different ways of breaking up the numbers, use manipulatives like Base 10 blocks to demonstrate.

Pause and direct students to their *Reflections* (*Student Book*, pp. 259–260) to answer the question: What do you want to remember about the mathematical idea of borrowing?

Math Inspection: Showing What the Shorthand Means

This inspection is meant to help students see how subtraction with borrowing, or renaming, works. They regroup, taking an extra step to show explicitly what is happening when problem-solvers borrow. Regrouping is a valid approach, an application of the associative property.

The steps are not meant as a new algorithm for borrowing (although students can use the steps as illustrated in the example); rather, they are meant to focus students' attention on *why* borrowing works. This is an opportunity to show explicitly the associative property of addition. For instance, to subtract 59 from 71, you need to regroup 71: **71 = 70 + 1**. 70 is the same as **60 + 10**. **(60 + 10) + 1 = 60 + (10 + 1)**.

If students are struggling, have them do a few more examples with two digit numbers before they move on to #2, 3, and 4. If students are confused by the notation involved, you could have them draw columns for each place value: hundreds, tens, ones. Then, as they regroup, they can move the "borrowed" amount from one column to another.

$$859$$
$$-370$$

HUNDREDS	TENS	ONES
800	50	9
700 + 100	50	9
700	100 + 50	9
700	150	9
-300	-70	-0

This could be made even more visual and tactile with Base 10 blocks moving from one group or location to another. When students understand the process, show them how parentheses can be used as notation for regrouping.

Note that #4 is more challenging as it requires regrouping twice.

Ask students to work individually or in pairs to determine the solution to each problem. Then, as a whole group, ask for volunteers to share how they expanded the problem in order to regroup and then subtract. The focus of the discussion should be on when borrowing was useful and why it worked rather than solely on the correct answer.

Note that students who have learned arithmetic in other countries often use different effective and efficient algorithms for subtraction. If so, have them share theirs and investigate how and why their methods work.

Summary Discussion

Give students time to write responses to the
Reflection question (*Student Book*, pp. 259–260):
What are (three) different ways to think about what
subtraction means?

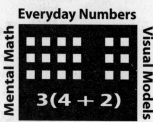

Everyday Numbers

Mental Math

Visual Models

3(4 + 2)

If students are searching for ideas, you may ask them
to give an example of a time when they want to find
a difference or make a comparison and a different situation when they had an
amount and some was to be taken away.

Check to see if the ideas about borrowing are clear at this point. Say:

 **"Borrowing a 1" means different things depending on the "1" you are
borrowing.**

What would the 1 borrowed in this problem mean?   52 – 36

What would the 1 borrowed in this problem mean?   325 – 242

Refer students to *Vocabulary* (*Student Book*, p. 254) to record their definitions
and examples.

Practice

Check Both Sides of the Equal Sign—Addition, p. 89
For reinforcement on the importance of paying attention to both sides of the
equal sign.

Check Both Sides of the Equal Sign—Subtraction, p. 90
For reinforcement on the importance of paying attention to both sides of the
equal sign, and exploring mathematical ideas, such as $a - b = (a + c) - (b + c)$.
Revisits concepts explored in *Lesson 4, Math Inspection: Check Both Sides of the
Equation*.

Heads Up!

As students work on *Practice: Check Both Sides of the Equal Sign—Addition*, and *Practice:
Check Both Sides of the Equal Sign—Subtraction*, they are working with **equivalent
expressions**. If those words don't come up as they explain what they notice about the
expressions given, bring them up yourself. You may define equivalent expressions as
numbers and operations that describe the same value. For example, **5 + 3 = 6 + 2** are
equivalent expressions; they are both equal to 8.

What's My Purpose for Estimating?, p. 91
For practice on estimating the degree of precision called for by the situation.
Solicit ideas from students related to shopping, bill-paying, estimating amounts of
food or cleaning supplies. Ask learners: When is it practical for an estimate to be
low or high?

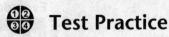 **Test Practice**

Test Practice, p. 92

 Looking Closely

Observe whether students are able to

Identify and use three models (or interpretations) of subtraction

Are students moving beyond seeing subtraction as take-away? Encourage (insist upon) a visual to go along with their verbal interpretations. What is the picture they see of the take-away? How do they see it? Are they employing the number line? Is it set up right with equal intervals?

If students insist on "sticking with what they learned before," check to see if they can articulate the connection between expanded notation and their algorithms for addition and subtraction.

Historically, expanded notation was drilled into people. Expanded notation is useful as a way to show place value, because it makes explicit the amounts that are borrowed and carried in addition and subtraction problems.

Because expanded notation reveals the quantities of 10's and 1's within a number, expanded notation reinforces work with 10's and 1's for students whose place value knowledge is not solid.

Examine, understand, and explain why algorithms for addition and subtraction work

Adults can mostly add and subtract in some way. Their ways may be cobbled together or remembered from long ago.

Though many educators are comfortable with the standard algorithm and would like to teach it, the goal of teaching these models is to give learners a sturdy, reliable way to compute. By discussing the many algorithms that work, everyone can learn something about taking apart and manipulating numbers. Someone with a half-remembered algorithm will benefit from working with someone who can help them reconstruct the steps, as opposed to starting from scratch. The one that has stuck with them in some form will be the go-to algorithm, remembered for years as opposed to a new piece of information to remember.

Few people subtract with pencil and paper in everyday life. Subtraction is either a mental process or carried out on a calculator. The reason to look inside the algorithm is to demonstrate why you can do things differently and still get the right answer (not just once, but reliably).

64 Everyday Number Sense: Mental Math and Visual Models

EMPower™

Rationale

This lesson helps learners connect the stories and pictures to the operation of subtraction. This book avoids teaching the algorithm, instead embracing the exploration of concrete models and meanings. When a class does get to the algorithm, we want to keep the meaning in tact. Teachers can do that if they ask students to match a picture, story, and notation.

Math Background

Lesson 5 expands the concept of subtraction to include "missing amount" situations, such as the scenario offered in *Activity 1*:

> Myrna had $80 when she went into the store. She came out with $30. How much did she spend?

These types of problems tend to be a little more challenging for students, because they have a different underlying structure. The problem above could be represented algebraically by

$$\$80 - a = \$30$$

To see how the problem above can be solved using $80 - $30 requires a deeper understanding of addition and subtraction. If we think in terms of a whole and its parts, $80 is the whole and it has been broken into two parts: $30 and the unknown quantity a ($80 = $30 + a). Subtracting either of the parts will give us the other. Students may need guidance to see this connection.

The expanded notation used in the exploration of the traditional addition and subtraction algorithms is based on an understanding of place value. In the explanation of "borrowing," the associative property of addition is used. The associative property says that we can regroup addends (often notated with parentheses) without changing the sum. For example,

$$(50 + 10) + 2 = 50 + (10 + 2)$$

In effect, this is changing the order in which we add the numbers, but without changing the order in which they appear (which would involve the commutative property of addition, explored earlier in *Lesson 1*). While the final sum does not change, changing the order or grouping of addends does change the partial sums

$$(50 + 10) + 2 = 50 + (10 + 2)$$

$$60 + 2 = 50 + 12$$

which is what allows the traditional "borrowing" subtraction algorithm to work— we get the extra value "moved over" into the place value where we need it to subtract.

Borrowing methods of subtraction are not always the easiest to do mentally, since they often require holding a large number of digits and steps in working memory. This lesson also provides more practice with the strategy of adding the same amount to the subtrahend and minuend, first introduced in *Lesson 4*. In this way, the amounts being subtracted can actually be changed (usually, to friendlier numbers) while the difference between them stays the same.

This can be modeled on a number line: if the difference between numbers is the same as the distance between them on a number line, imagine that set distance sliding towards the right. Both numbers would be increasing, but the distance between them would stay constant. This could also demonstrate the reverse: sliding the distance left on the number line would decrease the subtrahend and the minuend while the difference remained constant.

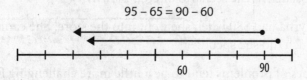

$$95 - 65 = 90 - 60$$

Context

Collect problems that students have struggled with recently or introduce a scenario related to cutbacks in services, wages, etc. Acknowledge that the idea of cutting sounds like take away, but raise the question "Is subtraction the best or only way to think through the consequences?" Another way to compare different models of subtraction is to look at sale advertisements, in which some emphasize the sale price and others highlight the amount saved. How can subtraction be used to find the missing information?

Facilitation

Students may not be accustomed to talking about the "why" behind the algorithms they have learned and apply regularly. You may need to explain that slowing down to discuss these problem solving moves is not pulling them back to elementary math, but laying a foundation for algebraic problem-solving.

Making the Lesson Easier

Stick with numbers 1-20 in examples. Have single or two-color chips, paper clips or other countable objects handy. Have a tape measure, number line or yardstick available as well to help students see the operation in linear space.

Making the Lesson Harder

Have on hand examples from the news.

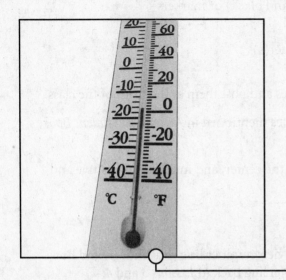

6

Extending the Line

> **What do you wear when the temperature drops below zero?**

Synopsis

This lesson introduces negative numbers (**integers**) on an extended number line, which continues to be employed as a problem-solving tool.

1. The class shares knowledge about negative numbers and reviews use of the number line. You show how the number line extends below zero.

2. Pairs construct an extended number line to track checking account actions.

3. Pairs find differences between world-record high and low temperatures using a picture of a thermometer's number line.

4. The class summarizes, sharing what they know about finding the difference between any two numbers.

Objectives

*   Locate **negative** and **positive** integers on the number line
*   Determine the difference between integers

Materials/Prep

- Calculators
- 8.5" × 14" paper or strips made from easel paper
- Colored pencils (including red and black) or markers
- Rulers
- Non-digital outdoor thermometer(s)
- World map

Prepare some large blank number lines and post them at the front of the class.

Post a world map with the various cities mentioned in *Activity 2* (*Student Book*, p. 95) located and labeled.

Construct a number line with zero in the center, and mark some positive and negative numbers on the line.

Opening Discussion

To prepare students for this lesson, review number line conventions and how numbers on the line are compared, referring back to *Lessons 3* and *4*:

- Numbers increase to the right.
- Numbers decrease to the left.
- Intervals are evenly spaced.
- Make jumps from one number to the next, count the spaces covered, and label the jumps.
- Add up the numbers on the jumps to find the total difference between two numbers.

Survey the class about previous experience with negative numbers.

If no one raises the following points, raise them yourself:

- Negative numbers are located to the left of the zero on a number line and below zero on a thermometer.
- When they are recorded, they are preceded by a minus sign (-).
- They represent amounts less than zero.

Heads Up!

See *Lesson Commentary: Math Background*, p. 73, for ways to address misconceptions.

Post a class definition of negative numbers and solicit some examples of negative numbers occurring—a business operating in the red, budget deficits, overdrawn bank accounts, feet below sea level, etc. Add to the class vocabulary list a definition for integers.

Introduce (or review) the term **integer**. Post the definition: zero or a whole number that can be positive or negative. Have students list examples of numbers that are integers.

Ask:

💬 **Why can't we refer to integers as all positive and negative numbers?** (Leave out zero, includes fractions and decimals like 1/2, 0.23, and so on.)

🌀 Activity 1: In the Red

Pair students. Distribute an 8.5" × 14" sheet of paper, a red pencil, a black pencil, and a ruler to each pair. Refer them to *Activity 1: In the Red* (*Student Book*, p. 94). Make sure everyone understands what a bounced check is and what the terms "in the red" and "in the black" mean.

As students show George's balance for each date on the number line, ask questions that emphasize the negative amounts. For example:

💬 **How did you know it was -$75? What does a negative amount of money mean?**

💬 **Is George's balance on January 27 enough for him to pay his $650 car loan?**

Reach agreement on George's final balance.

If it has not come up in the discussion, mention that zero is neither a positive nor a negative number. If George has a balance of $0, he is neither in the red nor in the black.

🌀 Activity 2: Record Highs, Record Lows

Begin a discussion about number lines and temperature by saying something such as this:

💬 **In today's newspaper, the weather report says, "high 60°F to 65°F, low 52°F to 57°F." Those temperatures represent a range of temperatures that we can expect.**

💬 **By the end of the day, though, there will be a high and a low.**

Discuss the term **range**. You might use as an example the range of ages in the class. Note:

- The range in everyday language describes highest to lowest or lowest to highest (such as, 18-years-old to 60-years-old).

- The range can be described by a single number that represents the difference between these two values (a range of 42 years).

Post a class definition of the term "range" as described by students in their own words. Continue:

💬 **Depending on where you live, temperatures may dip into negative numbers. What is the coldest temperature you have ever known?**

Draw a line on the board. Ask a volunteer to set up the number line so all suggested temperatures can be posted on it. Watch for correct placement and notation of negative numbers. If no one mentions a temperature below zero, mention one or two yourself.

Ask:

What is the warmest temperature you have ever known?

Ask volunteers to place their temperatures on the number line on the board and to initial them.

Heads Up!

The activity refers to Fahrenheit temperatures. Be sure to ask whether temperatures mentioned are Fahrenheit or Celsius, and make sure students distinguish between the two.

Refer students to *Activity 2: Record Highs, Record Lows* (*Student Book*, p. 95). After they complete Part 1 on the thermometer, ask students to find partners for Part 2.

As you circulate, observe how students mark the thermometers and number lines. Ask:

What is similar about marking temperatures on a thermometer and on a number line? What is different?

Make sure the fact that negative numbers on a thermometer appear *below* zero while negative numbers on a number line appear *to the left of* zero is understood and that the connection is made between numbers on a thermometer and the horizontal number line.

Question how students arrived at the difference between the highest and lowest recorded temperatures. Push for number-line explanations.

Heads Up!

Focus students' attention on marking jumps using 10's and 1's, as they did in *Lesson 4*. Remind them to total only the numbers recorded above the jumps.

Because different pairs have likely chosen different temperatures to compare, ask students to share their methods. End by asking them what they noticed about finding the difference between two numbers (as in Problem 14).

Summary Discussion

Expand students' awareness of the use of negative numbers by posing a question with a different context:

What do you now know about finding the difference between any two integers?

You want students to use mental math to find an answer and then to show the class their reasoning on a number line.

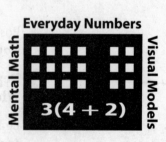

Refer students to *Reflections* (*Student Book*, p. 260), where they should write what they know about negative numbers and finding the difference between integers, and to *Vocabulary* (*Student Book*, p. 254) to record their definitions..

Practice

Planting Zones, p. 98
For practice finding ranges and differences on the number line.

What's the Range? p. 100
For practice finding differences between integers using a variety of visual models.

Ordering Numbers, p. 101
For practice ordering positive and negative integers.

Mental Math Practice

Count Up and Down by 10's, p. 102
For practice skip-counting by 10 along the extended number line (positive and negative regions).

Extension

Sorry, Account Overdrawn, p. 103
To challenge reasoning about numbers and applying number-line strategies to a money situation.

Below Sea Level, p. 104
For a challenge finding differences between large numbers.

Test Practice

Test Practice, p. 105

Looking Closely

Observe whether students are able to

Locate positive and negative integers on the number line

Most students are comfortable counting up, moving to the right on a number line; however, counting down, or "backward" to the left, can pose some problems, especially when negative numbers are involved.

First make sure students can easily count forward and backward with positive numbers. Then help them see the symmetry in the number line. Draw attention to the zero as the pivotal point that separates positive numbers from negative numbers. Zero itself is neither positive nor negative. It may be helpful to mark positive numbers in black and negative numbers in red.

Examination of thermometers and elevation markers may help students focus on the "up-ness" and "down-ness" of the positive and negative numbers, but they should see the connection to the horizontal representation, where going left is similar to going down and going right is analogous to going up.

Determine the difference between two numbers

Although students have been working on the difference between two numbers in *Lessons 4* and *5,* in this lesson they encounter negative numbers for the first time. Locating them on a number line is intended to help them see the difference as the distance between any two numbers, including negative numbers. If they have difficulty with this at first, use smaller numbers. For example, ask them to find the difference between 8 and -6. If students think about the difference in terms of the distance model, they will be able to see 8 to the right of zero and 6 to the left, which totals 14 altogether.

When they are comfortable with small numbers and have begun working with larger numbers, remind them to think in terms of the distance between the two. Examples that use money seem to be helpful, as most people are familiar with gains and losses.

Two issues may arise for students as they seek to determine a range. They may think of the range as the listing of high and low values and not the interval between them, and they may think that a range of negative numbers is negative.

To help students see the interval, mark it off and label it "range." Then apply counting techniques within the established range. Ask questions such as, "How many spaces (numbers) does the range cover?"

Explain that whether the numbers are located above or below zero—that is, whether they are positive or negative—is irrelevant when determining the range. One needs to know how many intervals, or spaces, are between the highest and lowest numbers that mark the boundaries of the range. Students can mark the spaces off and count the total, as discussed in *Lesson 4.*

Rationale

Negative numbers are relevant, particularly in light of budget deficits, personal debt, and scientific research. A familiarity with a number line expands students' ability to follow or participate in public discourse on a variety of topics.

Math Background

The focus in this lesson is on locating positive and negative integers on the number line. Finding differences between two points on the number line continues that focus. Rely on the distance model of subtraction because when finding the difference between two numbers (say, 107 and -125), locating and then seeing the space between the two numbers is what makes the answer (232) reasonable. The mathematics anticipates, but does not cover, formal operations with integers.

The introduction of negative numbers challenges ingrained ideas about positive numbers. For example, the number -500 is less than -50. With positive numbers, the larger numbers are more than the smaller ones: +500 is larger than +50. Further confounding understanding is the fact that when talking about debt, –$500 actually indicates *more* debt than -$50, and -45°F is colder than -25°F. Help students reframe the ideas—when the temperature is -45°F, there is *less* heat in the air (and a thermometer measures "heat" not "cold") than when it is -25°F. These language issues can lead to deep confusion; address them when they arise.

Context

Most people are familiar with rising and dropping temperatures. You might use this opportunity to introduce the Celsius and Fahrenheit scales, both derived from the temperatures at which water freezes and boils.

Facilitation

Stay away from rules on operating with negative numbers. The lesson is designed to build intuitive understanding.

Making the Lesson Easier

Build number lines together as a class. Work with familiar numbers (multiples of 10 or 5). Avoid pinpointing the exact differences at first. Concentrate on weather change scenarios, such as those where the temperature was 10°F and then dropped to -20°F. (How many degrees did it drop?)

Encourage students to do the *Mental Math Practice: Count Up and Count Down by 10's* (*Student Book*, p. 102).

Use real thermometers and have students demonstrate on those, counting up or down by 10's. Then work with number lines or mental strategies. Assign *Activity 2: Record Highs, Record Lows* (*Student Book*, p. 95) only when students are comfortable with these easier numbers.

Making the Lesson Harder

Use messier numbers and have them first estimate what they think the difference or range will be. Also, have students create real-life story problems illustrating examples of when they have had to deal with negative and positive numbers.

The following dialogue illustrates how one class began the discussion on negative numbers and worked on Activity 2.

Teacher: "When have you heard of negative numbers?"

Student 1: "Paying bills. Money not coming in, but going out."

Teacher: "States have hard times right now. There are huge budget what? (Silence) Starts with a 'd.'"

Student 1: "Deficit."

Student 2: "What's that mean?"

Student 1: "Loss, debt."

Teacher: "How about temperatures?"

Student: "Below zero, -10°F, when it freezes."

The class looked at a sample number line from -9°F to 9°F.

Teacher: "Which temperature is higher or warmer? -1 or -9? Let me see whether you have it right: Is -9 more than -1?"

Students seemed to grasp that -9°F is less, that is, a lower temperature. The class did three more problems together. In one, a student at the board read, "Start at 25. Go down 30." He ended up at -10°F, then changed his mind and chose -5°F. Once he showed the jumps above the number line, everyone agreed with his answer.

The class read over the information about high and low temperatures worldwide. Several students started their number lines with zero in the middle. This meant that the extreme highs and lows were squished together at one end. Lynn had the most trouble getting started. Her classmate tried to explain her own number line, where the increments were listed by 25°F increments. Lynn wondered how to determine where to place Africa's high temperature of 136°F. She seemed puzzled by how Una had known to number up to 150°F, and she asked, "Is there another way to do it?" Alex was able to explain what he did. He began with a list of the high temperatures from highest to lowest. Then he numbered his line in increments of 10. With his strategy, it was easier to see where to place 136°F.

Alex knew to subtract 59°F from 136°F to find the range of high temperatures. I asked him to show the difference on the number line. He counted back from 136°F ("6°F + 10°F, 20°F, 30°F, 40°F, 50°F, 60°F, 70°F. That's 76°F + 1°F, 77°F"). Would it work the same way if you started from 59°F? He tried it and it worked.

Martha Merson, Observer
Community Learning Center, Cambridge, MA

Ups and Downs with Addition

> *Does addition always make things bigger?*

Synopsis

This lesson continues to explore integers, using both a number line and **zero-pairs** model. The focus is on visualizing the addition of signed numbers.

1. The class uses a classroom number line to track addition of bank deposits and withdrawals.

2. Students record movement back and forth on the number line with symbols.

3. Pairs use two-color chips and zero-pairs to model the bank deposits/ withdrawals and other contexts.

4. The class makes generalizations about integer addition.

Objectives

- Use visual models and symbolic notation to express addition with integers

- Describe patterns that occur when adding integers (e.g., commutative and associative properties, the additive inverse, connecting subtraction of a positive amount with addition of a negative)

Materials/Prep

- Metric rulers or meter sticks
- *Blackline Master 6: Number Lines -1,000 to 1,000*, one per pair
- *Blackline Master 7: Number Lines -20 to 20*, optional resource for *More Practice*, one per student pair
- *Blackline Master 8: Bank Balance Cards*, five of the same cards from the full set per pair, cut apart
- *Blackline Master 9: Balance Ups and Downs,* optional resource for *More Practice*
- Two-color chips, or two colors of paper squares, several per student, or red and black markers along with paper squares
- Material for large number lines (masking tape, strips of paper, Post-it Notes)
- Play money for *Activity 2: Concentration*

Prepare several large number lines (at least two meters long, marked off in 10 cm intervals) on the floor using masking tape with sticky notes or two-inch wide paper. Label extending from -1000 to +1000, marked off in 100's. .

Heads Up!

If time allows, have student pairs make their own large number lines from -1,000 to +1,000 on long strips of flip chart paper or on adding machine tape. They can label increments of 100 or possibly 50. It is a valuable experience that requires planning equal intervals, as well as thinking about how the numbers progress on each side of the line.

Opening Discussion

Start by saying:

 In the last lesson, you explored numbers below zero—the negative integers. Now we are going to look at how to add positive and negative integers. So, first let's discuss what you know about the operation of addition by looking at some statements.

Write four true-or-false statements on the board:

1. Addition, subtraction, multiplication, and division are the four mathematical operations.

2. Addition can be thought of as an act of combining amounts.

3. The answer in addition is called the sum, or total.

4. The sum, or total, is always larger than each of the parts that are added, or the addends.

Answers: 1. true 2. true 3. true 4. false

Ask small groups to discuss and come to agreement about the truth or falseness of each statement. Then ask for each group's decision, listening carefully to various perspectives. Expect disagreement, especially on the fourth statement, and ask for people's reasoning with examples. Record what people say. Acknowledge that it is not unreasonable to think statement 4 is true. In basic arithmetic, with positive numbers, the sum is generally larger than each of the parts (4 + 10 + 7 = 21, and 21 is larger than each addend). An exception occurs when at least one of two addends is zero (9 + 0 = 9, and 9 is equal to one of the addends). When you extend the numbers to include negative numbers, all bets are off!

Say:

 In this lesson, you are going to explore addition with a number line including positive and negative numbers. You'll do that addition in two ways—with the number line and with color (chips, markers, or paper squares).

 ## Activity 1: Bank Balance Ups and Downs

This activity begins with a -1,000 to +1,000 number line on the floor, large enough to walk along. If floor space is limited, it could be posted on the wall for all to see and to physically move along. This kind of physical movement creates some muscle memory.

Heads Up!

One goal of this activity is for students to view combining deposits and/or withdrawals as the operation of adding them. When you add a deposit, it brings your balance up. When you add a withdrawal, it brings the balance down. At some point, students will most likely assert, "Withdrawing just feels like subtracting to me!" Pause for emphasis at this point, saying "Exactly! You can think of adding a negative amount the same way you think about subtracting (taking away) a positive amount. (-150) added to 400 (400 + -150) is the same as 150 subtracted from 400 (400 – 150). They both bring the total down!" Encourage students to practice thinking of adding amounts, whether they are negative or positive.

The language of banking may not be familiar to all students. Words like balance, deposit, bounce, and check all have different meanings in other contexts. Explain them as needed.

Begin the activity by explaining that the number line on the floor/wall will be used to represent actions with a personal checking account.

 Imagine that this line is a record of your bank account balance. What would the negative numbers represent? The positive numbers? Zero? Where should we place your account balance the day you walk into the bank, before you make your first deposit?

Demonstrate. Ask for a volunteer to stand at a number line at "before I make the first deposit." Then give directions and ask him/her to move the appropriate number of spaces in the appropriate direction. Encourage coaching from the group.

💬 **You begin with a balance of $0. Your first deposit is $400. Where are you now?** [400 to the right of $0, 400 above zero, 400 positive, plus 400] **What did you do to get there?** [added 400 to 0] **Which direction did you move?** [toward the right (up) or positive direction]

(Write on the board)

We could record that as:

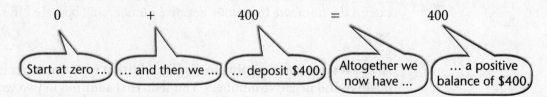

0   +   400   =   400

Start at zero ...   ... and then we ...   ... deposit $400.   Altogether we now have ...   ... a positive balance of $400.

💬 **Now you write a check (withdrawal) to pay your cable TV bill of $150. Which direction did you move?** [to the left, negative] **Where will that bring you?** [$250 above zero, positive 250, in the black 250]

After reaching agreement, write on the board.

💬 **We could record that as:**

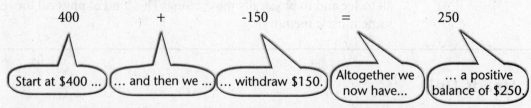

400   +   -150   =   250

Start at $400 ...   ... and then we ...   ... withdraw $150.   Altogether we now have...   ... a positive balance of $250.

💬 **Now you pay your part of the rent with a check for $600. Which direction will you move?** [to the left, negative] **Where will that bring you?** [$350 below zero, negative 350, $350 in the hole]

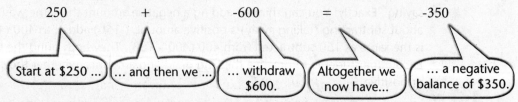

250   +   -600   =   -350

Start at $250 ...   ... and then we ...   ... withdraw $600.   Altogether we now have...   ... a negative balance of $350.

💬 **We could show the three actions on the number line as:**

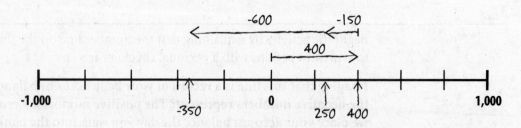

💬 **What happens now, when you overdraw? Some banks just return (bounce) the check and also charge a fee. Some cover the check, but charge a fee. Some give you a safety valve (overdraft account) if you have a minimum in your savings. Let's assume this one is an overdraft account with no fees.**

Once students are comfortable moving in the appropriate direction and have seen several examples written symbolically, ask them to complete *Activity 1* in pairs. Direct attention to *Activity 1: Bank Balance Ups and Downs (Student Book,* p. 108). Pass out five cards from the cut up set of *Blackline Master 8: Bank Balance Cards* to each pair, making sure each pile is shuffled. Also, distribute copies of *Blackline Master 7: Number Lines -1,000 to 1,000.*

As students are finishing up, ask two or three pairs to record their equations on the board.

Bring the whole class together to examine what students notice. They might say:

"We all got to the same balance in the end, even though we did in it different order" or "Order doesn't matter when you add."

Heads Up!

Be careful not to assign black/white as negative/positive. Better to start with red as negative ("in the red") and black or another color as positive.

 ## Activity 2: Show the Bank Activity with Objects

Begin a discussion about the difficulty of "seeing" negative amounts of money. In this activity students use color and objects to count positive and negative amounts—to make these amounts concrete. This will give the class a way to visualize combining negative and positive numbers. Look for agreement and understanding among students—you can't hold negative amounts of money in your hands, even though you know debt is a heavy weight.

> **In this activity we are going to use markers or chips to "see" what positive and negative amounts of money look like. This will give you a chance to visualize what is happening when negatives and positives are combined.**

Distribute two-color chips or two colors of markers to pairs of students. Explain that one is positive and the other is negative (if red is one of the color choices, it would be the side preferred for negative). Be sure there is agreement about which is positive and which is negative. Hold up the red, or negative item.

> **If this were money, what would it represent in your checking account?** [withdrawing $1]

Ask the same about the other color. [depositing $1]

> **What if I put the two of these together? What do I have?** [nothing—the positive and negative have cancelled each other out]

$$+1 \ + \ -1 \ = \ 0$$

Discuss the term *zero pair*: the positive and negative numbers which, added together, total zero. Then place four positive chips and four negative chips together where the students can see them.

How much money did I deposit? How much did I withdraw? Did I change the balance? Why or why not?

Write the following on the board and ask for responses, along with explanation of thinking:

$70 + (?) = 0

-$50 + (?) = 0

Discuss the term **additive inverse** of a number. -70 is the additive inverse of 70. Likewise, 50 is the additive inverse of -50.

Then model several examples of adding with positive and negative numbers. For example, model the situation of depositing $5. Put out 5 positive chips. Then add a withdrawal of $7. Put out 7 negative chips. You can find five zero pairs, which leave you with a balance of negative 2, or -2.

$(+ + + + +) + (- - - - - - -) = (- -)$

Direct students to *Activity 2: Showing the Bank Activity with Objects* (*Student Book*, p. 109) using the same six bank balance cards and the math they recorded in *Activity 1*. Ask the pairs to now use chips. Assign a convenient value to each color: positive $50 = 1 color chip, and negative $50 = 1 other color chip.

Ask them to see if they end up with the same balance as they did when they used the number line.

Suggest students add these terms to their vocabulary lists (*Student Book*, p. 255): zero pair, additive inverse.

 # Math Inspection: Check Both Sides of the Equal Sign

This inspection builds on the previous lessons—addition and subtraction with positive whole numbers. This inspection is another opportunity for students to see the connection between adding a negative amount and subtracting that same amount.

Ask students to work individually or in pairs to determine the solution to each problem. The three equations illustrate adding a negative integer on one side of the equation and writing equivalent expressions using subtraction of a positive integer on the other side.

When you debrief with the whole class, you want students to be able to state that adding a negative number is the same as subtracting the positive of that number. Use the term "additive inverse" as needed. The intent is for students to attach meaning to the concept and recognize it when it appears. With students, list some examples of when adding a negative shows up in daily life, e.g., working with debts or deficits that need to be taken into account.

Summary Discussion

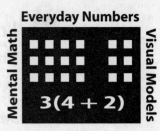
Start the summary by reviewing the rules the class members generated about adding withdrawals and deposits (*Activity 2, Student Book*, p. 109).

Then remind the class that together you tried two ways to show addition with positive and negative numbers. Ask:

💬 **Which is easier for you to see, the two color chip model or the number line?**

Listen for responses.

💬 **Let's go back to the four statements about addition we started with in this lesson. What do you agree with? How would you change the fourth statement to make it true?**

💬 **Write down two more true statements about addition of integers that will be important to remember. Did you discover any shortcuts?**

End with this statement:

💬 **When you study algebra, you will want to think about "addition of the opposite" rather than "take away." So when you see 40 – 30 you think 40 + (-30).**

Give students a minute to tell a partner or the class in their own words why that is different.

Refer students to *Vocabulary* (*Student Book*, p. 255) to record their definitions and examples.

🎯 Practice

Number of the Day: -10, p. 111
For practice writing expressions that total to negative 10.

More Practice Adding Integers, p. 112
For practice adding positive and negative numbers. Provide copies of *Blackline Master 9* for students to use with this exercise.

Adding Integers in Different Situations, p. 114
For practice adding integers using number lines or chips in contextualized situations.

Up and Down the Elevator, p. 116
For practice adding integers on a vertical number line.

① ② ③ ④ Test Practice

Test Practice, p. 117

Looking Closely

Observe whether students are able to

Use visual models (number lines or two color counters) and symbolic notation to express addition with integers

These models give all students, and particularly those who are visual learners, the chance to see what the action of combining looks like. With the two-colored counters, red may be negative, black may be positive. Pairing one of each color to cancel each other and make zero is very explicit. Likewise, moving along a number line, to the right for positive values and to the left for negative values, is a strong visual aid. Do students recognize the effect of combining amounts that cancel each other out?

Describe patterns that occur when adding integers

What language do students use to express how quantities change when negative or positive amounts are combined? See if they can anticipate in which direction the total is moving, toward a positive or negative extreme or toward zero, the neutral point. For example, listen for students to explain that adding negative numbers results in a number that is more extremely negative, further from zero on the number line. As an example, can they see that debt grows when you add negative amounts? You lessen debt by adding a positive number.

If students are able to attach meaning—real-world examples—to the mathematics they are working with, it will help them lay a sturdy foundation. Look for other ways to play with these ideas that involve falling and rising through a neutral point such as an elevator going to above and below ground levels of a building or parking garage or descending into and rising above the ocean from sea level.

Do students notice and use zero pairs to simplify their calculations (as exemplified in 5 + -5 = 0)? Can they see the connection between adding a negative and subtracting a positive? These are some important number properties that lay the foundation for algebra.

Rationale

Negative numbers are as much a part of students' lives as positive numbers. Since students have a sense of what it means to go below zero, this lesson engages students in further developing their intuitive sense of the effect of combining positive and negative numbers. The lesson sticks with the concept of combining because the symbols, action, and meaning can then be explored and connected.

Math Background

This lesson continues to develop important mathematical ideas:

1. The effect of subtracting is the same as adding a negative;

2. The action of adding a negative can be visualized on a number line.

The properties of the operations underlie what students do in arithmetic and in algebra. At this point students should be pretty confident that the order in which they add two numbers does not change the answer. This lesson is a chance to see whether this holds for combining negative and positive numbers. If $15 + 3 = 3 + 15$, is this statement also true: $15 + -3 = -3 + 15$. Why is this true and an allowable move when subtraction is not commutative?

When you rewrite $15 - 3$ using addition, you have $15 + -3$. The important point is the negative sign stays with the value 3. It signifies that 3 is less than zero on the number line, that any quantity in combination with it will be less 3. To the student it looks as though the operational sign of subtraction morphs into a negative sign.

To say this in words, $15 - 3$ and $15 + -3$ can both be interpreted as I have 15 with a loss of 3. They are equivalent expressions. Because addition is commutative, you can say, I had a debt of 3 in combination with 15. However, you cannot attach the negative sign to fifteen and make the 3 positive: that would change the meaning of the problem.

Another way to think about this is that the starting point matters when considering subtraction on the number line. However, the starting point does not matter with addition. One combines parts to make a total and these parts are easily interchangeable whereas one starts with a total and removes a part when subtracting. You could not reverse that and start with a part and remove a total.

Context

Apply new ideas to contexts like football (yards gained, yards lost) or breaking even when a certain dollar figure is reached.

Facilitation

Making the Lesson Easier

Slow down. Do a few more examples. Stick with the picture, connect with the story. Have students act out the story, if possible. If not, ask them to represent the story using a picture or number line. Students should have at least one model they understand and are able to use and check for themselves.

Two-color chips or a number line should make sense. At least one should be a tool they feel comfortable using to check themselves.

Making the Lesson Harder

Push students to articulate generalizations. Ask them to support their conjectures with examples. You could ask students to say what is the same or different about two problems with similar-appearing numbers, such as these:

$$-1,257 + 999$$

$$1,257 + -999$$

You might also ask students to evaluate expressions with messier numbers such as this one:

$$-1,099 + 257$$

Teachers often note that it is not trivial to get the students to try to learn conceptually instead of using the algorithms exclusively.

Students really enjoyed *Activity 1: Bank Balance Ups and Downs.* Almost everyone got it right. [They] appreciated the number line for practice adding integers. Before really beginning *Activity 1*, students asked if everyone would end up at the same final answer. I threw the question back to them and asked why yes and why no, leaving the question unanswered until the end of class.

The activity was a stretch for almost everyone. All remembered that the order of adding and subtracting doesn't matter. I was surprised how few caught onto the idea that adding a negative is the same as subtracting a positive.

When doing this material, the students were generally able to make sense of the problems, generally. It sort of naturally evolved into a discussion of absolute value because all the problems were addition problems. They were able to explore the varied approaches for solving these problems (i.e., doing the computation in the same order in which it was described verbally was only one way to do it). My advice is to relate the lesson as much as possible to everyday life.

I used a bank analogy to teach addition and subtraction of integers after I taught the skills and concepts using a football analogy.

Questions I am glad I asked:

What happens in life when you gain something negative?

Is adding a negative the same thing as taking away?

Paul Tardy
Bronx Adult Learning Center

I don't use any special supplies. One year I had chips that are red on one side, yellow on the other, but sometimes I use pennies where I paint a negative sign on the tails. Sometimes I use blue squares and red squares.

I also show students how I organize a problem, like -7 + 8 on paper.

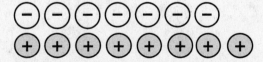

They like this because they can do it quickly on a piece of paper.

Donna Parrish
Rogue Community College, Oregon

FACILITATING LESSON **8**

Take Your Winnings

> *What is the largest amount you have ever won?*

Synopsis

In this lesson, students examine and record the make-up of whole numbers. In the context of lottery winnings, they think about how a number is composed in terms of 1's, 10's, 100's, and 1,000's. Then they play a game of concentration, matching equivalent amounts.

Mental math remains the focus when calculators are introduced. Savvy students can "beat the calculator" in arriving at an answer by examining the change in place values.

1. The class relates concrete experiences with $10, $100, and $1,000 bills to math operations and notation.

2. Student pairs use the context of a lottery to consider the make-up of large amounts of money in terms of 1,000's, 100's, and 10's. They use notation with *parentheses* to record their various solutions.

3. In pairs, students play a game of concentration, matching amounts written in expanded notation.

4. Individuals predict calculator operations by deconstructing numbers.

5. Students interpret and notate multiplication problems with exponents.

Heads Up!

Lesson 8 uses the context of lottery winnings as a jumping off point. If gambling is a sensitive issue in your class, reword the problems with the total representing a shared bonus or gift.

Objectives

- Examine and identify the composition of a number in terms of 10's, 100's, and 1,000's

- Mentally add or subtract multiples of 10, 100, and 1,000 and then check mental math with a calculator

- Use notation (parentheses, exponents) in investigating and representing the connection between exponents and multiplication with powers of ten.

Materials/Prep

- Calculators

- Play money or slips of paper marked in denominations of $1, $10, $100 and $1,000 (Monopoly™ money works well)

Make copies of *Blackline Masters 10* and *11*: *Concentration Cards*, one per student pair. Cut each into a set of 12 cards, and clip each set together or place in an envelope.

Opening Discussion

Tell students that today they will work more with tens, hundreds, and thousands. They will need to think about the make-up of large amounts of money.

As an introduction, pose the following questions:

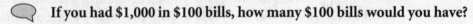 **If you had $1,000 in $100 bills, how many $100 bills would you have?**

How do you know?

Ask a volunteer to demonstrate the solution using play money or slips of paper marked in appropriate denominations. Then ask someone to describe that solution process with numbers and math symbols.

Students might write

$100 + $100 + … + $100 = $1,000

or

$10 × $100 = $1,000

or

$1,000 ÷ $100 = 10.

Make explicit the connection between the concrete task in the money demonstration and the symbolic math notation.

Then ask:

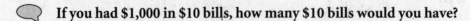 **If you had $1,000 in $10 bills, how many $10 bills would you have?**

How do you know?

Again ask for a demonstration of the solution both in paper money and symbolically.

Students might write

$100 \times \$10 = \$1,000$

or

$\$1,000 \div \$10 = 100$.

Lead "Count Around."

Students stand in a circle and count around—beginning with 0 and counting by a friendly number, such as 100. Then start with a less friendly number such as 6,750 and have students count up by 100's or 1,000's. Have a student up at the board jotting down each number as it is shared. Make sure some numbers go across next grouping, e.g.,

Count up by 100. Start: 6,750; 6,850, 6,950; 7,050, 7,150

Count up by 1,000. Start: 6,750; 7,750; 8,750; 9,750; 10,750

Count up by 100. Start: 139,800; 139,900; 140,000; 140,100

Count up by 1,000. Start: 139, 800; 140,800, etc.

 ## Activity 1: How Do You Take Your Winnings?

Ask a volunteer to read the story aloud at the beginning of *Activity 1: How Do You Take Your Winnings?* (*Student Book*, p. 120). When everyone is clear about the directions, encourage student pairs to talk with one another to reach agreement on the ways each woman (Andrea, Barbara, and Carla) will receive her winnings.

Observe who is doing mental calculations, who is using pencil and paper, and who is counting out money. Ask those who finish early to seek an alternative solution method. For those who are having difficulty, offer the play money as a way to work out the problem.

When everyone has finished the first problem, ask for volunteers to explain their solutions for the three different distributions of $3,843. Ask:

Who wants to share how they solved this problem?

Who solved it differently?

How can you be sure your answer is right?

Write all offerings on the board. If there is disagreement, ask for verification with play money.

Correct solutions are as follows:

Andrea receives three $1,000 bills and the rest ($843) in various denominations. There are many ways to combine the rest. They might be:

- three $1,000 bills, eight $100 bills, four $10 bills, and three $1 bills, or
- three $1,000 bills, 84 $10 bills, and three $1 bills, or
- three $1,000 bills, seven $100 bills, 14 $10 bills and three $1 bills.

Barbara receives 38 $100 bills and the rest ($43) in various denominations.

Carla receives 384 $10 bills with three $1 bills for the remainder.

Use this activity as an opportunity to reinforce the convention of **parentheses** in notation. Establish the practice that from now on the class will write three $1,000 bills and eight $100 bills and four $10 bills and three $1 bills as

3($1,000) + 8($100) + 4($10) + 3($1).

Have pairs continue with Problems 2 and 3, asking students now to use parentheses in the notation. In other words, "3($1,000)" will be a way to write "three $1,000 bills." Post offerings for Problems 2 and 3 on the board and reach agreement on possible ways each woman might receive her money.

Say:

💬 **We have looked at various ways that an amount of money can be given; now we are going to think about a different situation.**

Post these questions or share them on a transparency one at a time:

💬 **Suppose Dora won the lottery and asked for her winnings in $10 bills. The clerk gave her 28($10) + 5($1). What were her winnings?** ($285)

💬 **Suppose Emilia won the lottery. The clerk gave her 36($100) + 5($10). What were her winnings?** ($3,650)

Conclude this activity by pushing for some generalizations about the relationship between 1,000's, 100's, and 10's.

Ask:

💬 **What patterns have you noticed about the make-up of a number?**

Students might offers statements such as these:

> "Three thousand, four hundred can be read as thirty-four hundred."
> "One thousand is the same as 10 hundreds."
> "One thousand is the same as 100 tens."

If no one mentions that a number such as 3,000 is the same as 30 hundreds or 300 tens [3(1,000) = 30(100) = 300(10)], ask people to fill in the missing amounts in number sentences such as these: 3(1,000) = ?(100) = ?(10). Then ask students again what patterns they notice, especially with the zeroes.

🌀 Activity 2: Concentration

Distribute one set of *Blackline Masters 10* and *11: Concentration Cards* to each pair of students.

Ask for a volunteer to read the directions for *Activity 2: Concentration* (*Student Book*, p. 121). When everyone understands the directions and the goal of winning the most money, ask pairs to play the game, reminding them to replace the cards if there is not a match. Pairs that finish quickly might play the game a few more times.

After everyone has played the game successfully at least once, bring the class together and ask how that went. Then have some students to write equations on the board that describe their matched pairs, using parentheses in their notation.

Some possible equations are listed here:

$5(\$1,000) + 2(\$100) = 52(\$100)$

$\$5,200 = 520(\$10)$

$50(\$10) + 2(\$1) = 5(\$100) + 2(\$1)$

$\$502 = 502(\$1)$

$2(\$1,000) + 5(\$100) = 25(\$100)$

$\$2,500 = 20(\$100) + 50(\$10)$

Conclude by asking:

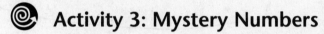 **How do you know that your equations are correct? Who matched equations to get the most money?**

🌀 Activity 3: Mystery Numbers

This activity presents a game in which students figure out the amount that has been added or subtracted to change one number into another on the calculator screen. The goal is to investigate the effects of adding and subtracting **multiples of 10, 100, and 1,000.** The activity should go quickly, but it will afford another opportunity to concentrate on deconstructing numbers. Students will need to pay attention to place value.

Make sure everyone has a calculator.

On the board, write a three- or four-digit number as the starting number. Ask students to clear their screens and enter that number in their calculators. Now secretly add 100 to the number and write the result as the end number.

Set up the board like this:

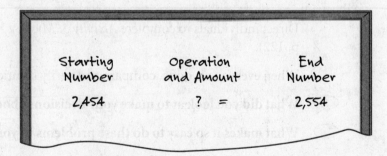

Starting Number	Operation and Amount	End Number
2,454	? =	2,554

Ask:

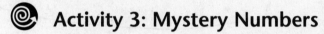 **What could you do to the starting number to arrive at the end number? Do this in your head.**

💬 **How do you know?**

Take all suggestions and ask students to verify accuracy, using the calculator to check the operation with the number of the proposed answer and then pressing the "=" key to arrive at the result.

Do another problem, this time secretly adding or subtracting a multiple of 10, 100, or 1,000 to a starting number to get the end number. Students first arrive at the operation and amount using mental math and then verify their answers with calculators.

For example: You write "6,753" and students enter in their calculators "6,753." You secretly subtract 300 and write down "6,453"for the end number. Students again use mental math to find the answer and calculators to check its accuracy.

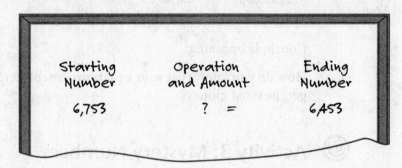

Next, ask students to suggest some starting numbers. Proceed with each number as you did with the previous problems, and give students the end number. For example:

$$7,541 - 40 = 7,501$$

Heads Up!

Be prepared for issues about calculator use to arise. For example, students who are accustomed to seeing a comma divide decimal and whole numbers may be thrown off. Some students may need to be reminded to press the equals key.

Direct individuals to complete *Activity 3: Mystery Numbers* (*Student Book*, p. 122).

When everyone is done, compare and verify solutions and summarize by asking:

💬 **What did you look at to make your decisions about the operation and amount?**

💬 **What makes it so easy to do these problems in your head?**

Students should notice which digit changed, the value of the digit in that place, and whether there was an increase or decrease. In each case, they should see that adding or subtracting a multiple of 10, 100, or 1,000 made the math easy to do mentally.

When you review this activity, call attention to "wrap-around" numbers, those that change in more than one column as you add or subtract. Ask students to share their strategies for solving these, and illustrate their comments with a number line. Provide a few more examples if these problems interest students (for example, $526 - 80$; $739 + 70$).

Conclude by asking:

💬 **When you found the mystery numbers, were you faster than the calculator?**

🌀 Activity 4: How High Can You Go?

The goal of this activity is to add the exponent to students' repertoire of symbols that makes sense to them.

Begin by asking students to call on and share previous knowledge. Ask:

💬 **If you received a message saying you won $\$10^6$, would you be happy? How much money would that be?**

Ask pairs to come up with a value, and record the values on the board. Ask for explanations. Then, depending on the knowledge in the class, clarify what the small raised 6 means, and describe an exponent as a signal as to how many times a number (the base, here 10) is used as a factor.

Say:

💬 **Today you are going to use exponents to write some numbers, especially powers of 10.**

Direct students' attention to *Activity 4: How High Can You Go? (Student Book, p. 123.)*

Students will probably point out that the exponent matches the number of zeros when working with powers of ten. Ask them if they can explain why this is the case.

⊖ Math Inspection: Symbols for Multiplication

This inspection builds on the various ways that multiplication can be represented by illustrating that exponents can be used when multiplying the same number by itself. By now, students should have had some exposure to the different symbols for multiplication ($\times$, $\cdot$, and parentheses). Students should be able to explore the difference between symbolic structure such as $10(3)$ vs. 10^3 so that they can begin to build automaticity in thinking about the exponent not as a number to be multiplied but rather an indication of how many times the base must be multiplied times itself.

Students often confuse expressions for exponents with expressions for multiplication. Be prepared to review many times how to interpret exponential notation.

In this inspection, students work in pairs to address each of the questions. Be sure to take time to have students create their own examples using exponents. They will further explore the idea of multiplying with exponents ($a^2 \times b^2$) vs. ($a \times b$)^2 in a later *Math Inspection*. For now, ask them to try to figure out which expressions are the same without focusing on any rules that they might not remember.

Summary Discussion

Give students time to write in the *Reflections* section (*Student Book*, pp. 261–262) what they want to remember from this lesson about the make-up of whole numbers and especially about any shortcuts they used. Then ask for volunteers to share what they have written.

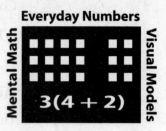

Have students record definitions in *Vocabulary* (*Student Book*, p. 255).

Practice

True or False? p. 127
For practice interpreting equivalent amounts written in expanded notation.

More Mystery Numbers, p. 128
For practice mentally adding or subtracting multiples of 10, 100, or 1,000 to a given amount and then checking the answer with a calculator.

Calculating With Money, p. 129
For practice entering dollars and cents into the calculator. Students will need to be careful with decimal points and zeroes.

College Registration, p. 130
For practice thinking about and calculating with 100's in context.

Number of the Day, p. 131
For practice writing large amounts, using exponents.

Mental Math Practice

Double Trouble, p. 132
For practice doubling or halving amounts quickly.

Test Practice

Test Practice, p. 134

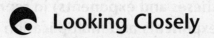 **Looking Closely**

Observe whether students are able to

Examine and identify the composition of a number in terms of 10's, 100's, and 1,000's

Are students developing confidence and flexibility as they consider the various ways to think about numbers as in *Take Your Winnings*? Allow time for them to make confident connections between the concrete play money and the written amounts.

Are students noticing number patterns? For example, do they see that when 3($1,000) = 30($100) = 300($10), the total amount of zeroes remains the same? Make sure there is explicit discussion about such patterns. For more practice, assign *True or False?* (*Student Book*, p. 127).

Finally, are students able to read a number such as 6,500 as "six thousand, five hundred," as well as "sixty-five hundred," and thus see the connection between 6(1,000) + 500 and 65(100)?

Mentally add or subtract multiples of 10, 100, and 1,000 and then check mental math with a calculator

Are students readily able to identify multiples of 10, 100, or 1,000? See *Lesson 8 in Action*, p. 101, for how one teacher took time to list examples of multiples before starting *Mystery Numbers*.

In the *Mystery Numbers* activity, also assess the students' comfort with calculators. If you think they might benefit from more calculator practice, assign the practices *More Mystery Numbers* (*Student Book*, p. 128) and *Calculating With Money* (*Student Book*, p. 129), where their attention is focused on the zeroes and decimal points. When dealing with dollars and cents, several dilemmas often arise:

When adding $3 and 7¢, punching in "3 + 7" does not lead to a reasonable answer. One needs either to convert all numbers to dollars ($3 + $0.07 or $3.00 + $0.07) or to cents (300¢ + 7¢).

The calculator leaves out some (unnecessary) zeroes. For example, 3 + .50 = appears as 3.5 on the calculator. On the other hand, the calculator will often append zeroes (.70 + .10 = 0.8). The interpretation of $0.8 as 80¢ can be puzzling.

Commas are not the same as zeroes. In fact there are calculator models that do not use commas at all.

Be aware that if students come from other countries, decimals and commas may have been used very differently than the ways they are used in the United States. For example, in South America, a comma indicates a separation between the whole and the decimal fraction, whereas the point marks off the thousands and millions. In other words, the comma and the decimal point have opposite meanings than they do in the United States.

Use notation (e.g., parentheses and exponents) in representing the connection between exponents and multiplication with powers of ten.

Do students recognize exponent notation as repeated multiplication of the same number—for example, interpreting 10^3 as $10 \times 10 \times 10$, not as 10×3? Are they able to explain the connection between powers of ten and the number of zeros? Numbers with many digits, especially if most of them are zeros, can be visually confusing for many students. If students struggle to accurately count zeros or determine place value, see if they know the conventions for placing commas in large numbers (which are intended to break up the string of digits for easier reading). Students who struggle with visual alignment may benefit from using grid paper or lined paper turned sideways to create columns.

Do students understand the use of parentheses as a convenient convention to represent repeated groups? Do they understand 4($1,000) to mean "four 1,000's, or $4 \times \$1,000$?" This notation is common in algebraic models and scientific contexts.

Rationale

Students' familiarity with denominations of money provides a basis for developing a deepened awareness of the composition of numbers in the base-10 system. This familiarity also is a foundation for an intuitive understanding of an expanded notation for a number, place value, and ease with mental calculations.

Math Background

This lesson develops three important mathematical ideas.

Noticing patterns in the composition of base-10 numbers provides a basis for more powerful mental math calculations

The lottery activity requires students to go beyond identifying the place value of the digits in a four-digit number. Although it is important to be able to note the place value of each digit (the usual treatment of place value in basic math books), this excercise is designed to go a step further. By calculating how many $1,000, $100, and $10 bills they can derive from a certain amount of money, students not only attend to place value but at the same time develop connections between 10's, 100's, and 1,000's. Knowing that there are 10 hundreds in 1,000, 100 tens in 1,000, and 10 tens in 100 is important and provides a basis for later work, such as mentally multiplying and dividing by 10's, 100's, 1,000's, and their multiples.

A repertoire of notation conventions offers multiple ways to record and represent concrete experiences

Knowing equivalent expressions for a quantity and connecting those expressions to concrete representations is important. Play money can be useful here.

Parentheses are introduced in this lesson as a way to group and separate amounts. Their connection to multiplication, e.g., that $2 \times 30 = 2(30)$, and their use as a way to impose order, e.g., $3(4 + 5) = 3(9)$, will be explored in the next lesson.

The lesson also treats expanded notation more broadly than merely writing a number to show the value of each place, e.g., $679 = 6(100) + 7(10) + 9(1)$. Although students should be familiar with what is traditionally understood as expanded notation, they are asked to think about alternative and equivalent expansions of the number, such as $67(10) + 9(1)$.

The *Math Inspection: Symbols for Multiplication* and *Activity 4: How High Can You Go?* take this notation one step further. Students explore the connection between powers of ten and exponents. As numbers get larger, exponents provide us with a compact way to preserve place value without writing out so many zeros. Instead of writing 60,000,000, we recognize that this number is equal to $6 \times 10,000,000$, which can be written as 6×10^7. Notating this way makes very large (and, later on, very small) numbers easier to read by drawing our attention to the place value of the 6 and avoiding the need to count zeros, which is often a source of human error. This is the basis for scientific notation, which records numbers as a product of non-zero digits times a power of ten. For example, 23,000 becomes 2.3×10^4. Some students will encounter scientific notation if they are preparing for High School Equivalency tests in math or science or if they pursue other scientific or technical training.

The calculator can be used in tandem with mental calculations

This lesson focuses on the calculator as a way to check against reasonable mental calculations. Dissonance caused by answers that vary when both a calculator and mental math are used presents an opportunity to bring in concrete examples as the arbiter.

Context

Money launches the lesson with the lottery context of the first activity, but students are also encouraged to leave context for a while as they attend to number patterns that support mental math computation.

Facilitation

Making the Lesson Easier

Slow down and keep examples concrete. It is more important to focus on the concept of the make-up of a number than alternative notation.

Making the Lesson Harder

Introduce larger numbers that involve 10,000's, 100,000's and 1,000,000's. Introduce non-whole numbers (dollars and cents).

In one class, the teacher took the time to solidify the multiples of 10, 100, and 1,000 as a prelude to Activity 3: Mystery Numbers.

> Today we worked on *Activity 3: Mystery Numbers*. We started off with the question "What is a multiple?" and then made lists of multiples of 10, 100, and 1,000. I put all answers on the board, whether they were correct or not. If we weren't sure, we put the answer up with a question mark. Then I asked the students whether they could make any observations, which I recorded on the board, for example, "There are a lot of zeroes" and "All numbers that are multiples of 100 have at least two zeroes." We used these statements to reconsider our numbers with question marks and move them to the correct columns. I gave the students time to copy these notes from the board.
>
> Then I put a box on the board with a number in it and asked whether it was a multiple of a certain number. For example, I'd write "30" and ask, "Is this a multiple of 100? How do you know?" I gave different students a chance to come to the board and put numbers in the box.
>
> Finally, we started working on mystery addition and subtraction, on the board only. I encouraged students to use their calculators to figure how to get from the beginning number to the end number. First, we would decide whether to add or subtract; then we would decide how much we needed to add or subtract.
>
> *Jonna Rao*
> *SafeSpace, New York City, NY*

Patterns and Order

> *Which is faster—mental math or a calculator?*

Synopsis

Students identify patterns when multiplying and dividing by 10, 100, and 1,000 and then test their mental math skills against the calculator. Using mental math and the calculator, they begin to explore the importance of **order of operations**.

1. The class agrees upon patterns that occur when multiplying and dividing by 10, 100, and 1,000.

2. Working in pairs, students test whether they can solve multiplication and division problems faster using mental math or with calculators.

3. Students solve equations involving the numbers 3, 4, and 5 and addition and multiplication and compare their results with those of the calculator.

4. Students use and examine the role of parentheses in determining the order of operations in various equations.

5. The class summarizes findings.

Objectives

- Identify and use patterns when multiplying and dividing by 10, 100, and 1,000

- Use order of operations to solve problems

Materials/Prep

- Scientific calculators, one per student; make sure they follow order of operations as some do not

Prepare to display *Blackline Master 12: Patterns with 10, 100, and 1,000* or copy the numbers on the board.

Opening Discussion

Start by saying:

> 💬 **In math, noticing and making use of patterns is important. Some people have said mathematics is the study of patterns.**

> 💬 **Let's look at some of the patterns from the previous lesson, where people took their winnings in different ways.**

What are the different ways people could take their cash lottery winnings for $5,000?

Ask volunteers to write solutions on the board. If necessary, prompt by asking how many $1,000 bills, $100 bills, $10 bills, or $1 bills there could be. If no one uses parentheses as notation, ask whether someone could rewrite any of the answers with parentheses.

Focus on 5($1,000), 50($100), 500($10), and 5,000($1) by circling them. Next, ask:

> 💬 **What about $900?** [9($100), 90($10), or 900($1)]

Ask:

> 💬 **Do you see any patterns in the numbers here? What do you notice?**

Students might say:

> "There are always the same number of zeroes."
>
> "It always means multiplication."
>
> "You just count the number of zeroes at the end."

If it does not come up in the discussion, connect the notation with parentheses to multiplication, pointing out that 3(1,000) is one way to write 3 × 1,000.

Display *Blackline Master 12: Patterns with 10, 100, and 1,000* or copy the numbers on the board. Ask individuals to try the multiplication problems, first doing all the multiplications by 10, using patterns whenever they can; then the multiplications by 100; and finally all the multiplications by 1,000.

When students are done, ask pairs to check answers with one another, and then ask for responses to the question:

> 💬 **What is the rule or pattern you notice?**

Make the connection between multiplication and division. Ask:

> 💬 **How could knowing these patterns in multiplication help with a division problem, such as 70 ÷ 10? How do you know?**

Make sure the relationship between multiplication and division is explicit. Ask:

 If you know that 261 × 10 = 2,610, then what is 2,610 ÷ 10?

Ask for a few more examples of connecting division to the multiplication problems.

 ## Activity 1: Mental Math or Calculator?

Introduce the activity by asking:

 Mental math or calculator—which is faster?

Refer students to *Activity 1: Mental Math or Calculator?* (*Student Book,* p. 136). Pair students and go over the directions.

After students finish the first 10 problems, they will write some of the things they notice about multiplying and dividing by 10, 100, and 1,000. Bring the class together to share.

Students may give examples such as these:

> "Multiplying by 10 or 100 is easy because I just add one or two zeroes."
>
> "Dividing a number that ends in zero by 10 is easy—I just take out the last zero."

Ask for explanations.

Anticipate that the issue of order may arise as a result of the use of a calculator. Although order does not make a difference for multiplication (e.g., 90 × 10 = 10 90), it does for division (e.g., 300 ÷ 10 does not give the same result as 10 ÷ 300).

Reinforce the importance of estimation for arriving at reasonable answers.

 ## Activity 2: 3, 4, 5

Heads Up!

While most scientific calculators (as well as those on cell phones) use order of operations, some, like desktop calculators, do not. Verify that your calculators do before beginning this activity. Point this out to students to help them avoid confusion in the future.

Refer students to *Activity 2: 3, 4, 5* (*Student Book,* p. 138).

Review the directions for Part 1.

 Use the numbers 3, 4, and 5 and two operations, addition and multiplication. Write as many number sentences as you can. Use each number and operation exactly once in each sentence.

Ask students to work on this individually at first.

💬 **Now check your number sentences with the calculator.**

Then ask:

💬 **Which answers are different? What did the calculator do differently?**

Record some sentences that resulted in different responses.

For example, $3 + 4 \times 5 = 23$ if the operations are performed with the calculator, but if done left to right, $3 + 4 \times 5 = 35$.

After a few examples, establish that the calculator always does the multiplication first.

Post the rule "Multiply first and then add" in students' words.

Next, students work on Part 2 (*Student Book*, p. 139), through Problem 4. They complete each part in Problem 3 the way a calculator would and they do the problems according to the rules of order of operations.

Verify answers with the whole class and then ask:

💬 **What answers would you get if you did the operations left to right?**

Post answers. Note that three of the answers would be different from the ones obtained with a calculator.

💬 **How would you write these three number sentences if you wanted the answer to match your left-to-right order?**

If no one mentions parentheses, introduce them. Draw parentheses around the addition where appropriate, and explain that when there are parentheses, they indicate that you perform the operations inside of the parentheses first. For example, $1 + 9 \times 5$ would be written as $(1 + 9) \times 5$ if left-to-right order were wanted.

Add:

💬 **Order matters! In mathematics, parentheses help us communicate order. If there are no parentheses, then the order of operations is to multiply first and then add.**

💬 **What happens if we work with division and subtraction? What did you find in Problem 5?**

The problem is similar to the ones with multiplication and addition. Push for the rule "Divide first and then subtract."

Students will have opportunities to pursue this further in *Practice: Just Like the Calculator* (*Student Book*, p. 143).

Activity 3: How Many Different Ways Can You Solve It?

The goal of this activity is to introduce the distributive property (of multiplication over addition and subtraction) beginning with students' intuitive sense of numbers. Depending on the level of your students, you may want to use more informal language around the distributive property rather than using the more formal structure:

$$a(b + c) = ab + ac$$

Begin by asking students to call on and share previous knowledge.

Ask:

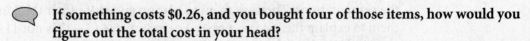 **If something costs $0.26, and you bought four of those items, how would you figure out the total cost in your head?**

Give everyone time to think through the problem on their own, then ask for some solution strategies. You want to focus on the strategy related to the distributive property—such as multiplying **0.25 × 4** and then adding 4 cents (**0.01 × 4**).

Then ask:

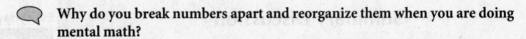 **Why do you break numbers apart and reorganize them when you are doing mental math?**

You want to make sure students see the value of breaking numbers apart in order to make the problem easier and more efficient to solve.

Then ask them to tackle *Activity 3: How Many Different Ways Can You Solve It?* (*Student Book,* p. 140).

Once everyone has come up with at least two strategies, ask for volunteers to share. Watch for examples of how students broke numbers apart, solved each part separately, and then put the parts back together again.

If possible, use students' examples to illustrate the distributive property. If not, use a discussion similar to the following:

One way of determining the total cost of 12 monthly payments of $142 is to multiply 12 times 142. But that is the same as this:

$$12(142) = 10(142) + 2 (142)$$

In this example, 12 months was broken down into 10 and 2 months. The 142 represents the cost, and the 10 and 2 represent months.

Another way to solve the problem could be this way:

$$12(142) = 12(100) + 12(40) + 12(2)$$

What does the 12 represent in this situation? The 100? The 40? The 2?

Be sure that students can explain what was broken apart (months vs. money).

Have students explain what they are doing when they are "distributing" the numbers. They should understand that the distributive property allows you to "break a number apart and then multiply each part individually and add (or subtract) the parts back together again."

 ## Math Inspection: Who Is Right?

This inspection focuses on the order of operations, illustrating the types of mistakes students often make. Being able to analyze someone else's process helps students become more comfortable in assessing their own work. The examples intentionally include and exclude parentheses.

In this inspection, ask students to first work alone giving them time to go through the computations. Then ask them to pair up and share their thinking. Encourage them to explain the incorrect ones. For example, 4 (3 − 1) is not 11; ask students to articulate what went wrong. When you go over the problems together with the class, be sure to be explicit about the order of operations and the role of the parentheses. When there are no parentheses, the order of operations says to first perform any multiplication and division operations, then perform addition and subtraction from left to right.

Summary Discussion

Ask students:

 What are some of the things you need to be aware of when you use a calculator?

 How does estimation help when using a calculator?

Establish that although the calculator can help you find an answer, you may not catch a mistake made by pressing keys if you do not first have an estimate in mind.

Recap the order of operations:

 When a problem includes multiplication, division, addition, and subtraction, but no parentheses, what is the order of operations?

Refer students to *Reflections* (*Student Book*, p. 262), where they can write down some of these ideas, and to *Vocabulary* (*Student Book*, p.255) to write definitions.

 ## Practice

Number of the Day, p. 142
For practice creating expressions using more than one operation to focus on order of operations.

Just like the Calculator, p. 143
For more practice with order of operations.

More or Less? p. 144
For practice making estimates.

Mental Math Practice

Shopping Mentally, p. 145
For practice applying the distributive property in order to mentally solve problems.

Multiply and Divide with 10, 100, or 1,000, p. 146
For practice computing mentally with powers of 10.

 ## Extension

The Answer Is 24, p. 147
For practice with writing word problems and checking equations with the calculator.

Wrong Number! p. 149
For practice using mental math to solve problems.

 ## Test Practice

Test Practice, p. 150

Looking Closely

Observe whether students are able to

Identify and use patterns when multiplying and dividing by 10, 100, and 1,000

Do students use the strategies they have learned in the unit to make reasonable estimates? Realizing that they can solve the problems faster using mental math than by entering the numbers on the calculator should give them confidence.

Do students use the calculator correctly, finding the appropriate keys and reading the display? Review calculator use with those students who need the help or with the whole group.

As needed, review related material or sheets from previous lessons on rounding and making mental estimates.

Use order of operations to solve problems

Do students adjust to the convention of order of operations? Watch students as they begin a problem. Do they take a second to scan the equation, looking for multiplication and division signs? Encourage students to make notes on or around an equation. Colored markers or different colored pencils or pens might help students highlight the operations and put in parentheses as reminders.

Help students articulate the difference between working an equation left to right and following the order of operations.

As students are breaking apart numbers, informally exploring the distributive property, can they re-trace their steps using order of operations? Do they represent their steps correctly using math notation?

Rationale

Sound mental math computational skills depend on the ability to see patterns. One of the most useable patterns is the one that occurs when multiplying by powers of 10.

Because the lesson centers on calculator use, it introduces some conventions about order of operation. Although there are mnemonic devices for remembering the order (Please Excuse My Dear Aunt Sally, PEMDAS, etc.), the multiple experiences solving equations in a left-to-right manner and comparing them with the same equations solved by the calculator will help students see the importance of order of operation.

Math Background

Patterns with Powers of 10

Multiplication and division by 10 and powers of 10 involve zeroes. How many zeroes should be added or removed? It is important to have an idea of the magnitude of the result so that the answer makes sense. For example, 760×100 should be a large number because it can be thought of as 100 groups of 760—for example, 100 baskets, each filled with 760 cherries. That's a lot of cherries!

$760 \times 10 = 7,600$

$760 \times 100 = 76,000$

Similarly, $8,700 \div 100$ can be solved using the fact that $100 = 10 \times 10$, so $8,700 \div 10 = 870$, and $870 \div 10 = 87$.

Although a calculator will yield the answers, it is likely just as fast, if not faster, to solve these problems using mental math. In all cases, the reasonableness of the solution is important.

Order of Operations

As in reading, where commas indicate a pause and periods mean "stop," in mathematics, the operations in a string of numbers also have meaning, indicating order. Establishing order of operations determines universal reading and solving of equations: parentheses take precedence—anything inside of them is to be done or solved first; then exponents; after that multiplication and division; and last, addition and subtraction. For example, $62 + 8 \times 5$ is *not* solved left to right, but instead, by doing the multiplication first—$8 \times 5 = 40$—followed by the addition—$62 + 40 = 102$.

On the other hand, $(62 + 8) \, 5$ is solved by adding the amounts inside the parentheses first $(62 + 8 = 70)$ and then multiplying $(70 \times 5 = 350)$.

The two equations communicate different stories.

Distributive Property

Students first begin working with the distributive property in *Lesson 2*, when they work on estimating and adjusting. At first, some students may have made the error of only adjusting to account for one item, for example:

$$\$3.99 \times 4$$

$$\$4(4) - \$.01 \text{ (incorrect)}$$

The reason this doesn't work is because when we rounded $3.99 to $4, we added $.01 for each item, so a total of 4 times. In this case, the 4 has to be distributed to both the $4 and the $.01: the parts that, when subtracted ($4-$.01), make $3.99.

The distributive property can also be used to find unknown multiplication facts from known facts. For example, if I know that $5(15) = 75$, and that $2(15) = 30$, I can add five 15's and two 15's to figure out that seven 15's must be $75 + 30 = 105$. This is a powerful property for increasing facility and fluency with multiplication.

Facilitation

For those who question the need to use the order of operations, it will help to discuss other sequential activities and what happens when steps are done out of order—for instance, drying clothes before washing them. Students might also relate this mathematical convention to grammatical conventions they automatically follow, such as placing the verb after the subject of the sentence unless it is a question. English speakers do not put the verb first, saying, "Go I"; the convention is that the noun comes first: "I go."

Making the Lesson Easier

Stretch out the activities over a number of days. After doing one activity, choose a related practice and do that with the class.

Encourage students to do the *Mental Math Practice: Multiply and Divide with 10, 100, or 1,000 (Student Book, p. 146)* before they work on any of the other practices in this lesson.

Making the Lesson Harder

Use numbers that do not end in 0, and ask students to divide by 10, 100, or 1,000. This will yield answers with decimals.

Use dollars and cents. The inclusion of the decimal point requires more careful use and interpretation of the calculator. Refer students to *Extensions: The Answer Is 24 (Student Book, p. 147)* and *Wrong Number! (Student Book, p. 149)*.

Two teachers wrote the following about Activity 2: 3, 4, 5.

The group really enjoyed generating the number sentences for *3, 4, 5*. For most of them, using two operations in one number sentence was a big hit. At the point when we looked at which equations got different answers, the class started to diverge into two groups: a few who got it quickly and the rest who didn't.

Those who got it were excited. One woman wrote in her journal:

"Today is one of my best days. I actually look forward to [class] because I get to learn something new like using the parentheses. I was actually having fun doing it because I never knew it was so interesting. I got to like it. I also learned how to use the scientific calculator."

Deidre Freeman
Lehman College, Bronx, NY

All were engaged and attentive for most of the lesson period. Everyone learned something and felt successful. Ted said he had figured out how to use the function keys. Elana, a younger student, exclaimed as she checked her *3, 4, 5* problems on the calculator, "I know what's going on; you're trying to trick us. I see what I did wrong." (I had to urge her to refrain from spilling the beans to the other learners before they had a chance to see for themselves.)

Nora asked the key question: "Why are we getting different answers?" Nora's question led to a grand discussion of "Elana's Rule" that multiplication should always come first. Jay, a young and restless learner, said he did not think the rule would hold in all cases, so we tried each suggested number sentence to see whether her rule would work to get the same number as shown on the calculator. Lo and behold, it did! Everyone was convinced and, I think, surprised and pleased. Here was a fact, a "truth" they could hold: Do the multiplication first.

Jay was enthusiastic when it came time for everyone to write two or three of their own number sentences on the board. "We get to write the problems— all right!" Ted provided a great challenge to the class with his example — $(2 \times 3) + 4 \times 2$. Most people, including Ted, thought the answer was 16, though at least one person said 20. The "20" answer indicated that they had forgotten to do the multiplication first the second time around. Those who answered 16 acknowledged that they, for some reason, multiplied 6 by 2 before adding 4. When we worked it out by rewriting the sentences after each step, they all saw immediately what the answer was. Ted noted that, "I tricked everyone" (himself included).

Tricia Donovan
Pioneer Adult Education Center, Northampton, MA

FACILITATING LESSON

10

Picture This

> ## *How many are there?*
> ## *How do you know?*

Synopsis

Students explore ways to visualize and represent numbers and operations with arrangements of objects in arrays (rows and columns) and equal groups. This lesson is the first of two lessons that focus on totaling and breaking apart groups of items while making connections among visual representations, mathematical expressions and equations, and word problems.

1. The class discusses ways to total items without individually counting each object. They record ideas using words and equations and by marking off arrays.

2. Individuals find at least two ways to record the total number of items in pictured groups, and then student pairs match equations with arrays.

3. Student pairs arrange collections of objects for ease in counting and write equations that reflect their arrangements.

4. Student pairs solve the *Garden Pathway* problem, and the whole class reviews the problem.

5. Students compare the algorithms they use to solve multiplication problems.

6. Using arrays, students make visible the subtotals resulting from the US standard algorithm. Students see the distributive property at work.

7. The class summarizes what they learned about showing equations and writing equations. Then they discuss using math to find totals in their daily lives.

Objectives

- Write math expressions to reflect regular arrangements of objects in groups and arrays
- Represent equations using arrays and/or equal groups arranged to correspond with numbers and operations
- Identify **equivalent expressions**

Materials/Prep

- Colored markers
- Easel paper
- Uniform objects for counting, such as paper clips, pennies or counting chips, enough so that each student or pair can have between 30 and 60

Enlarge or project a copy of *Blackline Master 13: Windows.*

Take note of arrays around your classroom, for example, the arrangement of floor or ceiling tiles, desks, or windowpanes. Bring to class some items that come in arrays, for instance, egg cartons, six-pack containers, flats of garden plants, or booklets of stamps. These may be empty, as long as it is clear how many items they would contain. You could also take photographs and/or cut out magazine pictures showing things in rows and columns.

Opening Discussion

Set up the lesson by saying:

 We have discussed different ways we calculate with numbers—mentally, with a number line, or with a calculator. Today we focus on a way of using math to describe an arrangement of objects. In this lesson, you will concentrate on visualizing the operations of multiplication and addition or subtraction.

Post and say aloud the definition for **arrays**:

 **Arrays show items arranged in rows and columns.**

Show or sketch actual arrangements of 2×6 and 4×3 arrays.

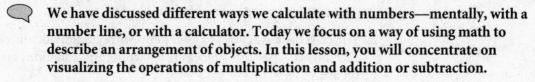

Direct students to look around the class for examples of other arrays. Ask:

How many items are in this array? In this one?

How did you count them?

There are many ways to count. Students will likely say, "I counted one by one"; "I counted one row and then multiplied by the number of rows"; or "I skip counted by 4's." Ask whether they might have counted the number differently if they looked at the array differently, vertically instead of horizontally, for instance.

Display *Blackline Master 13: Windows* and say:

 I know someone who *thinks* in arrays! She washes windows for a living and charges $5 a window. She needs to make quick estimates for her customers, so she never counts one by one. When she looks at a building like this, how many windows does she see?

Give students a moment to talk to a partner. As volunteers share approaches, record their ideas with equations. If someone says, "I counted by 3's," ask for details—what he or she said or thought when counting each group. Demonstrate on the board how the person saw the numbers in the array, and record the numbers as well as any explanation of mental arithmetic.

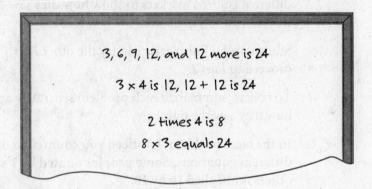

3, 6, 9, 12, and 12 more is 24

3 × 4 is 12, 12 + 12 is 24

2 times 4 is 8
8 × 3 equals 24

If someone explains, "I just knew that three 4's equal 12, so I added 12 and 12," post a copy of the picture and record:

- 3 × 4 = 12 (Box the first set of windows and label the sides with the numbers 3 and 4.)

- 12 + 12 = 24 (Box the second set of windows and label it "12.")

If the question "I saw 4 × 3—is that the same?" arises, take the opportunity to rotate the array pictured and ask, "Has the total changed?" You may wish to try a few more array examples to emphasize that 6 × 2 = 2 × 6, and these are equivalent because their total is equal.

Encourage a variety of approaches by asking questions such as these:

 Did anyone count by 4's?

Did anyone use only addition? What did you do?

Did anyone use only multiplication? What did you do?

💬 **Did anyone multiply different numbers together or multiply numbers in a different order?**

💬 **Did anyone use addition *and* multiplication?**

As you record equations, ask whether anyone is familiar with other ways to record. For instance, if you record "3 × 4 = 12," ask whether anyone knows another way to show multiplication. Occasionally, vary your own recording to help students learn the different notation, in particular, use the raised dot and parentheses, as in 3 · 4 and 3(4).

🌀 Activity 1: Pictures and Numbers

Refer students to *Activity 1: Pictures and Numbers* (*Student Book*, p. 152).

Part 1

Students find totals without counting each individual item; instead they focus on groups of things.

They record at least two ways to find the total and mark the chosen pictures with different colored markers to show how they saw the numbers. Each student does this for two sets of objects.

Students who finish early can try the other *Part 1* items or find a partner and proceed to *Part 2*.

To review, summarize each problem separately and ask students to demonstrate how they saw the numbers.

💬 **In the faces problem, I noticed you counted in different ways and wrote different equations. Some people counted by 1's, some people added 10's, and others multiplied 10 by 10.**

💬 **How are those ways alike? How are they different?**

💬 **Is the same true for the chocolates problem, where some people added and multiplied and some people counted?**

As connections are made between the expressions, take this opportunity to define **equivalent expressions**—those that result in the same total. Students may add this definition their list, *Student Book, Vocabulary*, p. 255.

Then focus on the counting:

💬 **Each way you counted involves multiplying some number a certain number of times.**

💬 **With counting by 3's, 6's, 10's, etc., and repeated addition, you say or think, for instance, of all the 3's up to the total of 18. Multiplication is shorthand for that.**

Part 2

Continue with *Part 2*, where the pictures are grids of squares and less literal.

First take suggestions for mathematical expressions, writing students' offerings on the board.

Probe:

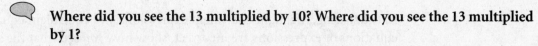 **Where did you see the 13 multiplied by 10? Where did you see the 13 multiplied by 1?**

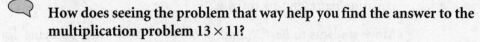 **How does seeing the problem that way help you find the answer to the multiplication problem 13 × 11?**

Have volunteers show the rest of the class how they matched the remaining expressions and arrays.

Bring into the discussion ideas about pulling apart numbers to make multiplying easier and "seeing" expressions in different formats that can be connected visually as well as by notation.

When you discuss the equation $10 \times 10 + 13 \times 1 + 3 \times 10$, highlight the 10×10 block, and introduce the raised **exponent** as another shorthand way to record an instance when a number is multiplied by itself (10^2). Numbers that can be drawn in arrays where the rows and columns are equal are called "**square numbers.**" In this case, the exponent 2 tells you that two 10's are multiplied by one another. Ask:

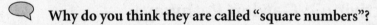 **Why do you think they are called "square numbers"?**

What other square numbers can you think of? How would you write equations for them using an exponent? How would you write equations for them *without* using an exponent?

⟳ Activity 2: Counting Smart

Refer students to *Activity 2: Counting Smart* (*Student Book*, p. 156) and review the directions for *Part 1*. Give each pair a small handful of paper clips, pennies, or chips (about 30 to 60).

As students work, ask them how they are deciding on their arrangements and supporting the arrangements by recording the expressions. Ask students who are done quickly to create an arrangement that involves two operations.

Student pairs that finish early look at another pair's arrangement and explain with an equation how they found the total without counting each item. Pairs then compare their equations, noting how they are alike and different.

Call the class together to share some of the ways they grouped the paper clips or tiles. Find one pair who made arrays and ask them to make their sketch on the board. Ask:

How many rows did you use? What did you do with the extra items that didn't make up a full row?

Who has another way to write an expression for this arrangement?

Did anyone put the paper clips or tiles in groups of the same size? What size groups did you use? Why?

 Which was easier for you to count? Why?

In the sharing, highlight equivalent expressions and equivalent equations. If equations or expressions are incorrect, show how *you* see what the student's equation represents pictorially.

Move students to *Part 2 (Student Book*, p. 157), where students draw pictures to match mathematical expressions. Pairs of students select two expressions to draw, and those pairs who finish quickly might draw a picture for all four expressions.

Students share and compare their pictures, checking to see that the pictures correspond to the expressions.

See *Lesson 10 in Action*, p. 128, for ways students connected expressions and visualizations.

By the end of *Activity 2,* students will have used objects to create arrangements which they then wrote as mathematical expressions and drew as pictures to represent expressions.

 ## Activity 3: Garden Pathway

Refer students to *Activity 3: Garden Pathway* (*Student Book*, p. 158).

When everyone is clear about the directions, allow time for individuals to create at least two ways to show the number of tiles mathematically. Then bring the class together to share expressions.

There are several ways that students might write the expression for 96 tiles. Some might see the double rows of two 10's on the sides and the corners with four tiles each. Possible answers include:

1. a row of 14 on top, a row of 14 on bottom and 4 rows of 10 on the sides

   $14 + 14 + 10 + 10 + 10 + 10 = 2(14) + 4(10)$

2. 2 rows of 12 on right and 2 rows of 12 on left and a row of 10 on top and a row of 10 on bottom

   $12 + 12 + 12 + 12 + 10 + 10 = 4(12) + (2 \times 10).$

Some students may figure out the number of tiles to cover the whole area, and subtract those that cover the garden:

$14(12) - 10(10)$ or

$14(12) - 10^2$

If no one brings up the subtraction, say:

 I saw this as $14 - 10(10)$. What did I see?

During the review, insist that students demonstrate to one another how they came to their expressions.

Conclude by having them evaluate each expression, using the rules of order to verify that each expression equals 68.

 ## Activity 4: Understanding the "Why" of Our Multiplication Methods

In this activity, students will have the opportunity to examine the mathematical principles behind their procedures, or algorithms, they regularly use for this operation. This is not a lesson on *how* to multiply with paper and pencil. It is assumed that students have learned to do this. If there are some who do not know how to, this discussion will uncover that, and you may want to provide extra practice.

Part 1: Students share their algorithms for multiplication

Launch from the algorithms that student use with a public display of "Our Multiplication Procedures (Algorithms)," similar to those suggested for addition and subtraction in *Lesson 5*.

Start by saying:

> I know you have been doing basic multiplication for a long time, sometimes in your head, sometimes using a paper and pencil, and sometimes with a calculator or computer. It depends on what the situation is.

> Right now, we're going to take a look at the paper and pencil methods you learned in school, and may still use, and discuss not just how they work, but why they work, connecting them to the arrays we have been working with. This knowledge is important groundwork for higher math.

Present the following problems to solve:

> What is the cost of 13 T-shirts @ $11 per shirt?

> Your three-year cell phone contract is almost up. For the last 32 months, you have paid $45/month. What have you paid on the contract thus far?

First ask the class for estimations, and record those on the board.

> How would you figure out the amount using paper and pencil?

Ask students to check with another person to see if they did it exactly the same way. Then have volunteers show various methods on the board, explaining how they did it.

Heads Up!

Students from other countries may not have learned the U.S. standard algorithm, but might still use a standard algorithm that is based on sound mathematical principles.

Part 2: Probing *why* school methods work mathematically

After methods are posted, direct students' attention to seeing multiplication with arrays, by completing and discussing:

- *Math Inspection: Rectangles, Arrays, Area, and the Distributive Property* (*Student Book*, p. 160), using single-digit rectangular arrays to visualize how the property works; and,

- *Math Inspection: Connecting Arrays to Multiplication (Student Book,* p. 164), using two-digit rectangular arrays to visualize how the U.S. standard algorithm for multiplication works. This is not designed to teach students how to multiply, but rather to show them why the algorithm works.

After completing the math inspections, return to the Public Display of "Our Multiplication Algorithms." Ask students to work in pairs to look for connections between the way they did 11 × 13 on paper and the array on p. 164, and between the way they did 45 × 32 and the array on p. 166.

 ## Math Inspection: Rectangles, Arrays, Area, and the Distributive Property

This inspection illustrates the distributive property. For example, the first situation, (6 × 7), has been regrouped to show 6(5 + 2), or 6(5) + 6(2). Seven could have been regrouped as 6 + 1, 3 + 4, or some other combination totalling 7. Being able to break amounts apart makes it easier for problem solvers to use the math facts they know, which lessens the cognitive burden of mental math. If, for example, the student doesn't know the product of 6 × 7 is but knows his 5 facts, breaking the 7 into 5 + 2 allows him to do the multiplication mentally.

In this inspection, ask students to work in pairs. Provide them with graph paper so that they can easily sketch the array. Encourage them to come up with different strategies for breaking apart numbers so that they can see that, no matter how the amount is separated, the total (product) is always the same. Be explicit in illustrating the distributive property, that is, no matter how 6 or 7 is divided, there is still distribution of amounts. For example, in 6 × (3 + 4) = 6(3) + 6(4), the operation of multiplication has to touch both parts of 7: 3 and 4.

 ## Math Inspection: Connecting Arrays to Multiplication

The previous inspection focused on using arrays to illustrate the distributive property. This math inspection continues to build on this idea, and in doing so it clarifies why the standard multiplication algorithm works with multi-digit numbers. The point of this activity is to have students regroup using place value. For example, the number 25 would be regrouped into 20 + 5 to focus on two tens and five ones.

Once the numbers are regrouped, students compare the steps and resulting products with each of the products in the array. This should help students see the way the standard algorithm works. In the example 11 × 13, the amounts being multiplied are $(10 + 3) \times (10 + 1)$ … . Therefore, the 3 is multiplied by 10 and by 1. The array clearly shows these sub-products [(10×10), (10×1), (3×10) and (3×1)] so students can understand why they sometimes need "to move a space to the left" when they multiply and then eventually add everything together.

Summary Discussion

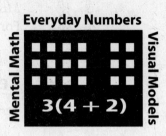

Refer students to *Reflections* (*Student Book*, p. 263).

After students have written their responses, take statements from volunteers.

Give students time to write responses to these questions:

1. By sharing our different methods, what did we learn from one another in this lesson?

2. Many people say, "I just know how to do the procedure—I don't know why or what it really means." What do you understand clearly about why your multiplication procedure works the way it does?

3. What is still confusing?

Have students record their definitions in *Vocabulary* (*Student Book*, p. 255).

Practice

Number of the Day, p. 168
For practice finding factor pairs for the number 120.

Cartons of Eggs, p. 169
For practice writing equations to match arrays.

Expressions, Arrays, and Stories, p. 170
For practice connecting arrays with various expressions and relating stories to each array.

How Do You See It? p. 171
For practice writing equations and finding totals without counting.

Stone Paths, p. 173
For practice with rectangular arrays.

Sketch the Two Expressions, p. 176
For practice sketching two expressions to show that they are equal, illustrating why the distributive property works.

Mental Math Practice

Square Numbers, p. 177
For practice squaring numbers and using exponential notation.

Extension

Seeing Squarely, p. 178
For practice visualizing arrangements for expressions that include exponents.

Missing Rolls of Film, p. 179
For a challenge counting objects in a three-dimensional arrangement.

 Test Practice

Test Practice, p. 180

Looking Closely

Observe whether students are able to

Write math expressions to reflect regular arrangements of objects in groups and arrays

Can students find the total number of objects in such an arrangement without counting (e.g., by adding or multiplying)?

Can students explain their approaches with reference to arithmetic and record their approaches using equations? Encourage them to explain their thinking using words such as "multiply" or "add." Say, for example, "You knew that there were three rows and each row had six squares. What did you do to find that there were 18 squares in all?"

Help students become familiar with the appropriate arithmetic terms: "So, you knew that three 6's are 18—you multiplied 3 by 6 and got 18."

Refer students to equations you (or others) recorded for the class and, as needed, model correct recording yourself. Some students may be familiar with different ways of recording operations and equations. For this lesson, encourage them to record in ways that are comfortable—as long as they are correct—but also point out alternative notation, e.g., $3 \times 4 = 3(4) = 3 \cdot 4$.

Ask those students who struggle to explain how they are counting the objects or to count aloud for you so you can repeat or record for them what they said. With a pencil, mark off the sets of objects to reflect how students are seeing them.

Do students notice commutative relationships among operations—in other words, that three rows of four is the same as four rows of three?

Represent equations using arrays and/or equal groups arranged to correspond with numbers and operations

Do students recognize that arranging objects into equal groups makes it possible to find the total without counting each object?

Ask students to arrange the items into groups of a particular size (say, four or five items to a group) and then to find the total number of items without counting each item one by one. If needed, work with students to add or skip-count to find the total: "Okay, we have four groups of five items. So, this first group has five items; how many items are in these two groups together? How many are in three groups?"

Are students able to find a total number in an array by multiplication? As above, ask students to model the number with objects in groups of 10, and ask them to find the total by counting by 10's.

Can students make an abstract-looking multiplication problem concrete? Using arrays should make the key ideas of multiplication obvious—an accumulated total of equal groups. The algorithm for finding the product of two- and three-digit numbers should also make more sense once students have seen how an array can be broken apart into smaller multiplication problems whose products are then totaled. Three properties play a role: commutative in that any order or set up of the array is as acceptable as another (3×4 vs 4×3); associative in that the numbers can be broken down (into 10's and 1's for example); and the distributive (that the same number, the multiplicand, acts on all the parts of any number that has been broken up).

Identify equivalent expressions

Are students able to verify that equations are equivalent or nonequivalent by demonstrating with visual models? Take time to connect the visual models with the mathematical symbols.

Are they able to use rules of order to evaluate an expression? Return to *Lesson 9*, where order of operations was a main focus.

Rationale

Arrays provide a clear picture of multiplication and open the way for visualizing multi-operational equations. The lesson provides plenty of opportunity to practice multiplication facts, but the emphasis is on the conceptual understanding of multiplication.

This lesson also helps to build flexibility with breaking apart and putting together numbers, an essential skill throughout mathematics.

Math Background

Arrays are handy for organizing multiplication because rows and columns make it easy to see numbers of equal groups. Yet some students will not trust that multiplying rows and columns will yield the same result as counting by 1's. Are students persuaded that they can break apart an array, combining sub-totals of smaller multiplication problems to come up with a product? Start with a manageable area of 12 or 16 if needed. Use colored pencils or different pens to keep track of which parts of the array have been counted and calculated in a running total.

Arrays lend themselves to a discussion of commutativity; one can rotate the array to see the rows and columns change, but the total remains the same. Arrays are generally more useful than groups for quick totaling because arrays show at a glance that they contain equal numbers of items; groups do not.

Some students may be comfortable with commutativity in addition and multiplication. They may take it for granted that 40 + 7 is the same as 7 + 40, or that 3×5 is the same as 5×3. Others may be less certain and may benefit from a visual approach. For instance, suppose students are explaining how they know how many squares are in the following array:

One student may see this as three rows of five—3×5, others may see it as five columns of three and write "5×3." With repeated experiences such as these, over time students will gain understanding of commutativity in multiplication and addition.

The algorithm for finding the product of two- and three-digit numbers should also make more sense once students have seen how an array can be broken apart into smaller multiplication problems whose products are then totaled. Three properties play a role: commutative in that any order or set up of the array is as acceptable as another (3×4 vs 4×3); associative in that the numbers can be broken down (into 10's and 1's for example); and distributive (that the same number, the multiplicand, acts on all the parts of any number that has been broken up).

Using arrays to understand the partial sums in the standard multiplication algorithm (*Math Inspection: Connecting Arrays to Multiplication*) may be new for some teachers. The array model for two digit times two digit multiplication shows visually the four multiplication steps involved as the four sections of the larger array. The visual model not only shows why the procedure makes sense, but it also makes place value prominent. If we look at the example from the *Student Book*, p. 164, many students talk themselves through the algorithm without attention to place value: "One times three is three, one times three is three, put down a zero …" The array model reminds them that not all the 1's are really 1: 1×3 is 3, but the next sub-product is actually $10 \times 3 = 30$. The array makes this clear.

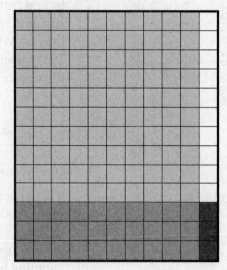

Facilitation

The more time devoted to notation, the longer this lesson will take.

Some students take the direction to sketch literally. Recommend the use of sticks, X's, or dots as ways to sketch a representation of an arrangement.

To connect the lesson more firmly with daily life, take some time to examine objects and photographs of real arrays and discuss how students see the total in each.

Do an internet search for images of architecture, items packaged in sets, items arranged for sale or storage, and art that involved repeating geometric patterns.

Making the Lesson Easier

Assign fewer sets in *Activity 1: Pictures and Numbers* (*Student Book*, p. 152) and limit selection to the simpler arrangements. In *Activity 2*, distribute fewer paper clips to student pairs.

Making the Lesson Harder

Discuss square and prime numbers with students. Assign *Extension: Seeing Squarely* (*Student Book*, p. 178) as a challenge.

LESSON 10 IN ACTION

Teachers commented on the value of connecting expressions with visual representations.

> When drawing out the situations for a number sentence, it was interesting to find that students see multiplication as addition. Having to illustrate a situation made them really think about what it meant. Once I suggested that they try to think a little differently, they began to change their illustrations. This has such potential really to bring so many big ideas of multiplication to the surface.
>
> *Phyllis Flanagan*
> *Adult Education Center, Rock Valley College, Rockford, Illinois*

> This lesson worked fairly well as an introduction to seeing and discussing multiplication. Students were immediately engaged in counting the numbers of things in each photo. The discussion went well, but there are such huge gaps in how people approach this problem (from counting one by one to counting by groups, and *not* often by multiplication). Making the pictures for the equations was equally as engaging, though the frustration level was higher. Again, multiplication was definitely seen as addition.
>
> One student began to see that three groups of three was also one group of nine. That was big to me, but the concept was a slippery one for a while and I'm not so sure that he solidly understands it.
>
> *Deidre Freeman*
> *Lehman College, New York*

11

What Is the Story?

> *What math do you see in this picture?*

Synopsis

This lesson draws attention to the various ways people successfully represent and solve word problems. Students explain possible solution paths to solve a problem and represent contextual situations with pictures and mathematical expressions. Individuals compare their solutions for *The Rose Problem*, using pictures and math symbols to support their reasoning.

1. Partners complete two possible solution paths for contextual problems, and students demonstrate their mathematical reasoning with arrangements of objects and mathematical expressions.

2. Individuals solve *The Rose Problem* and then share their own solution paths, using pictures and mathematical expresssions to explain and confirm their reasoning.

3. Students explore how to handle square roots and exponents attached to the same base number.

Objectives

- Represent word problems with pictures and mathematical equations
- Record problem-solving strategies with equations and pictures
- Find squares and square roots of perfect squares
- Generalize a rule for multiplying exponents

Materials/Prep

- Grid paper
- Uniform objects for counting such as paper clips, chips, small plastic or wood tiles, or pennies, 25 per student

Make copies of *Blackline Master 14: Multiplication Table* for students to use in *Mental Math Practice: Patterns in the Multiplication Table* (*Student Book*, p. 200) if they need a clean copy.

Set up your board so that equations, diagrams, and word problems can be situated next to each other.

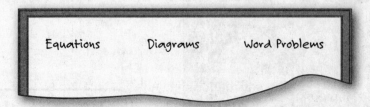

Equations   Diagrams   Word Problems

Opening Discussion

Introduce word problems as the focus of this lesson:

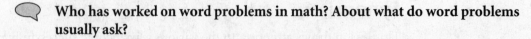 **Who has worked on word problems in math? About what do word problems usually ask?**

Record a list of word problem topics. Note that word problems often talk about amounts or quantities, such as miles, dollars, inches, etc.

Explain:

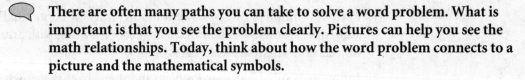 **There are often many paths you can take to solve a word problem. What is important is that you see the problem clearly. Pictures can help you see the math relationships. Today, think about how the word problem connects to a picture and the mathematical symbols.**

Point out the headings on the board: equations, diagrams, and word problems. Tell students to use each of these forms as they do the activities.

 ## Activity 1: What Is the Story?

There are two points to this activity. First, there are often various ways to enter a problem, second, pictures and math symbols are ways to see the structure of the problem.

Refer students to *Activity 1: What Is the Story?* (*Student Book*, p. 184). Ask a volunteer to read the problem aloud. Then ask students to partner up. One partner will be Person A; the other, Person B.

Problems such as this one might be solved in different ways. In this activity, one of you will solve the problem starting out the way Person A did; the other will solve the problem starting out the way Person B did.

Individuals work on the problem and then share with their partner the way they solved it as they continued the line of thinking for their role as Person A or Person B. Remind everyone to both draw a picture and write the math expressions and equations.

Bring the class together and focus first on Person A's thinking. Ask:

💬 **What would Person A's picture look like? What part of the picture would Person A look at first?**

💬 **What math would Person A do first? What would Person A's mathematical equation look like?**

Take all suggestions but insist upon continuing Person A's thinking. Because Person A thought first about the number of windows in each building, the drawing and mathematical equations should indicate that there are 34 windows in each building and that there would be four times as many in total. The picture and equations might look like these:

$4(10 + 12 + 12) = 4(34) = 136$

or

$4(3 \times 10 + 4) = 136$

or

$2 \times 12 + 10 = 34$

$4 \times 34 = 136$

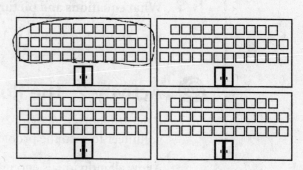

Seek explicit connections between each of the pictures and each of the equations.

Next, review Person B's solution path. Because Person B focused on each floor first, the picture and mathematical equation should indicate a totaling of the windows, floor by floor, and then a sum of the three floor totals. The pictures and equations might look like these:

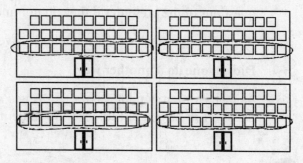

$4(12) = 48$ (total 1st floor windows)

$4(12) = 48$ (total 2nd floor windows)

$4(10) = 40$ (total 3rd floor windows)

$48 + 48 + 40 = 136$

or

$4 \times 12 + 4 \times 12 + 4 \times 10 = 136$

Conclude by asking:

💬 **What are the differences between Person A's and Person B's solutions?**

💬 **What is the same in both solutions?**

Continue with Problem 2, asking partners to take on the different roles, and then review, comparing Person A's and Person B's solution paths.

Say:

💬 **Person A started out by finding out how many children need T-shirts. What do you think he did?**

💬 **Did anyone else following Person A's thinking solve the problem differently?**

After students share equations and pictures, continue with Person B.

💬 **How did Person B start and then solve the problem?**

💬 **What equations and pictures did you use in solving the problem?**

See *Lesson 11 in Action*, p. 143, for two students' explanations.

🌀 Activity 2: The Rose Problem

Refer students to *Activity 2: The Rose Problem* (*Student Book*, p. 188). Ask for a volunteer to read the problem aloud.

Allow all individuals enough time to thoroughly think through the problem. Encourage students who finish early to think of another solution method or to start some of the practices or the extension.

When everyone has finished solving the problem, ask volunteers to come up to the board to explain their solution methods.

It is important that students follow and critique one another's reasoning and ask questions of the presenter if they do not understand the explanation.

Keep asking until all solution methods have been presented:

💬 **Did anyone do it another way?**

As we have seen in pilot classes, *The Rose Problem* has many solution methods. See *Lesson 11 in Action*, p. 140, for ways students have solved the problem.

⊖ Math Inspection: Perfect Squares and Their Square Roots

In an inspection in *Lesson 8*, students focused on exponents as a way to notate multiplication of numbers times themselves. This inspection builds on that idea by looking at the inverse of squaring a number. The square root sign may be new to students, but the exponent should not be. As students explore squares and square roots they should discover that squaring a sum isn't the same as the sum of squares (as in Problems **e** and **f**) and that $\sqrt{100} \neq \sqrt{25} + \sqrt{75}$. Also adding unlike bases that have the same exponent is not the same as first adding the bases and then using the exponent; for instance, $3^2 + 4^2 \neq 7^2$ even though $3 + 4 = 7$. Students need to be able to explore these ideas using sketches and manipulatives.

In this inspection, first pose the question, "Is $\sqrt{25}$ the same as $\sqrt{9} + \sqrt{16}$?" Have students explore the question using manipulatives or graph paper. When everyone has had a chance to "prove" the answer, ask for a volunteer or two to share their strategies of proving that $\sqrt{25} \neq \sqrt{9} + \sqrt{16}$.

Next ask students to determine whether $2^2 + 3^2 = 5^2$ and whether $(2 + 3)^2 = 5^2$. Again, have them use concrete models to show their reasoning. The point is not to have them begin to memorize rules about exponents. This is an opportunity for students to explore how exponents operate. In creating concrete examples, they are actually learning strategies that they can later use if they forget the rules. Some students may notice that in the first example ($2^2 + 3^2 = 5^2$), they have to first multiply and then add. In the second example, they first add $2 + 3$ and then multiply.

Now ask students to first work independently on the set in question 1, then share with a partner. Then have the partners work together on the next two questions.

Part 2

For *Part 2*, give each pair of students 25 square tiles. Explain they will be making arrays and remind them that an array organizes pictures or objects in rows and columns. Show an example and point out that an array must have all of the space in the middle filled in.

After everyone has had a chance to work through *Part 2*, discuss with the class— what did they come up with? Why won't 12 tiles make a square like the others? This experimentation is meant to give students a tactile experience with perfect squares and with numbers that are not perfect squares. Students might come up with a 3×4 rectangle, a 4×4 square with an empty center, or they may remark that the tiles would need to be cut. Can they see why 16 works and 12 does not? Push them to express the idea in words that there is no whole number multiplied by itself that equals 12. Therefore, 12 is not a perfect square. Use the opportunity to reinforce the vocabulary.

Parts 3 and 4

Students can work alone or in pairs on *Parts 3* and 4. For *Part 4*, you may want to provide a multiplication chart and have students highlight the perfect squares. In doing so, they should also be able to articulate the pattern that they see (there should be a perfect diagonal) and why that pattern exists (in each case, a number is being multiplied by itself).

Math Inspection: What's the Rule?

This inspection follows up on *Lesson 8* where students focused on exponents as multiplication of the same number. Here students learn some new vocabulary (*exponent*, *base*) and they explore a new multiplication—one where there are two bases that are the same. This is an opportunity to expose students to multiplying same bases by looking at patterns. There is no intent to have students master either the vocabulary or any rules. However, finding patterns will help students later when they may be asked to memorize rules. If their memories fail, at least they can revert to looking for patterns. A key idea to explore in this Inspection is the fact that, when multiplying numbers with the same bases, the base stays the same and the exponents are added; for example, $4^3 \times 4^5 = 4^8$. This builds on their exploration in *Math Inspection: Perfect Squares and Their Square Roots*.

In this inspection, ask students to work in pairs. If they use calculators, be sure to ask them to share what they did to solve the problem. Using a calculator can be a way to assess whether they understand the difference between 10^2 and 10×2. (Don't assume that they are comfortable using the calculator.) Another suggestion is to ask students to write out problems in expanded form; for example $2^4 \times 2^2 = (2 \times 2 \times 2 \times 2) \times (2 \times 2) = 2^6$. If they use the calculator, be sure to review the exponent key.

As a whole class, discuss their rules for multiplying numbers with exponents with the same bases. Also be sure to discuss the reasoning behind each answer in Problem Set 4.

Summary Discussion

Everyday Numbers

Mental Math | Visual Models

3(4 + 2)

Direct students to turn to a partner and tell one thing they already knew from this lesson and one thing they found challenging or new. Volunteers share their own challenges.

Wrap up by asking what students learned about ways to solve problems:

 Think about how you made up and solved problems in this lesson. What did you learn that helped you to solve problems?

Students might say, for example:

"Making a drawing can be helpful."

"There can be more than one way to start thinking about a problem."

"There can be more than one way to solve a problem. For instance, sometimes you can use multiplication or addition, sometimes both."

"Sometimes it helps to take numbers apart, to think of 12 as 10 + 2, for example."

Refer students to *Reflections* (*Student Book*, p. 263), where they write about what they learned, and to *Vocabulary* (*Student Book*, p. 256) to record their definitions.

Practice

Drawings and Equations, p. 196
For practice using pictures and equations to solve word problems.

Equations and Word Problems, p. 197
For practice seeing the math and a story in an arrangement of objects.

The Answer Is _____, p. 198
For practice making up and solving word problems.

One Day, I ... , p. 199
For practice making up and solving real-world word problems.

 # Mental Math Practice

Patterns in the Multiplication Table, p. 200
For practice seeing the patterns in the multiplication table.

 # Test Practice

Test Practice, p. 201

Looking Closely

Observe whether students are able to

Represent word problems with pictures and mathematical equations

Do students see an accurate picture of the situation? Do they also see the mathematical structures in the problem and connect the two?

Talk through the story in the problem. Suggest the use of grid paper or paper clips to represent the problem. Ask specific questions, such as, "How could you show the 10 six-packs? What about the packs that are missing two cans each? Where are the packs that are missing four cans each?" Encourage students to explain their pictures using words such as "multiplied" or "added."

Review with students what numbers and operations they see within the picture—are they seeing a larger whole with part taken away or a smaller whole with a few added? How are they building into the problem what they see?

Record problem-solving strategies with equations and pictures

Do students have ideas for how to begin solving the problems? Can they record their approaches with pictures? Can they record their approaches with equations?

If students' equations include numbers that are not transparent from the picture prompts, seek an explanation or draw what you see written in the equation.

Slow down the problem-solving process. The point of the lesson is to make confident connections between the three representations: pictures, equations, and word problems. Label numbers in the equations to relate the story problem to the mathematical symbols. Have students talk through their solution processes and model correct recording yourself.

Challenge those who perform ably to write their equations in different forms and to think about advantages and disadvantages of each form.

Some students should be able to write problems for situations related to, but extending beyond, the arrays pictured.

Find squares and square roots of perfect squares

Do students see relationships between squares and square roots? Prompt them to draw diagrams on grid paper (e.g., of squares 5×5 to show that relationship between the area of a square and length of its sides.) See if they can list in their own words the commonalities and differences among exponents and multiplication, division and square roots. Trial and error, such as trying to create a square with 16 tiles (doable) and 12 tiles (not doable) is a good way to develop an intuitive feel for square roots.

Generalize a rule for multiplying exponents

Do students see a pattern and come to the rule for multiplying exponents from there?

Rationale

As in literacy, making meaning is crucial in numeracy. Visualizing, or comprehending, and recording with notation story/word problems are among the essential numeracy skills adults acquire in order to make meaning. What makes these skills important is their practical application in out-of-school life. In this lesson, students have an opportunity to carefully examine word problems by entering into other people's thinking. The emphasis on sharing strategies develops flexibility.

Context

Visualizing mathematics problems, like visualizing scenes in books and poems, helps us understand them. The contexts used here vary, but the need to picture what is going on in each situation remains. Help students visualize what happens in a problem by dramatizing with real objects or by offering ways to picture a problem quickly and easily.

Some students may prefer to draw literal pictures of the situation. Accept this, but try to guide students to more efficient representations that will aid them when solving problems in other contexts. Using grid paper arrays, dots, X's and slash marks are all more efficient, albeit more abstract, ways to represent numbers of objects. For larger numbers, it can be helpful to make a box with the number in it and repeat the box however many times it is added or multiplied.

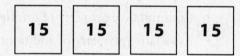

Mathematics Background

Because students generate most of the equations, the math on which you focus will depend on what issues students raise. As students compare equations and solution strategies, use the opportunity to probe for whether expressions are equivalent. You can then ask questions that bring attention to some regularities that occur in mathematics.

For example, you might focus on the commutative property by asking:

Does 5(4) = 4(5)? (yes) **How can you show that? Does order matter when you multiply two other numbers?**

Follow up with a request for students to provide examples and then to switch the order of two numbers while trying other operations such as adding, subtracting, and dividing. For example, instead of multiplying, ask does 5 + 4 = 4 + 5? (yes), but with subtraction and division, no, the order matters.

There may be opportunities to probe for understanding of the associative property, which allows problem solvers to regroup quantities in some cases. Test this out with a few examples:

Is (12 + 12) + 10 = 12 + (12 + 10)? (yes)
How about when you multiply three numbers?
Does (3 × 4) × 5 = 3 × (4 × 5)? (yes)

However, when you subtract or divide three or more numbers, it matters which pair you treat first. For example (20 − 10) − 6 does not equal 20 − (10 − 6). Similarly, (20 ÷ 10) ÷ 2 does not equal 20 ÷ (10 ÷ 2).

Knowing that addition and multiplication are commutative and associative, but division and subtraction are not, supports flexibility and creative problem-solving.

Another property is the distributive property of multiplication over addition. When doing *Activity 1: What Is the Story?* (*Student Book*, p. 184), students will have the opportunity to compare Person A's solution with Person B's. Ideally students will be critical, asking themselves and you if the amounts change when the groupings are altered.

Is 3(12 + 12+ 10) the same as 3(12) + 3(12) + 3(10)?
If yes, why are the statements equivalent?

Pictures or concrete examples can be used to verify responses.

The following general mathematical properties form the basis of this discussion.

- Commutative property of addition: $a + b = b + a$
- Commutative property of multiplication: $a \times b = b \times a$
- Associative property of addition: $(a + b) + c = a + (b + c)$
- Associative property of multiplication: $(a \times b) \times c = a \times (b \times c)$
- Distributive property of multiplication over addition, and multiplication over subtraction: $a(b + c) = ab + ac$ and $a(b − c) = ab − bc$

Facilitation

Solution paths depend on the first step taken, which in turn depends on which piece of information in a problem you choose to focus. For example, is the focus on the total number of windows in one building? Or on the total of first floor windows, then second floor windows, and then third floor windows in four buildings? One way is not more valid than another, though one can be seen to employ fewer steps or fewer opportunities for error. As students begin solving and analyzing solutions for math problems, it is not appropriate to push for efficiency. Only when students consistently understand problems is it useful to raise such issues.

Awareness of multiple pathways to solutions is crucial here and throughout the study of mathematics. Remain open to different ways of approaching each problem. What is important is that the steps taken make sense in context of the problem. Over time, by sharing and listening, everyone reaches his or her own conclusions about the best way to approach a problem.

Some students may notice that problems can be solved with a variety of operations. For instance, you can find how many cans are in three six-packs of soda with 3×6 or with $6 + 6 + 6$. Encourage these kinds of observations. As students explain and compare different ways to solve a problem, they learn about relationships among operations.

Students also need to learn which operations are not appropriate or efficient. If you want to find how many cans are in three six-packs, you could use multiplication or repeated addition; subtraction is not appropriate. As students make up and solve their own word problems, they deepen their understanding of which kinds of situations are best solved using which kinds of operations. Again, encouraging students to explain what operations they are choosing to solve a problem helps them gain better understanding. If students have difficulty either creating or solving problems, ask a volunteer to share what she or he is doing so far. This can help trigger ideas.

Making the Lesson Easier

Work on one problem at a time. Share results and then ask students to apply what they just learned to the next problem.

Use real objects that students can count and arrange. Have them copy the arrangements onto grid paper or in literal drawings. As needed, simplify the numbers so that students can easily draw pictures or model with objects to help them find solutions.

Making the Lesson Harder

Suggest that students substitute larger numbers in problems or consider alternate ways to solve the problem. Push for proof of generalizations of the properties (e.g., commutative, associative).

In one class, three solutions for The Rose Problem *emerged during a lesson. Though unique in framing and/or solving the problem, each method reveals sound reasoning.*

"Erin bought some roses to resell. She paid $6.00 for every 12 roses she bought. Later, Erin was charging $6.00 for eight roses. She sold them all and made a profit of $12.00. How many roses did Erin buy and resell?"

Miguel's Method

Miguel drew an arrangement of objects that focused attention on each dozen roses and used it to support his presentation.

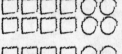 If she sells 8, she covers the cost of a dozen and 4 free.

 The 4 free ones give her $3 because eight gave her $6.

 $3 + $3 + $3 + $3 = $12, so 4 dozen or 48 roses.

Noreen's Method

Noreen started out by focusing on how much profit Erin made on each rose.

Bought 12 roses for $6 = 50¢ each

Sold 8 roses for $6 = 75¢ each

So Erin made 25¢ on each rose.

2 roses = 50¢

3 roses = 75¢

4 roses = $1

12 × 4 = 48

Monique's Method

Monique also began by focusing on each rose.

6 ÷ 12 = $0.50   "I divided to find the cost of one."

6 ÷ 8 = $0.75   "I divided to find the selling price of one."

12 ÷ $0.25 = 48   "Each one is 25¢ profit, so divide to find how many of those in total."

continued on next page

continued from previous page

The observer commented on students' reasoning and solution methods:

Miguel relies on his commercial experience. As a businessperson, he figures that the first task is to cover expenses. He demonstrates with a picture that Erin covers her cost by selling eight roses, leaving her four on which to profit. He further reasons that if she sold eight for $6, then the four left, being half of eight roses, will yield sales of $3. The reasoning is elegant. Miguel then shows that she needs to repeat her sales four times to yield the $12 target profit. The result is she needs to sell four dozen, or 48, roses.

Noreen finds the unit profit and then builds until she figures out how many roses are needed to make $1 profit. She is able to abstract that four roses equal $1, so she needs 12 times that many to get her targeted profit. Thus she needs 48 roses. Noreen clearly sees that an increase in the number of roses is matched by an increase in profits. If need be, she could build all the way to 48 roses = $12.

Monique determines the unit profit and then looks to find the number of those 25¢ profits in $12. She uses her equation to answer the question: How many single rose profits are there in $12 of profit?

Tricia Donovan, Observer
Notre Dame Education Center, Boston, MA

In another class, the observer commented on the back-and-forth discussion about The Rose Problem. *She wrote the following:*

The students had taken the problem home, and each showed his or her way on the board. When I arrived, the students were having a lively discussion about the problem. They had asked the lady in the lobby who sells flowers how she would do the problem (she said it was hard). Christina and her two kids (6th and 7th grade) had worked on it.

1. Carl went first

$12/6 - 8/6 = x/12$

$4/6 \qquad = x/12$

$2/3 \qquad = x/12$

$2 \cdot 12 \quad = 3x$

$24/3 \quad = x$

$8x \qquad$ (corrected by Judy, the teacher, to $8 = x$)

continued on next page

continued from previous page

I was at an impasse. Carl's confident mastery of algebraic symbol transformation floored me. But his conclusion was not correct. What question should I have asked? I did ask, "So what does the '8' mean?" He replied, "The profit." I think now I would have asked, "Could you confirm this another way?"

Judy asked if someone else could show how to solve the problem.

2. Maria went next

She spoke as she wrote:

"Buy 12 for $6 and sell eight for $6 to make it back." $12 = \$6$
                                                            $8 = \$6$

"You have four roses left that you can sell." 4 *Sell 8 for $6 profit*

"Buy another dozen." $12 = \$6$
                                                            $8 = \$6$

"You have another four roses left that you can sell." 4

"You have to do this twice.

"So, that makes four dozen that you had to buy … 48 roses."

3. Joe said, "I did it a little like that."

50¢   "12 for $6.00."

50¢   "8 for $6.00."

50¢   "4 for $2.00."

Judy said, "You're changing the prices." Joe lost his train of thought and went back to think about it.

4. Christina started next.

"12 roses @ 50¢ each is $6.00 (I divided 12 by 6 [sic])

"8 roses @ 75¢ each is $6.00 (I divided 8 by 6 [sic])

"She makes 25¢ a rose."

Christina made marks on the board:

/ / / / gives $1

/ gives $5; 40 gives $10

"We want two more dollars . . . that is eight roses."

Mary Jane Schmitt
Bridge to Learning and Literacy Program, Harvard University, Cambridge, MA

Sometimes starting with smaller numbers allows people to see the mathematical structure more clearly. An observer wrote this:

"T-shirts come in packs of three. Lana needs to get a T-shirt for each child in the preschool where she works. There are four classes and each has nine children. How many packs does she need?"

Tamika seems stuck on the T-shirt problem as she starts to make a picture.

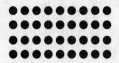

Teacher: "Hmmm, I see one class of nine kids, but can you show me the other kids in your picture?"

Tamika adds more dots to her sketch.

Teacher: "Okay, how can you show how many kids get T-shirts out of the first pack?"

Tamika circles three dots. She does this until she runs out of dots and then counts her circles. She arrives at the right answer, but I can see how this has become very abstract. It takes a lot of imagination to look at this picture and to see 36 nursery school kids in 12 packs of T-shirts.

When we review as a group, Sarita shares her array:

Teacher: "Can you show me the nine kids in each class? Sarita then draws a line through her array after every 3 × 3 grouping."

It was nice to have both models: 4 × 9 and 3 × 12. But I found these difficult to share on the board, as it takes some students quite a while to draw 36 dots. A document camera or enlarged copies of students' drawings would have made the discussion run more smoothly.

Martha Gray, observed by Martha Merson
Dimock Community Health Center, Roxbury, MA

Deal Me In

> *How much will it cost per month?*

Synopsis

This is the first of three lessons that focus on aspects of division. In this lesson, students build their sense of division as an act of equally dealing or splitting amounts into groups, and they generate notation and verbal language to connect with the action. They share strategies for dividing amounts by 4, 8, 12, and 24.

As students figure out *Payment Plans*, they practice and refine mental math strategies for dividing by 10 and 100.

1. Students divide a total number of items fairly into four piles, and the whole group lists several options for writing division notation and using verbal language.

2. Individuals estimate and find exact answers for problems that demand splitting the cost of a purchase or loan over different time periods: 4, 8, 12, and 24 months. They share their mental math methods.

3. Teams play a division game where they split the cost of purchases into 10 or 100 monthly payments.

4. Students use the fact that multiplication and division are inverse operations to solve division problems with multiplication.

Objectives

- Connect division to the act of splitting or dealing out an amount
- Match the verbal language and symbolic notation for division to a concrete model
- Apply mental math strategies for division to situations calling for splitting dollar amounts over 4, 8, 12, 24, 10, or 100 time periods

Materials/Prep

- Calculators
- Manipulatives, countable objects that are convenient to give to students in sets of 100, such as paper clips, pennies, tiles or cubes, playing cards, or Post-it Notes

Make copies of *Blackline Master 15: Payment Plans Cards*.

Cut up cards, one set per 4-6 students. Place in an envelope or keep clipped together for use with *Activity 2*.

Opening Discussion

Give partners a set of small manipulatives. Ask students to take 52 of these and make four equal piles. Observe the ways students split up the total, and then ask for different strategies for dealing out the 52 objects.

Students might say:

"We dealt them out one by one."

"We dealt them out 10 to a pile and then had 12 left, so we put three more in each pile."

"We dealt them out by two's until they were all gone."

"We knew $4 \times 10 = 40$ and $4 \times 3 = 12$, so $4 \times 13 = 52$."

Summarize:

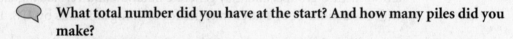 **What total number did you have at the start? And how many piles did you make?**

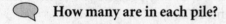 **How many are in each pile?**

Connect the concrete model to symbolic notation and verbal language.

Elicit students' wording for this division by asking:

What is another way to say, "Take 52 of something and make four equal piles" in your own words?

Listen and record expressions such as these:

"Fifty-two split up equally equals 13."

"Fifty-two divided by four equals 13."

"Four divided into 52 is 13." (This is incorrect.)

"Fifty-two shared among four people is 13."

"Fifty-two broken into four equal parts is 13."

Ask:

How could you write this problem in math notation? What could an equation look like that would describe what you just did?

Some may see this as multiplication, others as division. Students should generate different forms for writing division, e.g., the division sign, ÷; $\overline{)}$; or the fraction bar. List the problem in every format:

- Fifty-two divided by 4 equals 13
- $52 \div 4 = 13$
- $4 \times 13 = 52$
- $4\overline{)52}^{13}$
- $\frac{52}{4} = 13$

If students have gone to school in other countries, they may have learned to write and do long division with the dividend preceding the divisor and will write the quotient below, rather than above, the box.

- $\frac{52 \mid 4}{13}$

Check to see whether students' ways of writing equations and verbal expressions are all correct. Some students may not realize that the order of the numbers in division problems is important. Say and post:

Is $52 \div 4$ the same as $4 \div 52$? Why or why not?

Check to be sure that students can give a visual example demonstrating that the two expressions have different meanings. If students insist they are the same or are unsure, explore the problem using money: $52 divided among four people as opposed to $4 divided among 52 people. Acknowledge that in multiplication the order of the numbers makes no difference (4×13 or 13×4), but in division the order influences the meaning and the answer.

Connect this concept to using the calculator. Ask student to verify that $52 \div 4$ is different from $4 \div 52$.

Heads Up!

At this point, if you think students need practice on the various ways of expressing division, assign practice pages *Four Ways to Write Division* (*Student Book*, p. 209) and *Which Is Not the Same?* (*Student Book*, p. 210). Otherwise, proceed with the activities.

Heads Up!

The emphasis in this activity is on mental calculations. Encourage students who are confident about long division algorithms to break up numbers in a meaningful way using mental math. If they wish, they can use the algorithm to check their mental math.

Refer students to *Activity 1: Easy Payments* (*Student Book*, p. 204). Given an amount ($9,600), their task is to first estimate and then mentally calculate exact monthly payments for four different time frames: 4, 8, 12, and 24 months. Finally, they check their answers with a calculator and, if they wish, a paper-and-pencil method.

After individuals are done, ask each to partner up to compare answers and to share methods they used to do the mental calculations. Then bring the class together and reinforce the variety of useable methods:

Who had a mental math method that worked?

Spend time on the mental math methods. Ask individuals to come up to the board to explain and record their mental math strategies. Observe the ways students are breaking up the numbers or building on the previous answers. Some may choose to reason with multiplication, others with division. There are many valid ways to do this. For example, some might reason about splitting up the money this way:

$9,600 in 4 monthly payments means $2,400 per month.

4($2,000) = $8,000;

4($400) = $1,600;

$2,000 + $400 = $2,400.

or

$8,000 ÷ 4 = $2,000;

$1,000 ÷ 4 = $250;

$400 ÷ 4 = $100;

$200 ÷ 4 = $50;

$2,000 + $250 + $100 + $50 = $2,400.

or

$9,600 is close to $10,000;

$10,000 ÷ 4 = $2,500.

But there is $400 less, so I will take $100 away four times;

4($2,500) − 4($100) = 4($2,400).

$9,600 in 8 monthly payments means $1,200 per month.

I took the $2,400 and cut it in half because there are twice as many monthly payments now.

or

8($1,000) = $8,000;

8($100) = $800;

8($100) = $800;

$1,000 + $100 + $100 = $1,200.

$9,600 in 12 monthly payments means $800 per month.

I took the answer for four monthly payments ($2,400) and split each in three parts;

$2,400 ÷ 3 = $800.

or

10($800) = $8,000;

2($800) = $1,600;

so, there are twelve $800's.

or

I put $500 in each of the 12 piles, totaling $6,000;

I put $200 more in each, totaling $2,400;

then I took the $1,200 left and put $100 more in each pile;

$6,000 + $2,400 + $1,200 = $9,600.

$9,600 in 24 monthly payments means $400 per month

I see that 24 payments is twice as many as 12 payments, so I cut each of the $800 payments in half.

If $9,600 ÷ 12 = $800, then $9,600 ÷ 24 = $400.

or

$100 × 24 = $2,400;

$200 × 24 = $4,800;

$400 × 24 = $9,600.

Make sure everyone attends to the presenters' reasoning. Encourage critique and questions if a presenter's explanation is unclear. If there are disagreements or questions about answers or methods, ask for justification with diagrams.

Then ask for generalizations:

 Do you see any patterns here?

Students might say:

> "When you double the number of parts, you halve the amount of the payments."

> "The more payments you have, the smaller the payment."

> "Fewer payments mean you pay more each time."

Someone might point out that in reality paying on time doesn't quite work this way because the longer someone takes to pay, the more interest is charged. This activity does not take interest into account.

Acknowledge any paper-and-pencil methods. Depending on where and when they went to school, students may have learned different algorithms. Ask them to show those.

 Who has a paper-and-pencil method that works well?

 When you used the calculator, what did you have to keep in mind?

You are trying to elicit the idea that order made a difference when keying numbers in the calculator. Summarize by remarking on the variety of ways a number can be divided or split.

 ## Activity 2: Payment Plans

Explain that in this activity, students will practice mental math by figuring out *Payment Plans*. They will draw on what they know about multiplying by 10 and 100.

Refer everyone to *Activity 2: Payment Plans* (*Student Book,* p. 206). Review the directions. Use the cards from *Blackline Master 15* to illustrate.

Players place the cards print side down. Players take turns.

Player 1 picks a card and estimates the payment using mental math (no paper or pencils).

Player 2 checks the exact answer on the calculator.

Players make two piles:

> **Pile 1**—All agree the estimate fits.

> **Pile 2**—One or more players question the fit.

Player 2 picks a card and estimates the payment. Player 1 checks the exact answer on the calculator.

Players take turns until they run out of cards or time runs out.

Players keep track using the chart, *Student Book,* p. 206.

Pair students. Give each pair (or group) a set of cards and a calculator.

Before starting, ask why an estimate to the nearest dollar or 50¢ might be better than an exact answer. (If there are more mental math calculations, rounding $19.90 to $20 will make the next problem easier.)

Let students know how long they will have to play, and, if they are to use a timer, give each team about 1 minute to come up with an estimate.

Once players have run through the situations, convene the group. Ask if any groups had cards in their Question pile. Review these. Ask students to share their strategies and their reasoning for questioning the answers. Prepare to review rounding. Ask students to review their strategies dividing by ten mentally.

Listen for strategies such as:

- breaking a number into two smaller amounts
- rounding up and then dividing.
- guess and check—estimating how many times you could multiply a quantity by 10 to see if it is less than, more than, or equal to the target amount.

Ask students how they might use strategies for dividing by 10 mentally to help them divide mentally with 5, 20, and 100.

Listen for ideas related to doubling, halving, and multiples of 10.

Math Inspection: How Do You See It— Multiplication or Division?

This inspection is designed to emphasize the relationship between multiplication and division. Some problem-solvers think through a division problem by re-framing it as multiplication, multiplying up vs. dividing down. This approach is similar to the idea of counting up, for example, to give change on a purchase of $3.25 paid with $5.00. Even though subtraction works, many find adding up easier. When adults re-frame division problems, figuring what needs to be multiplied to get to the original amount, they are using the fact that division and multiplication are **inverse operations**.

In this math inspection, reinforce the relationship between multiplication and division. Be sure that students realize that the two are closely connected, that they are inverses of each other, so each has the power to undo the effect of the other and finding a missing factor in a multiplication problem is the same as dividing.

Ask students to first work independently so that they can really concentrate on their own thinking as they work on a solution to the problem.

Point out a key difference between multiplication and division—that the commutative property holds for multiplication but not division ($3 \times 12 = 12 \times 3$ but $3 \div 12 \neq 12 \div 3$).

During whole class discussion you may use the term inverse. Take the opportunity to ask students to name other inverse operations they have been using (addition and subtraction, squares and square roots). You might leave an open question: wonder aloud if there is any action in mathematics that does not have an inverse operation, a way to undo what was done.

Summary Discussion

Everyday Numbers

Mental Math   Visual Models

3(4 + 2)

Ask students to answer the following questions and to provide examples or models:

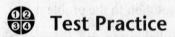 **What are some ways you can find a division answer if you have no paper and pencil or calculator?**

How do you know whether the exact answer would be a little less or a little more than an estimate?

Listen carefully to get an idea of what students understand.

Close by asking students to write in *Reflections* (*Student Book*, p. 258), where they consider ways to respond to a division problem presented in a workplace.

Say:

In the *Reflections* section, grade yourself on your ability to use mental math to solve division problems. Do you need to improve? Do you see yourself getting better at this as you practice?

Practice

Four Ways to Write Division, p. 209
For practice writing division with various notation.

Which Is Not the Same? p. 210
For more practice with division notation.

Those Monthly Payments, p. 211
For practice comparing payment plans, indicating whether the monthly payments are greater, less than, or equal to each other.

10's, 100's, and 1,000's, p. 212
For more practice breaking numbers apart to multiply and divide mentally.

Mental Math Practice

Flowers by the Month, p. 213
For more practice multiplying and dividing using number patterns.

Test Practice

Test Practice, p. 214

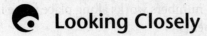

Looking Closely

Observe whether students are able to

Connect division to the act of splitting or dealing out an amount

Use manipulatives to reinforce how the operation of division relates to the act of splitting into equal amounts. This is the most basic and important idea of the lesson.

To cement the connection between the payment plan problems and the "dealing" division model, use play money and month markers to represent the situations.

Spiral back to multiplication strategies. Though this lesson centers on ways to divide mentally, the contexts can also be used to reinforce multiplication strategies by asking students how much a yearly bill would be if each month they paid X amount. In this way, they further practice breaking numbers apart, such as 12 into 10 and 2, in order to multiply. The fact that they cannot divide by 10 and then by 2 to divide by 12 raises some interesting questions. Explore these questions, only if they arise, with small totals.

Match the verbal language and symbolic notation for division to a concrete model

Are students secure with the order in division notation? During the *Opening Discussion* session, emphasize the need for common understanding when someone writes or speaks about division. If, for instance, someone reads a problem as "12 divided into 3," it is commonly understood to mean $12 \overline{)3}$ or $3 \div 12$. Yet if we add "12 divided into 3 parts," we would understand it as $12 \div 3$! Making the connection between words and notation is challenging without context. If a student means to read the problem $12 \div 3$ and be understood, one might expect to hear "three divided into twelve" or "three into twelve" or "twelve divided by three," etc. Making the notation connections between expressions remains important as well. Which number belongs *inside* the box when writing out a division problem? Although such issues are less likely to arise when solving contextualized problems, students often encounter problems translating division expressions during testing situations.

Keep the meaning of the situation by restating the problems, emphasizing what is known: the total payment and the number of groups or the number of payments.

Apply mental math strategies for division to situations calling for splitting dollar amounts over 4, 8, 12, 24, 10, or 100 time periods

Can students use what they know about multiplying by multiples of 10 and 100 to find a partial answer? Review mental math strategies for multiplication.

Do students draw on multiplication to solve problems and check their answers? Draw out silent class members with direct questions such as, "How did _____ use multiplication here?" or "How could you check _____'s work to see whether she is right?"

Do students see that breaking up numbers works along place value lines? Suggest thinking about 10-month increments.

Can students round and adjust appropriately? Rounding to a friendly number is the first step. Discuss the pros and cons of rounding with students, and make clear the difference between situations where a precise answer is necessary and those where an approximation will do. Another issue with rounding that may arise involves the question "Round to what?" Discuss in a case-by-case way with students whether they should round to the nearest multiple of 5, 10, or 100 and why.

To know whether to adjust by adding or subtracting, students must be aware of whether they rounded up or down and how that is likely to influence their answer. Talking through your reasoning may help. Also, reverting to smaller numbers as examples may help students visualize the situation. Working on rounding and estimating and holding off on adjusting until the first steps are solid may help some students feel more confident about tackling division mentally.

Investigate connections between multiplication and division and their properties. Do students use their knowledge of multiplication to assist them with finding missing factors or for checking their work when dividing? Can they offer related division facts given a multiplication equation? Make sure that students see the connection between multiplication and division as inverse operations with the power to undo each other. Offer concrete situations with manipulatives or visuals if students are struggling. See if they can create division equations from some of their arrays from *Lesson 10*.

Rationale

People use mental math skills all the time. Although the calculator is a very useful tool, as are paper-and–pencil algorithms, mental math strategies are the real basic skills for adults as they estimate and think on their feet in everyday life.

Math Background

Division problems are often classified into two cognitive models. One model is referred to as *sharing* or *partitioning*. In the sharing model explored in this lesson, the number of groups is given, but the number of objects in the groups is unknown. For example, "I have six payments to make. How much will each payment be?" or "I am going to cut this 10-foot board into four pieces. How long will each piece be?" The action here is one of dividing, splitting, or partitioning a set into a predetermined number of equal groups. In the sharing model, one interprets 12 ÷ 4 as 12 split into four equal groups of three.

●●●　●●●　●●●　●●●

The other model for division, referred to as *measurement* or *quotative*, will be explored in *Lesson 13*. In the measurement model, the amount in each group is given, and the task is to tell how many groups there are. For example, "How many $50 monthly payments would you need to make to pay off $2,000?" or "How many 18-inch segments could you cut from a five-foot long board?"

In the measurement model, 12 ÷ 4 would be interpreted as counting how many 4's there are in 12. There are 3 groups of 4.

●●●●　●●●●　●●●●

Numerate adults tend to blur the distinctions between the two models of division. They easily call on one or the other way to make sense of a problem, but adults who struggle with division may benefit from explicitly dealing with one model at a time.

In this lesson, students break apart numbers. Essentially they are using the distributive property. This is not so different from the algorithm, but it keeps the sense of the value of the digits intact. Reasoning that 9,600 ÷ 8 = (8,000 + 1,600) ÷ 8 = (8,000 ÷ 8) + (1,600 ÷ 8) = 1,000 + 200 is an application of the distributive property of division over addition.

Context

Dealing is a very kinesthetic way to internalize the sharing model; making monthly payments is an experience we have all had.

Facilitation

Remind students to consult with their teammates.

Making the Lesson Easier

Make play money available.

Minimize the pressure of being on the spot. Have teams huddle while considering the same three situations. They can spend up to three minutes. Then they can compare answers and check with a calculator.

Making the Lesson Harder

Payment Plans can be made more challenging by substituting 12 payments for 10 payments scenarios. Students can challenge each other by making up some payment plan scenarios that include interest.

Notice how the teacher guides the discussion to include everyone and extends beyond the familiar into algebraic expressions and non-U.S. (in this case Haitian) methods of expressing division problems. Following is a copy of the blackboard at the end of the Opening Discussion.

Math Symbols	Words
$3\overline{)6}$	How many times does three go into six? three divided into six three fits into six six divided by three
$12 \div 4$	12 divided by four
$\dfrac{18}{3}$ or 18/3	18 divided by 3 = 6 How many times does three fit into 18?

Teacher: "There is more than one way to say what we see; math has different ways to say or represent an idea, but we need to make sure we all understand each other, so if you have something different (than what was posted at first) written on your paper, please tell me. Did anybody say that differently?"

Observer: "Could we start a statement with the number six?"

Student: "Six people divided into three piles or groups."

Teacher: "So you could say six divided by three."

They move on to the second expression. A student posts "twelve divided by four."

Teacher: "If we use Pam's statement as a model, how might we say it?"

Student: "Four divided into 12."

Teacher: "How about this one (the third expression)?"

Student: "I know it's not multiplication or addition."

Student: "It's not a fraction, is it?"

Teacher: "It is."

Student: "Is it division?" (Teacher nods). "Okay."

A discussion ensues about the fraction form of division. Students report that it is "not familiar," "not outstanding like a daily routine."

Teacher: "It's more like algebra, like this. (She writes x/y on the board.) Use the language to say what that says."

Students: "x divided by y."

continued on next page

continued from previous page

Observer: "Can anyone put the second one in fraction form? In a box?"

Students offer up the new notation, which is correctly written.

Student: "Doesn't it all come out the same way?"

Teacher: "Yes, no matter how you write it, it's the same problem."

The class then launches into a discussion of the Haitian way of writing, and they practice with the Haitian form being changed into the American form and vice versa.

(They write: $12\underline{\smash{\big)}\,4}\atop{3}$ in Haiti, $4\overline{\smash{\big)}12}\atop{3}$ in the United States.)

Esther Leonelli
Notre Dame Education Center, Boston, MA

The following discussions took place during Payment Plans. *Playing by class rules can sometimes yield an answer that is mathematically troubling.*

Teacher: "Who can estimate what you would pay for each of 10 payments on a layaway for $48?"

Student: "Three dollars."

Student: "No, four dollars."

Student: "Three is too low."

Teacher: "How do you know?"

Student: "Well, three times 10 equals 30."

Student: "Ten by four is 40."

Teacher: "How far off are we?"

Student: "Ten by three is 30."

Student: "That's too low. You have some left over. It has to be four."

Everyone agrees the answer is four. The teacher suggests five, saying that it might actually be closer; but the students insist that the familiar game rule "closest without going over" should hold in this game. The teacher accepts their ruling.

Later, when mentally dividing $988 into 10-month payments, students explained:

Student: "It's close to 1,000."

Student: "A hundred for 10 months; it will be 1,000."

continued on next page

continued from previous page

Student: "Ninety will be 900."

Teacher: "Which is closer?"

Though the answer to her question was 100, the students were playing by the rule that the estimate had to be the closest without going over the target amount; however, they continued refining their answers.

Student: "Ninety-four is closer—940."

Student: "Ninety-eight times 10 is 980."

Esther Leonelli
Notre Dame Adult Education Center, South Boston, MA

One teacher wrote of students' initial reluctance to perform division using mental math.

The students seemed very engaged in the work today. There were still a couple who insisted the only right way to do the problems was by long division. I had said that if you do the math in your head, you are less likely to make a mistake. The ones who ignored the instructions and used long division usually got the problems wrong. When I started to repeat my statement, most of the class finished it for me because one of their classmates had proven what I had said. The new student, who was not to be won over without a battle, said, "I know my way is right because my daughter is in grade three, and I do her math homework and she always gets an A on it."

Phyllis Flanagan
Rock Valley Community College, Rockford, IL

13

String It Along

How will this woman use division?

Synopsis

There are two meanings of 52 ÷ 4 (or, more generally, $a \div b$). In the last lesson, students connected this notation to splitting 52 into four groups. Another way to understand division is to think of how many groups of a certain size are in a total. In other words, one can also interpret 52 ÷ 4 as "How many fours are in 52?" Using this second interpretation of division, students find how many of one measurement are in a larger one.

1. Students take on complex, multi-step problems, applying their number and operation sense to solve equations.

2. Students work in pairs with pieces of string, equations, and numbers to explore "how many _____ in a _____" using linear measurement.

3. Pairs apply division knowledge to solve map scale problems.

4. The class discusses how division is used to find the number of groups of a given size in a total.

5. Students revisit several generalizations, discussing models and properties related to the four operations.

Objectives

- Work with direct measurements and scale to find the number of groups of a given size in a total

- Use mathematical symbols to express the action of division

- Find commonalities and differences between division and multiplication (e.g., identify factors and divisors of 48 and 72, consider the applicability of the commutative property)

Materials/Prep

- Measuring containers: 2-oz. jigger (or 1/4-cup measure), 8-oz. paper or measuring cup, and a half-gallon jug or bottle full of some liquid

- String (approximately five yards per group of three students; 3 colors is ideal but not absolutely necessary)

- Envelopes, two per every group of three students

- Tape

- An atlas or a variety of road maps or maps of the United States

For *Activity 1*, prepare two envelopes for every group of three students. Envelope A should have four strings: a 48″ long piece, and shorter pieces 3″, 4″, and 6″ long. Envelope B contains four strings: a 72″ long piece, and shorter pieces 6″, 9″, and 18″ long.

Heads Up!

Precise measuring of strings is crucial. Use string, avoid yarn or elastic that is stretchy.

Opening Discussion

Open by saying:

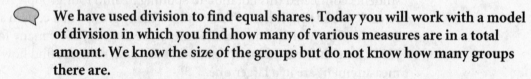 We have used division to find equal shares. Today you will work with a model of division in which you find how many of various measures are in a total amount. We know the size of the groups but do not know how many groups there are.

For instance, I have a 2-oz. measure. How could I figure out how many 2-oz. measures of water are contained in this cup?

Solicit ideas. If no one mentions physically pouring, suggest it. Fill the 8-oz. cup of water and keep pouring out 2-oz. measures until the cup is empty. Write numbers on the board that correspond to what you do.

1 c. − 2 oz. − 2 oz. − 2 oz. − 2 oz. = 0 oz.

1 c. ÷ 2 oz. = 4 portions

or

8 oz. ÷ 2 oz. = 4 portions

Repeat the process, this time using the cup and the half-gallon containers. Ask:

How many of these cups are in the half-gallon? How could we find out?

Again, if no one mentions pouring out or filling up, using the numbers, or a number line, probe by asking:

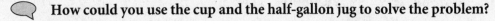 **How could you use the cup and the half-gallon jug to solve the problem?**

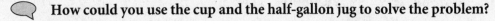 **If you knew the cup held eight ounces, how would that help you solve the problem?**

Start a number line and ask:

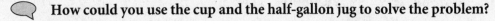 **What would a diagram of this problem on the number line look like?**

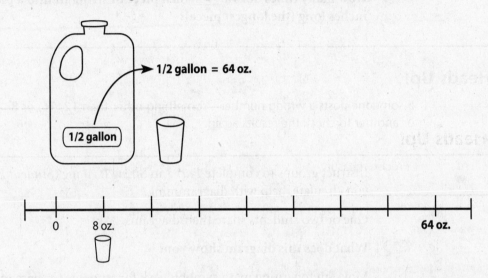

1/2 gallon = 64 oz.

1/2 gallon

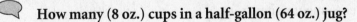

0   8 oz.   64 oz.

Mark the number line from 0 to 64 in increments of eight, as shown above.

Take a moment to re-read the problem emphasizing the language:

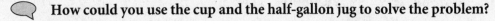 **How many (8 oz.) cups in a half-gallon (64 oz.) jug?**

Write on the board:

$8\overline{)64}$

$64 \div 8$

$\dfrac{64}{8}$

 ## Activity 1: String It Along

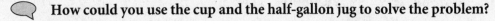 **We just worked with cups and ounces, or liquid volumes. The next problems involve linear measurements.**

Connect the word "linear" with the word "line" to help students think of what linear means. Ask for some words for linear measurements, such as inches, feet, miles, centimeters, etc.

Form groups of three students and distribute Envelope A to each group. Say:

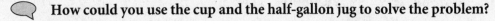 **Each group has a long piece of string and three short pieces of string. You will find how many of each of your short pieces could fit into your long piece. All you know is that the short strings are 3″, 4″, and 6″ long.**

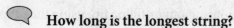 **How long is the longest string?**

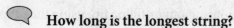 **How do you know?**

As students work, each member of a group with a different length of string, figuring out how many times their short pieces fit into the long piece, they may want to tape the longest string to a space on the wall.

Post on the board the question:

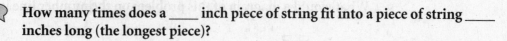 **How many times does a _____ inch piece of string fit into a piece of string _____ inches long (the longest piece)?**

Heads Up!

If someone posts a wrong number—something other than 12, 16, or 8—ask this student or another to check the results again.

Instruct groups to complete *Part 1* in *String It Along* (*Student Book*, p. 216). As you circulate, help with diagramming.

One or two students share their diagrams. Ask:

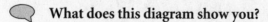 **What does this diagram show you?**

Move on to writing math symbols. Ask for students to share the ways they wrote their problem in math symbols when using the 3″ string. Then ask for ways they wrote explanations for the 4″ and 6″ strings. Some may see this as a division problem, others as a multiplication (or even an addition or subtraction) problem. Students might write:

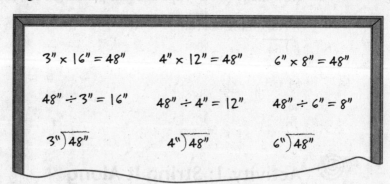

In each case, ask students where they see the operation in the string situation.

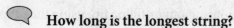 **Where do you see the multiplication?**

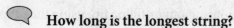 **Where do you see the division?**

Ask students to generalize:

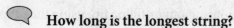 **As the size of the short strings gets longer, what happens to the number of times each fits into the long string? Why?**

Keep these equations on the board to refer to later.

Repeat the exercise, using Envelope B. After students see how many of each of the shorter strings physically fit in the longest, post all mathematical statements.

The board should be filled with statements such as these:

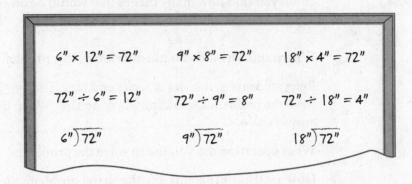

$6'' \times 12'' = 72''$ $9'' \times 8'' = 72''$ $18'' \times 4'' = 72''$

$72'' \div 6'' = 12''$ $72'' \div 9'' = 8''$ $72'' \div 18'' = 4''$

$6'')\overline{72''}$ $9'')\overline{72''}$ $18'')\overline{72''}$

•   Conclude *String It Along* by introducing a question that leads to the definition of factors:

💬 **Look at the 48″ length. Would strings of any other size (cut in whole inches) fit neatly and exactly into the long one (besides the 3″, 4″, and 6″ strings)?**

Write down all suggestions, asking for verification. Possible whole number answers are 1″, 2″, 8″, 12″, 16″, 24″, and 48″.

Say:

💬 **In mathematics, whole numbers that divide evenly into a number are called the divisors of that number. Because of the relationship between multiplication and division, the divisors may also be thought of as factors.**

Ask:

💬 **What are the factors of 72?**

Write down all suggestions, asking for verification. Possible whole number answers are 1, 2, 3, 4, 6, 8, 9, 12, 18, 24, 36, and 72.

Ask:

💬 **Is 9 a factor of 48? Why or why not?**

🌀 Activity 2: Scales on Maps

Now the context changes from string lengths to scales commonly found on maps. To make sure that everyone understands scale, ask:

💬 **How have you used scales on maps?**

Pass around a few road maps and, if you have a wall map, ask someone to find and read that scale as well. Students might share that they have approximated or exactly calculated distances using scales on maps. Start by saying:

💬 **When a scale reads "1 inch = 40 miles," how many miles would 5 inches represent?**

Suggest a few other amounts (6″, 10″, 20 ″), and ask students how they found the actual distance represented. Then ask:

💬 **If instead you knew that the distance between two places was 143 miles, how could you find how many inches that would be on your map?**

Ask:

💬 **Where and why did you use division in this problem?**

Refer students to *Activity 2: Scales on Maps* (*Student Book*, p. 218) and ask pairs to solve the problems, rounding where needed. When they are done and share their answers, ask:

💬 **What operation did you use to solve the problems?**

💬 **How are these problems like the string problems you did in *Activity 1*? How are they different?**

Math Inspection: Working with Symbols

In this math inspection the problems intentionally look "ugly." They incorporate exponents, multiplication, and division. The intention is for students to move from noticing patterns, drawing, and acting out math ideas to problems that are presented and solved symbolically.

Begin by putting $2^3 \times 4^2 \div 2(4) = ?$ on the board. Give students a chance to try to solve the equation and encourage them to talk to a partner. Then work through the problem, one step at a time. (If students struggle with this example, back off and present only the numerator (dividend) first ($2^3 \times 4^2$).

Direct students to work in pairs so that they can articulate what the different symbols mean. The focus should be on understanding each part of the problem, not just getting the correct answer.

Math Inspection: The Commutative Property and the Four Operations

This inspection brings several of the ideas from the unit together. The statements focus on generalizations related to the commutative property (for which operations does it apply?) and to the conceptual understanding of the operations and their relationship to one another. Students should come away with these big ideas:

- The commutative property holds for multiplication and addition but not for division and subtraction.

- Subtraction not only means take away but also can be used to compare two amounts (How much older is Joe than Tom?) and to find the missing part (Sarah had $20 but now has $4.32 in her pocket. How much did she spend?).

- Division can be considered repeated subtraction although the two are not inverse operations, just as multiplication can be considered repeated addition although the two are not inverse operations.

In this math inspection, ask students to work in pairs to decide whether each statement is true or false. Then discuss all ten statements as a whole class. If there are disagreements about the answers, encourage students to offer concrete examples (or counterexamples) to support their thinking.

Summary Discussion

Tell students:

💬 **In this lesson, you worked on two types of problems that used the measurement model of division. You found how many of the shorter strings fit in the longer string and how many inches or centimeters represented a distance given in miles on a scaled map.**

💬 **Many of you used division to solve these problems. What made them division problems?**

On the board write the following:

$$60 \div 5$$

Ask students to write two word problems and draw a sketch in the *Reflections* section (*Student Book*, pp. 264–265) for the following:

1. Split 60 into five equal parts.

2. Find out how many fives are in 60.

Ask volunteers to share some examples of what they have written.

🎯 Practice

How Many Blanks in a Blank? p. 222
For practice finding how many of one measure are in another.

About How Many Times as Large? p. 224
For practice finding out about how many times larger one amount is than another.

Coin Rolling, p. 225
For practice thinking with 5, 10, 25, and 50.

Vacation Spots, p. 227
For practice thinking about distance and time.

Collecting Frequent Flyer Miles, p. 228
For practice with larger numbers.

➕ Mental Math Practice

Factors, p. 229
For practice finding factors of some common numbers.

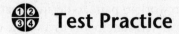

Test Practice

Test Practice, p. 230

Looking Closely

Observe whether students are able to

Work with direct measurements and scale to find the number of groups of a given size in a total

Are students able to demonstrate the operations of division and multiplication using the measured strings? Are they able to "talk it out" as they do so? Make sure the words and actions are well connected. Help students see that the situation is one of dividing or measuring out a certain size group (length) within the larger total.

If students struggle with demonstrations, offer a diagram such as this:

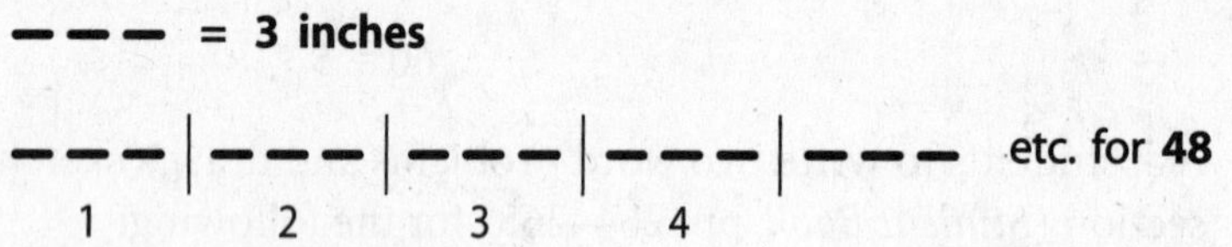

Or use a number line:

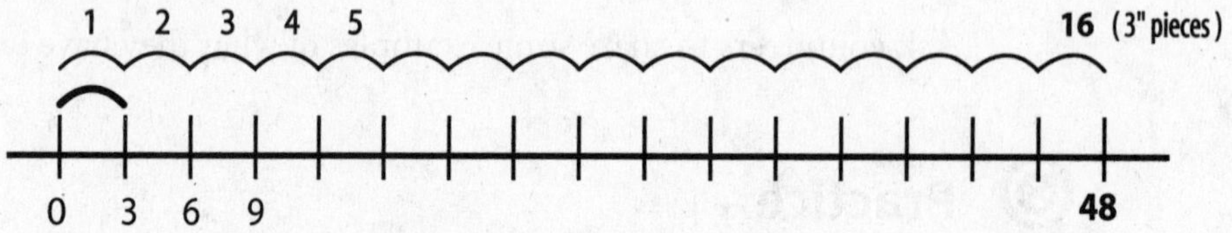

Do students have experience with scales on maps? It might be helpful to examine some actual road maps.

Use mathematical symbols to express the action of division

Do not insist on any one notation, but make sure all possibilities are shared. As students talk through how they solved the problem, model writing division in various ways:

- Horizontally, as in $8 \div 4 = 2$
- As a fraction, as in $\frac{8}{4} = 2$
- In the traditional way of writing division, as in $4\overline{)8}$

Also ask what the difference is between $8 \div 4$ and $4 \div 8$, and discuss this so students get a deeper understanding of division and how the order in which the numbers are written in a division problem matters. Be specific about the language: How many groups of four go into or make eight, as compared with how many groups of eight go into or make four? If students find it helpful, use objects to demonstrate the two situations.

Find commonalities and differences between division and multiplication (e.g., identify factors and divisors of 48 and 72, consider the applicability of the commutative property)

The numbers 48 and 72 used in *Activity 1* were chosen because they have many factors. Using these numbers supports the notion that multiplication can be used to solve division problems. Do students see that finding two numbers (the two factors) that multiplied together equal the amount being divided is an equally satisfying way to solve a problem with a missing divisor?

Do students see that the commutative property holds for addition and multiplication but not for subtraction and division? Using number facts that students are certain of, experiment with the order and ask students to compare the outcomes (e.g., $10 \div 2$ is 5; $2 \div 10 = 1/5$, less than one, not nearly 5). Use drawings or objects for counting to play out experiments with order.

Rationale

Learners who can think flexibly about division can be more efficient in computing division problems. For example, $150 ÷ 75 is much easier to solve when you ask the question: How many $75's are in $150? It is more difficult to think about how much money is in 75 piles. Many students intuitively approach division using the sharing model: how many *x*-sized groups are in the total given? Building on this intuition makes the repeated addition or subtraction in division apparent. The mathematical goal of this lesson is to cement a second meaning for the division operation.

Math Background

Division problems are often interpreted using two models: *sharing* and *measurement*. In the sharing—or partitive—model discussed in *Lesson 10*, the number of groups is given, but the number of objects in the groups is unknown. For example, "We are sharing 52 objects among four people; how many objects does each person get?" This can be thought of as doling out one object at a time to each person in turn so that each person gets the same number. We start out knowing we need four groups but do not know how many are in each group.

In the measurement—or quotative—model, the size of the groups is known, but the number of groups is not known. For example, "I need to order enough cars to transport 52 people for a field trip. A car holds four passengers. How many cars do I need?" In this case, the problem is to find how many groups of four will build to get to a total of 52. This model can also be seen as repeated subtraction or adding up.

Any decontextualized division problem may be approached either as a sharing or measurement model. For example, 10 ÷ 2 can be seen in each of these ways:

How do two people share $10? (sharing)

$$$$$ $$$$$

How many $2 piles are in $10? (measurement)

$$ $$ $$ $$ $$

As students understand the concept of division, they are more able to abstract the numbers and interchange the two models according to which is easier to visualize.

Context

The premise for this lesson could be anything; some of the examples given here are liquid and linear measurements, coins in a roll, and distances on a scaled map.

This lesson is a jumping-off point for practice with maps and scale, ordering numbers, and multi-step problems, such as those that require students to find miles per hour and miles per gallon. The lesson could easily extend over multiple class sessions if all these possibilities are explored.

Facilitation

Making the Lesson Easier

Move from *Activity 1: String It Along* (*Student Book*, p. 216) to *Practice: Coin Rolling* (*Student Book*, p. 225).

Making the Lesson Harder

In *Activity 2*, use actual numbers rather than rounded numbers. Compare results for rounded and actual numbers, and account for the difference.

Push for generalizations based on factors. If one factor is doubled, the other one is halved (6×8 is 6×2—or 12—multiplied by 1/2 of 8—or 4—or 12×4; likewise, 50×6 is the same as 100×3). Ask whether $40 \div 4$ is the same as $4 \div 40$ and why.

Students try to make sense of cups and gallons and then lengths of string as the motivators for looking at division, multiplication, and factors.

The teacher closed the cup-gallon demonstration, summing up, "We say this [amount] divided by this [amount], and our answer is how many *times* one goes into the other." She opened the string activity by saying, "I will give you a short and a long piece of string. You find how many times the short piece goes into the long one."

Student pairs determined how many times their short piece of string fit into the long piece and then posted their results on the board. The teacher taped the short pieces of string to the board and recorded the number of times each fit into the long piece posted above them.

The teacher wrote on the board:

"How many short pieces of ___ length are in this long piece?"

She had the students fill in their answers and then said, "So, we're supposed to write an equation. Let's do that together." Then she asked, "So what did you do?" A few students said, "We took the long piece." The teacher continued, "We started with this long piece of rope. What letter can we use to represent the long piece of rope?" The students chose "R," and the teacher wrote it under the posted data.

Teacher: "What did you do then?"

Students: "We found how many times it [the short rope] fit in [the long one]."

Teacher : "What are you doing there?"

Students: "Division."

Michael: "Adding—you're adding up the small pieces."

The teacher did not hear Michael and so posted the division symbol after the "R" and then the length of the short rope, coming up with the following equation:

$R \div 6'' = 8$ times

Rope divided by a short length equals the number of times it fits in.

Teacher : "Okay. Write the equation you came up with on your sheet. Then see if you can figure out how long your piece was."

The students did this and then shared their equations and answers: "We said how many times does x go into 48, and we had the answer of six."

Student: "How long was the short piece? Eight inches because six times eight is 48."

continued on next page

continued from previous page

As students shared, it became clear that those who found an answer asked themselves the question, "What *multiplied by* six (or 24 or 16 or 12) equals 48?" Some even rewrote their equations after finding an answer by thinking about multiplication: 48 ÷ 6 = 8 or 48 ÷ 16 = 3, showing a deeper understanding of division and equations.

Teacher: "Why is this division, and how do you use multiplication?"

Students: "You have to make it equal" (referring to the equation).

Teacher : "How do you do that?"

John: "Multiply. You have the long piece, and you divide it by the short piece to find how many times it goes in. The whole piece divided by this (shows short piece)—find how many times it (shows short piece) goes in."

The teacher then made a diagram. She said, "Drawing pictures is a good way to solve a problem."

$R = 48''$

Teacher : "How would the picture change if we used 2″ lengths?"

Carol: "It would make it longer." (I think Carol meant the small piece would fit into the longer one more times, but I'm not sure.)

Teacher : "But we know how long the long piece is; it's 48″.

Sandra: "More pieces."

John: "You would draw more pieces."

The teacher shared the equation and changed the drawing, saying, "See how the picture changes?"

$R = 48''$

She then asked, "What happened to your answer as the little pieces got bigger?"

Everyone said, "Less," meaning the short piece went in fewer times.

Teacher : "What happens if the pieces get smaller?"

Students: "More."

continued on next page

continued from previous page

Teacher: "Let's generalize then. The smaller your piece, the more times it goes into the big one. The larger your piece, the fewer times. I have a vocabulary word for you: factors. When you have two numbers multiplied together to equal a number, they're called factors of that number. The factors of 48 are 2 and 24, 6 and 8, 12 and 4, and 16 and 3."

When I asked if those were all the factors, Michael, who is great with his times tables, suggested 1 and 48.

When asked what they were learning today, the students said, "Inches, ounces, feet, yards." Clearly the measurement context made an impression.

Esther Leonelli, observed by Tricia Donovan
Notre Dame Education Center, Boston, MA

14

Making Do

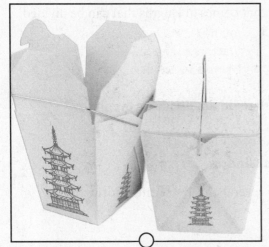

> ### *What do I do with the leftovers?*

Synopsis

Students refine their division skills by handling **remainders** with division in a sensible way.

1. The class discusses past experiences with division when the results did not come out evenly.

2. Student pairs look at various party favors and decide how to split them up sensibly among six children.

3. Students describe remainders in words and with mathematical notation.

4. Individuals apply these skills to another scenario that requires allocation of supplies and compare ways they handled the remainders.

5. Students examine and compare algorithms for division.

6. Students document the connections they see among the four operations.

7. The class synthesizes what has been learned about division with remainders and writes a question or statement of understanding about remainders.

Objectives

- Deal with remainders in a sensible way, given the context of the problem

- Write and understand remainders written as decimals, fractions, and whole numbers

- Explore why paper-and-pencil division algorithms work

- Explain the relationship among the four operations, including number properties and inverse operations

Materials/Prep

- Packs of gum (six pieces per pack) and Lifesavers™ or a similar type of candy that comes in rolls
- Small manipulatives, such as paper clips or chips
- Rope, string, or wire (something that comes in lengths that can be divided)

Opening Discussion

Pose a question such as this:

💬 **Did you ever try to divide something that did not divide up evenly?**

Share several stories and then say:

💬 **In math, those leftovers are called "remainders."**

Connect the term "remainder" back to several of the students' stories. Post a definition.

@ Activity 1: Party Favors

Refer students to *Activity 1: Party Favors* (*Student Book,* p. 232). Ask a volunteer to read the directions aloud, and when everyone is clear about the goal, have partners work together to complete the activity.

While they work, post on the board the three categories:

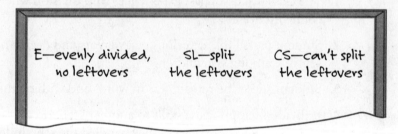

E—evenly divided, no leftovers   SL—split the leftovers   CS—can't split the leftovers

Bring the class together to share conclusions. Listen for and acknowledge disagreements, and encourage students to use pictures or objects to demonstrate their reasoning. All of the favors require dividing the total by six. Some of the favors can be easily redistributed in whole number amounts. For some, it makes sense to save the leftovers for another party. Other remainders can be split up and included in the party bags.

Ask first about the favors that divided up easily:

💬 **Which favors divided up evenly with nothing left over?**

Correct responses are the 30 stickers and the 60 marbles.

Next, ask about the favors where the leftovers could be split up:

💬 **Which favors had leftovers that you could split up?**

Correct responses are the 15 packs of Lifesavers and the 15 packs of gum; however, students may argue that there are no leftovers with the gum because the 90 sticks could be divided evenly among the bags. Others may argue that because the remainders of Lifesavers (3 rolls of 11) cannot be divided evenly by 6 that the Lifesavers cannot be split.

Finally, ask about those favors where there were leftovers, but it didn't make sense to split them up:

Which favors had leftovers that you did not split up? Why?

Correct responses are the 15 balloons, the 10 picture books, the 35 gummy candies, the 25 sparklers, the 15 quarters, and the five gift certificates. For instance, trying to cut a balloon into six pieces would be unrealistic. The gift certificates cannot be used at all for this party because there are only five, and ripping them into parts would make them unusable.

Encourage the use of demonstrations and pictures to support reasoning and solutions.

Connecting Division with Remainders to Notation

When the class has agreed on the categories, connect division with remainders to symbolic notation, but make sure students relate their numbers back to real objects. Ask students to take turns coming to the board to write some division equations for each favor.

For those categorized as "E," expect:

$$30 \text{ stickers} \div 6 = 5 \text{ or } 6\overline{)30}^{\,5} \text{ or } 30/6 = 5$$

$$60 \text{ marbles} \div 6 = 10 \text{ or } 6\overline{)60}^{\,10} \text{ or } 60/6 = 10$$

Thoroughly talk through the examples of the packs of gum and Lifesavers. Have students do the division mentally and physically, opening the packs of gum and Lifesavers to deal out the pieces equally among the five goody bags. Then say:

You had 25 sparklers. You said each child received four and there was one left over. How could you write that in math language?

For those favors categorized as "SL," there are several ways to express how much of each favor would be in each party bag:

15 packs of gum ÷ 6 = 2 3/6, or 2 1/2 packs for each bag (or 15 pieces per child).

Ask someone to use the calculator for the division. Connect 0.5 (five-tenths) with a half-pack of Lifesavers. Discuss whether or not student pairs' original answers on this support the calculator answer, how, and why.

15 packs of Lifesavers ÷ 6 = 2 1/2 packs each, or 2.5 packs

Listen for any of the three options: fractions, decimals, or writing "r" next to what is left to show that number is a remainder. Probe further, asking:

💬 **If we did not open up the packs of gum and divide out the pieces, if instead we kept the leftover packages whole, which way would you write that? Why?**

💬 **Some people write remainders with a fraction bar. How would this look written as a fraction? When would you do that? Why?**

Make clear that the fraction 3/6 could be used to show either that they have three *out of* a total of six that they need or to show that they need to *divide* the three packs left into six piles. In either case, the children get two whole packs and part of another pack. Use labeled objects or diagrams to support the concepts—whole pack; half pack.

For those favors categorized as "CS," fractions and decimals do not make sense:

> 15 balloons ÷ 6 = 2 r3
> (meaning two for each child with three leftovers to save for another time).
>
> 5 gift certificates ÷ 6 = 0 r5 (They cannot be divided by six because there are only five, and ripping them into parts would make them unusable.)
>
> 10 picture books ÷ 6 = 1 r4
>
> 25 sparklers ÷ 6 = 4 r1

Take time to put into words what the remainder means when notated as r___ .

Ask:

💬 **How was dividing up the 15 Lifesavers packs the same as or different from dividing up the sparklers or the gum? How many packs of Lifesavers did each of the six children get?**

Pictures are absolutely necessary here to appreciate fully how remainders present themselves in different problem contexts.

Activity 2: Making Do

Pair or group students. Assign *Activity 2: Making Do* (*Student Book,* p. 233). This problem is similar to the party favor scenario, but this time students must go one step further to divide up the supplies, deciding on a fraction or decimal to show the remainder.

Have partners compare ways they figured out and wrote their answers.

Review this activity with questions similar to those used for *Activity 1*:

💬 **Which items divided up evenly?**

💬 **What did you do with those items that did not divide up evenly?**

💬 **Which ways did you write the remainders? Why?**

Check students' decision-making processes. Regardless of whether you think so, in each case ask the class:

 Does that way make sense?

 ## Activity 3: Understanding the "Why" of Methods for Division

The lessons on division are intended to give students the opportunity to examine the mathematical principles behind the steps, or algorithms, they regularly use for this operation. Like *Lessons 12* and *13*, this is not a lesson on *how* to divide with paper and pencil. It is assumed that students have learned to do this. If there are some who do not know how to, this discussion will uncover that, and you may want to provide extra practice.

Part 1: Students share their algorithms for division

This activity launches from the algorithms or methods that student use. Document and post a record of division methods similar to those suggested in earlier lessons for addition and subtraction.

Start by saying:

 I know you have been doing basic division for a long time, sometimes in your head, sometimes using a paper and pencil, and sometimes with a calculator or other device. It depends on what the situation is.

 Right now, we're going to take a look at the paper-and-pencil methods you learned in school, and may still use, and discuss not just *how* they work but *why* they work. This knowledge is important groundwork for higher level math.

Present the following problem:

> You buy a car for $10,600 and will pay for it in four equal installments. How much will each installment be? (Ask for and record estimates on the board before the calculations.)

 How would you figure out the amount using paper and pencil?

Ask students to check with another person to see if they did it exactly the same way. Then have volunteers show various methods on the board, explaining *how* they did it.

Heads Up!

Students from other countries may not have learned the U.S. standard algorithm, but the algorithm they were taught is likely based on sound mathematical principles.

Part 2: Probing *why* school methods work mathematically

After methods are posted, direct discussion to the mathematical reasoning behind the procedures or algorithms. Say:

💬 **Hmmm, I see a variety of strategies. What's going on here? How do they work?**

If a strategy of breaking up the $10,600 using expanded notation is not included, bring it up yourself, making connections to the real values of the digits by expanding the number:

💬 **I see you broke the 10,600 into 10,000 + 600. How did that help you?**

I know that $10,000 \div 4 = 2,500$ and also $600 = 400 + 200$, so dividing each one by 4, $400 \div 4 = 100$ and $200 \div 4 = 50$, so the whole thing is $2,500 + 100 + 50 = 2,650$.

💬 **So when dividing we can break the number into parts and divide the parts by the number, in this case 4 ... let's see how others solved it.**

Point to the long division for the U.S. standard algorithm (if anyone did it that way), and say:

$$
\begin{array}{r}
2\,6\,5\,0 \\
4\,\overline{)\,10{,}600\,} \\
-\,8\downarrow \qquad\quad 2\times4=8\\
\hline
2\,6 \\
-\,24\downarrow \qquad 6\times4=24\\
\hline
2\,0 \\
-\,20\downarrow \qquad 5\times4=20\\
\hline
0\,0 \\
-\,0 \qquad\quad 0\times4=0\\
\hline
0 \qquad \boxed{2{,}650}
\end{array}
$$

💬 **What does the 10 represent in that first "goes into" part?**

The 10 is 10,000; and the 6 is 600, so when you "bring down" the 6, you have 2,600; not just 26.

💬 **One way to show what this means is looking at it this way—where you see the real value of every number.**

$$
\begin{array}{r}
4\,\overline{)\,10{,}600\,} \\
\underline{8{,}000} \quad (4 \times 2{,}000) \\
2{,}600 \\
\underline{2{,}400} \quad (4 \times 600) \\
200 \\
\underline{200} \quad (4 \times 50) \\
0 \quad (4 \times 2{,}650)
\end{array}
$$

Each installment will be $2,650.

We have now looked at two ways in which you solved the division problem. One could even argue that you used multiplication to solve the division problem. Some of you used other methods. Let's look at them as well.

💬 **Now try one more problem. Do it in a way that we showed here that is different from your way.**

Your friend also buys a car, but hers is $10,999 and she will pay it in four equal installments. How much will each installment be?

Ask for estimates and record them on the board.

This problem has a remainder. If students didn't think of starting with what they already know (that $10,600 ÷ 4 = 2,650), you might call that to their attention later, since this ($10,999) is about $400 more, and that's an important thing to notice.

```
4 ⟌ 10,999
    8,000    (4 × 2,000)
    2,998
    2,400    (4 × 700)        39
     199                      36    (4 × 9)
     160     (4 × 40)          3
```

The remainder 3 is 3/4, so the total is $2,749 and 3/4, which is of course $2,749.75 for each installment. Alternately, if anyone noticed that this problem is the same as the previous one, but $399 more, you can start with the previous answer and add $399 ÷ 4.

```
4 ⟌ 399
    360    (4 × 90)
     39
     36    (4 × 9)
      3
```

The remainder is again 3/4, or $0.75. So $90 + $9 + $0.75 is a total of $99.75 more per month.

⊖ Math Inspection: The Four Operations

This inspection serves as a way to assess students' understanding of the four operations, including their relationships to each other.

Ask students to begin working independently and then to work with another student. They can compare and discuss relationships one found and the other did not list or does not recognize. Encourage students who struggle writing their ideas to use concrete examples to help clarify their thinking. As you circulate, you might prompt with examples of short-cuts or tricks that rely on these relationships. For example, you can calculate the multiplication facts for 9 by multiplying by 10 and subtracting.

Once students have done what they can, discuss their ideas. Create a large version of the four operations and record all of the interrelationships students' listed. Listen for the following key points. If students do not say them, add them to the mix.

Addition means to find the sum, to combine amounts. It is the inverse of subtraction. Repeated addition can be used for whole number multiplication situations: $4 \times 3 = 4 + 4 + 4$). It is commutative.

Subtraction has several different meanings: taking an amount away, finding the difference between two amounts, or comparing two amounts. It is the inverse of addition. Repeated subtraction can be used for whole number division situations ($10 \div 2$ can be found by subtracting 2 from 10 until you run out of groups of 2). It is not commutative.

Multiplication means to find the product. Multiplication is about equal groups. It can also be repeated addition. Exponents can be used to show repeated multiplication of the same base: ($4^2 = 4 \times 4$). Multiplication is the inverse of division. It is commutative.

Division means to find the quotient. Division has two meanings: finding how many of an amount in a total ($12 \div 3$ can mean to find how many groups of 3 there are in 12), and splitting up an amount into parts ($12 \div 3$ can also mean to find how many are in each group if 12 is evenly divided into 3 groups). Division is the inverse of multiplication. It is not commutative.

Summary Discussion

Synthesize the learning in this lesson by asking:

 What can happen when we divide up amounts of things?

Expect statements such as these:

"Sometimes the items will divide up evenly."

"Sometimes there will be items left over because there are not enough to deal one out to everyone again."

"Sometimes you leave the remainders alone and do not divide them up further—like the sparklers."

"Sometimes you do divide up the remainders into parts of things—like a half pack of gum."

Ask students to write about remainders in *Reflections* (p. 265) Record that and any other new words in *Vocabulary* (*Student Book*, p. 256). Reinforce the learning by asking:

 How can you identify or write remainders in a division answer?

Give students time to write responses to these questions:

1. By sharing our different methods, what did we learn from one another?

2. Many people say, "I just know how to do the procedure—I don't know why or what it really means." What do you understand clearly about why your division procedure works the way it does?

3. What is still confusing?

4. Do you see other operations when you encounter a division problem? How can addition, subtraction, or multiplication help you?

⊚ Practice

Interpreting Remainders, p. 236
For practice with remainders in different forms.

Pill Problems, p. 237
For another context in which to think carefully about remainders.

Meaningful Remainders, p. 238
For practice matching reasonable ways to express the quotient.

⊞ Mental Math Practice

Money in My Pocket, p. 240
Provides a challenging experience with divisibility and remainders.

⊞ Test Practice

Test Practice, p. 241

◉ Looking Closely

Observe whether students are able to

Deal with remainders in a sensible way, given the context of the problem

Are students able to stay with the realistic meaning of the problem? Are they able to justify their decisions based on the context? That is the focus of the lesson, so take time for physical demonstrations.

Write and understand remainders written as decimals, fractions, and whole numbers

Are students able to relate the different expressions of the remainders to the meaning of the problem? Spend time on breaking the answer apart. For example, in the equation 15 packs of gum ÷ 6 = 2 1/2, ask what the "2" means and what the "1/2" means. Is it two people, two packs, or two sticks? Is it a 1/2 pack or a 1/2 stick of gum? Students must be attentive to the context of the numbers.

Are students confused by fractions and decimals? The use of fractions in this lesson is limited to the fraction 1/2, which is relatively easy to demonstrate with visuals.

Explore why paper-and-pencil division algorithms work

Are students able to see place values within standard division algorithms? (For example, when students divide 4 into 2,400, do they see that the first "step" is really dividing 4 into 2,400, not just 24?) Are students able to recognize that standard division algorithms work by breaking the dividend into parts (usually by place value)?

Using multiples of 10 to get partial products and therefore find partial quotients, as shown in the examples in *Activity 3: Understanding the "Why" of Methods for Division, Part 2*, should help explain how the division works. Many students find that doing those partial products and keeping track of "how many so far" helps them get to the answer with understanding.

Explain the relationship among the four operations, including number properties and inverse operations

Look particularly to see if students identify which operations are inverse operations (multiplication/division and addition/subtraction) and if they identify number properties (either by name or description) with the proper operations. The lessons in this book have repeatedly covered the commutative property of addition and multiplication and have explored the distributive property as well. Students may be familiar with identity properties, such as a $x^1 = x$ and $a + 0 = a$, without necessarily identifying them formally. Pointing out that these are also number properties can be useful: for example, it is the identity property of 0 that makes additive inverses so useful (5 + -5 = 0) and the identity property of 1 that allows us to change denominators on a fraction.

Rationale

Even the students most confident with division tend to look unsettled when they find they have an answer with a remainder, and this lesson seeks to raise awareness of the meaning of the remainder in a division problem. By laying out the three options for notating remainders and distilling the differences, students can make decisions on a case-by-case basis about how to treat remainders.

Several research studies have shown that students are often careless with remainders and offer nonsensical answers after doing the computation. Everyone should be helped to develop a deeper understanding of what quotients and remainders mean. Without this understanding, silly but common mistakes occur, such as, "11.5 buses are needed to take 322 children on a field trip, if 28 children can ride in each bus."

Math Background

Most of the division in this lesson focuses on the partitioning, or splitting, model of division. When you split something up, what you do with the remainder is the central question. However, the issue of remainders is also central to questions in the form "How many ___ in a _____?"

Consider the question, "How many weeks are in a 30-day month?" One might answer "4" if one is thinking of full weeks, or "4 weeks and 2 days" to interpret the division $7\overline{)30}^{\,4\,r2}$. Another reasonable answer is 4 2/7 weeks, but somehow the answer in a nonterminating decimal, although mathematically correct, is contextually not very satisfactory (4.28572428451 …). The context usually dictates the representation of the remainder.

Facilitation

Making the Lesson Easier

Spend most of the class time on the party favor scenario. Introduce students to the context and involve them in a multiplication and division review by asking students first to create a list of goodies for favor bags for five kids. Begin with the list on p. 232 (*Student Book*) and add to it.

Students should figure out how many of each party favor should be in each of the five goody bags. Then ask them, "How would you change the goody bags to keep things fair for six children?"

Making the Lesson Harder

Increase the difficulty level and size of the numbers.

Give students a division problem such as 30 ÷ 4, and challenge them to write two different scenarios: one where the sensible answer is 7 r2 and one where the answer is 7 1/2.

A teacher recounted this after facilitating Math Inspection: Four Operations ...

Sound principles and methods in this lesson — very relevant to students' needs, especially for those on the road to high school equivalency tests. I'm glad I asked:

Who remembers what the four basic operations are?

How and why can using money help you when you're solving division problems?

The basics of the relationship between the four basic operations were pretty well understood by the class.

Students made memorable comments about the four operations:

"What do you mean 'multiplication is addition speeded up'?"

"Addition and subtraction are each other turned inside out."

"In my country, we don't do division that way."

Adam Weiss
Bronx Adult Learning Center, New York City, NY

Facilitating Closing the Unit: Computer Lab

> ### *How would you plan for your community?*

Synopsis

Students draw upon their number skills as they work on a performance assessment planning project. Then they complete a written *Final Assessment*.

1. You introduce the *Computer Lab Project* to the class.

2. Student pairs complete four *Computer Lab Warm-Up* exercises.

3. Student pairs plan for the computer lab purchases and then write up a report to share with the class.

4. Individuals complete an assessment that mirrors the opening lesson's assessment activities and provides a direct before-and-after comparison of knowledge (optional).

5. The class reflects on what they have learned in the unit.

Objectives

- Consolidate content taught in the unit
- Identify areas of strength and weakness

Materials/Prep

- Calculators
- Markers
- Easel paper
- Scrap paper (if doing optional *Activity 2, Number of the Day*)

For *Activity 1*, make copies of *Blackline Master 16: E-Z Computer Mail Order Catalog*, and *Blackline Master 17: Computer Lab Scoring Rubric*, one per student pair.

For *Activity 3*, make copies of *Final Assessment*, pp. 201–205, and *Final Assessment Checklist*, p. 206, one each per student. Prepare to display *Blackline Masters 18–20: Mental Math Challenge #1.*

Heads Up!

The closing will take two sessions.

Opening Discussion

Explain that this final major activity in the unit presents a chance for students to show what they have learned. Working with a partner, students use mental math and estimation to figure prices for a computer lab and then use a calculator to make the final plan. They will make presentations to the whole class that will be scored. Then everyone will complete an individual final written assessment.

 ## Activity 1: Computer Lab Project

Together, read aloud the scenario for *Activity 1: Computer Lab Project* (*Student Book*, p. 244).

Ask students to partner up. Distribute *Blackline Master 16: E-Z Computer Mail Order Catalog*, one per student pair.

Explain:

 Before you start planning your lab, there are four activities to do first. These will help establish your mindset for planning. You can work on these activities in any order, but you may not use a calculator yet.

Tell partners to read through the *Computer Lab Warm-Ups* (*Student Book*, pp. 244-248) and decide where they want to start. They will have about 20 minutes to work on these problems.

As they work, observe whether students are providing two solution methods when asked and whether they are using mental math. Encourage students to show their work or explain how they solved problems, so you can understand better how they are thinking.

After 20 minutes, bring the class together, and go over the answers and solutions.

Suggest to students that they reread the directions for the *Computer Lab* activity and begin their planning by reading through the list of necessary equipment and supplies. Remind students that they will present their final plans to the class next session. Distribute and read together *Blackline Master 17: Computer Lab Project Scoring Rubric* by which the presentations will be judged.

Final plans are then copied onto chart paper for sharing with the class.

Each student pair presents their final plan to the class and explains how they made their choices. If they do not mention any estimates or calculations, encourage them to do so by asking questions such as these:

> **What strategies did you use to figure out what you could buy?**

> **How did estimation help you?**

> **What helped you most to create a workable plan?**

> **How did you keep track of all the prices to make sure you were close to, but not over, your spending limit?**

> **Did you come up with any combinations of items that you wanted that were over your limit? What did you do?**

> **What estimates did you make? How did you decide when to use the calculator and when to work in your head?**

> **Once you made your choices, how did you find out whether you were over or under your spending limit?**

Other points to make that focus on the mathematical thinking include these:

Discuss when students multiplied and when they added, reinforcing the idea of using multiplication for repeated addition. Raise issues of commutativity and associativity by commenting:

> **This pair of students added the items in this order, while this other pair added the items in a different order; did the order in which the pairs added make a difference in the total amount?**

> **This pair entered "3" into the calculator first and then "699." What would happen if we entered "699" first and then "x 3"?**

If everyone says, "I just punched the numbers in the calculator," explore other ways they might have totaled amounts without using a calculator, as well as exactly how they entered numbers in the calculator in terms of keys and sequence.

Take this time to elicit from student pairs a few examples of equations that could represent all or a portion of the calculations. Assess skills with order of operations by having a few students insert parentheses on equations written on the board to indicate what operation would be done first by the calculator, or if the numbers are simple enough, have the class do the calculations using mental math and compare results with the calculator's.

For example, you might post $40 \times 2 + 20 + 4 \times 15$ to represent the two surge protectors, one mouse, and four 25-packs of CD's that a group chooses to buy and then ask for parentheses or a comparison of calculation methods. You might suggest that you arrived at an answer by multiplying 40×22 and then adding 4×15; then ask, "What did I do wrong?"

Move the conversation to a broader topic by posing questions such as these:

💬 **How far apart were your estimated grand total and your actual grand total? Whose were the closest?**

💬 **Which plan seems to be the most reasonable? Why?**

Activity 2: Number of the Day

Optional: This activity is recommended if you skip *Activity 1*.

Facilitate *Number of the Day* as explained in *Opening the Unit*, p. 4. Announce a number such as the year or select a number from a recent event. Distribute scrap paper.

Activity 3: Final Assessment

The *Final Assessment* mirrors the *Initial Assessment* in the opening session. This is an opportunity for you and students to compare the quality of their work at the beginning and end of the unit.

Distribute a copy of the *Final Assessment* to everyone.

Explain that there are five tasks:

Task 1: Mental Math Challenge

Task 2: Picturing the Math

Task 3: Four Operations

Task 4: Is It Always True?

Task 5: Four Problems

Facilitating Task 1

Tell students:

💬 **I am going to show and read some problems. Your challenge is to do the math in your head and then write down the answers. Do not use pencils and paper or calculators!**

Starting with *Blackline Master 18: Mental Math Challenge*, cover up the problems, revealing each problem one at a time and reading it aloud. Allow a few moments for students to think about each problem and write the answer. This is not a timed test, but move along at a good pace. You are trying to see how fluent students are with the numbers. Continue with the next two *Mental Math Challenges* (*Blackline Masters 19* and *20*).

Facilitating Tasks 2–5

Before students attempt the problems in Tasks 2–5, you may read through the problems together. Then ask students to complete the tasks using methods of their choice. See the *Final Assessment Checklist,* p. 206, to evaluate work. Share these with students after you have reviewed their work. Consider scheduling individual conferences.

Summary Discussion

Ask students to comment.

 What challenged you today and through this book?

 What did you find out about your strong points?

Remind students that they may not have known all the answers. That is okay. Learning is a process and this was a chance to take stock of what they know and where they need more work.

Students record thoughts in *Reflections* (*Student Book,* p. 266.)

Looking Closely

Observe whether students are able to

Apply content covered in *Everyday Number Sense: Mental Math and Visual Models*

The final assessment will give you information about how students handle mental math and visual models. To complete the assessment successfully, they will:

- Solve problems mentally with estimates and exact answers.
- Represent operations ($\times, \div, +, -$) using objects, pictures, arrays, and number lines to explain and support reasoning.
- Select appropriate operation(s) to represent problem situations (e.g., when to multiply and when to divide) and write expressions in mathematical notation.
- Explain and develop strategies for rounding, adjusting, and using benchmark numbers (10's and 100's) to solve problems.
- Understand basic number properties that form the basis for algebra.
- Use the scientific calculator.

As students work on the activities, keep these questions in mind:

> Are students demonstrating mastery of mental math and estimation, as well as flexibility with various solution methods?
>
> Are they using visual models that match math symbols?

Assess areas of strength and weakness

There are two guides for assessing student work.

For the *Computer Lab Project*, fill out *Blackline Master 17: Computer Lab Scoring Rubric* for each student pair. Use the *Final Assessment Checklist*, p. 206, for each individual student. Share these with students as a way to conclude the unit.

As you assess the various activity tasks, check for the following:

- Accuracy: Are totals and notation representation in equations accurate?

- Solution path choices: Are they appropriate and efficient?

- Flexibility: When asked for more than one solution method, does student represent multiple methods?

- Fluency: Did student work easily on each task or struggle with some? What blocked fluency?

Appendices

Name _____ Date _____

Everyday Number Sense: Mental Math and Visual Models

INITIAL ASSESSMENT

Task 1: Mental Math Challenge

After you see and hear each problem, do the math in your head and then write the answer here.

1. _____   8. _____

2. _____   9. _____

3. _____   10. _____

4. _____   11. _____

5. _____   12. _____

6. _____   13. _____

7. _____   14. _____

© 2015 TERC

Task 2. Picturing the Math

1. Tony and Marina each walk to the Learning Center. Tony lives eight blocks from school. Marina lives 12 blocks from school.

   a. Draw a picture of how you see this situation.

   b. Write a word problem for the situation. Then tell how you would solve it.

2. What if Tony lives eight blocks east of the school and Marina lives 12 blocks west of the school.

   a. Describe or draw how you see the situation.

   b. What changed from your drawing in Problem 1?

3. Write a number sentence to go with the picture:

© 2015 TERC EMPower™

4. Circle the picture that shows 8 × 4 + 3. Explain how you know.

Picture A 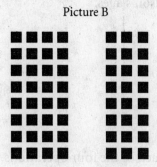 Picture B

5. Make a picture for each of these expressions:

   a. 2(3) + 6   b. 2(3 + 6)

6. Rosa and Ida agreed to split costs for a two-day trip.

Ida: I got cash and paid for gas and meals. Out of $600, I have $40 left.

Rosa: I paid for two hotels—$180 total.

   a. How much should each pay? Explain how you know with pictures, words, or an equation

   b. How much does one owe? Explain how you know with pictures, words, or an equation.

7. Carl is 57 years old. His grandson is 39 years younger. Draw a number line to show the age difference. Label Carl's and his grandson's ages.

Task 3: Four Operations

1. Write three things you know about each of the four operations.

Addition

_____

_____

_____

Subtraction

_____

_____

_____

Multiplication

_____

_____

_____

Division

_____

_____

_____

2. Then, on the connecting lines below, describe all the relationships that the operations have with one another. Give examples.

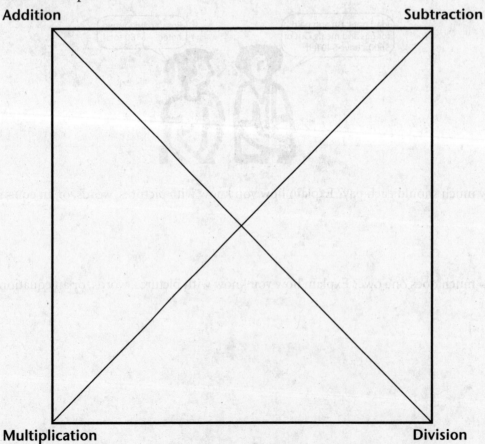

Addition   Subtraction

Multiplication   Division

Task 4: Is It Always True?

1. Mara knows a rule that saves time: if n is a whole number, it is always true that $n + -n = 0$.

   a. Do you agree or disagree?

   b. Give two examples that show that Mara's rule works or doesn't work.

Task 5: Four Problems

Show two different ways you could find the answer for each problem.

1. $382 + 49 + 118 =$	2. $1{,}003 - 98 =$
3. $78 \times 5 =$	4. $689 \div 13 =$

INITIAL ASSESSMENT CHECKLIST

Use a ✓, ✓+, or ✓– to assess how well students met each skill. Note strengths as well as areas for improvement.

Student's Name _____

Task	Skills	Lesson Taught
1. Mental Math Challenge	Doubles and halves Pairs numbers that add to 100 Adds or subtracts a multiple of 10 or 100 from an amount Multiplies by powers and multiples of 10 Divides by powers and multiples of 10 Estimates Rounding	All lessons
2. Picturing the Math	Connects diagrams, arrays, and number lines to word problems and mathematical expressions	3, 4, 5, 8, 9, 10, 11, 12
3. Four Operations	Makes true statements about the four basic operations Explains connections between and among the four basic operations	2, 4, 5, 6, 10, 11, 12, 13, 14
4. Is It Always True?	Generalizes about combining positive and negative numbers Explains mathematical ideas in words	5, 6, 7, 9, 14
5. Four Problems	Knows various ways to add Knows various ways to subtract Knows various ways to multiply Knows various ways to divide	All lessons

OVERALL NOTES

Strengths and Areas for Improvement

_____

_____

_____

_____

_____

_____

_____

© 2015 TERC

Name _____ Date _____

Everyday Number Sense:
Mental Math and Visual Models

FINAL ASSESSMENT

Task 1: Mental Math Challenge

After you see and hear each problem, do the math in your head and then write the answer here.

1. _____   8. _____

2. _____   9. _____

3. _____   10. _____

4. _____   11. _____

5. _____   12. _____

6. _____   13. _____

7. _____   14. _____

Task 2: Picturing the Math

1. John was born 25 years before his son Mark. John's father is 52 years older than Mark.

    a. Draw a picture or use a number line to show the situation.

    b. Write a word problem for the situation. Then solve it.

2. The distance from Seattle to Boston is approximately 3,000 miles (3,112 miles).

    Estimate the number of miles a driver has to travel each day on a cross-country trip, The driver will travel the the same number of miles each day, but is still deciding how many days it will take to make the trip.

NUMBER OF DAYS	ABOUT HOW MANY MILES COVERED EACH DAY
3 days	a.
4 days	b.
5 days	c.
8 days	d.
10 days	e.

    f. What patterns do you see as you calculate and check your answers?

3. Write a number sentence to go with this picture:

4. Which picture is correct for 8 x 2 + 4? How do you know?

Picture A

Picture B

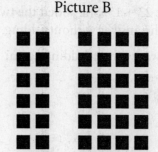

5. Make a picture for each expression:

   a. 5(2) + 4

   b. 5(2 + 4)

6. Carl lives in Boston, 200 miles north of New York. His mother lives in Washington, D.C., 175 miles south of New York. Draw a number line showing approximately how far Carl lives from his mother.

Task 3: Is It Always True?

1. Mara's teacher asked her to solve 23 + 15. She added the two numbers and got 38. The teacher asked her to solve 15 + 23. Mara gave the answer without adding.

   a. How did Mara know the answer without adding again?

   b. Write the rule you think Mara is using in math symbols.

   c. Will Mara's rule always work? Why or why not?

Task 4: Four Operations

1. Write three things you know about each of the four operations.

   Addition

   _____

   _____

   _____

   Subtraction

   _____

   _____

   _____

   Multiplication

   _____

   _____

   _____

   Division

   _____

   _____

   _____

2. Then, on the connecting lines below, write about the relationships you see between the operations..
Give examples.

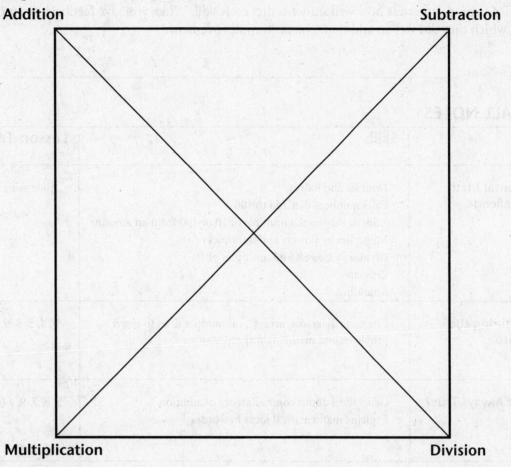

Addition

Subtraction

Multiplication

Division

Task 5: Four Problems

Show two different ways you could find the answer for each problem.

1. 491 + 48 + 107 =	2. 2,005 – 97 =
3. 56 x 25 =	4. 736 ÷ 23 =

FINAL ASSESSMENT CHECKLIST

Use a ✓, ✓+, or ✓– to assess how well students met each skill. When you give feedback to students, note areas in which they did well in addition to areas for improvement.

Student's Name_____

OVERALL NOTES

Task	Skills	Lesson Taught
1. Mental Math Challenge	Doubles and halves Pairs numbers that add to 100 Adds or subtracts a multiple of 10 or 100 from an amount Multiplies by powers and multiples of 10 Divides by powers and multiples of 10 Estimates Rounding	All lessons
2. Picturing the Math	Connects diagrams, arrays, and number lines to word problems and mathematical expressions	3, 4, 5, 8, 9, 10, 11, 12
3. Is It Always True?	Generalizes about commutativity of addition Explains mathematical ideas in words	5, 6, 7, 9, 14
4. Four Operations	Makes true stateements about the four basic operations Explains connections between and among the four basic operations	2, 4, 5, 6, 10, 11, 12, 13, 14
5. Four Problems	Knows various ways to add Knows various ways to subtract Knows various ways to multiply Knows various ways to divide	All lessons

Strengths and Areas for Improvement

_____

_____

_____

_____

_____

1. Double $10

2. Double $23

3. Halve $56

4. Double $1,500

5. Add 85¢ and 15¢

6. $1,500 − $20 =

7. $8,565 – $200 is

8. 10 times $25 is

9. 15 x $20 =

10. 22 x $100 =

11. How many $10 make $180?

12. $360 ÷ 4 =

EMPower™
© 2015 TERC

Yes or No?

If you have $10, do you have enough money to buy

13. Two books of stamps at $6.80 each?

14. Movie tickets for 4 children at $2.50 each?

1. $1.95 + $3.95

2. $12.75 + $3.19

3. $15.79 + $29.99

4. $11.88 + $18.00

5. $1.05 + $6.00 + $19.99

6. $4.00 + $8.95 + $5.75

EMPower™
© 2015 TERC

Blackline Master 5: U. S. Historical Events

President John F. Kennedy Assassinated

Photo courtesy Library of Congress Prints and Photographs Division
Washington, D.C. 20540 USA LC-USZ62-117124

United States Civil War Starts

Photo courtesy Library of Congress Prints and Photographs Division
Washington, D.C. 20540 USA

World War II Ends

Photo courtesy of Veterans History Project, American Folklife Center,
Library of Congress, August, 1945. Photo by Robert Lee Olen.

Civil Rights Act Passed

Photo courtesy Library of Congress, Prints & Photographs Division,
U.S. News & World Report Magazine Collection, LC-USZ62-95480 (9-12)

American Women Are Granted the Right to Vote

Photo courtesy Library of Congress Prints and Photographs Division
Washington, D.C. 20540 USA LC-USZ62-75334

The Vietnam War Ends

Blackline Master 6: Number Lines -1,000 to 1,000

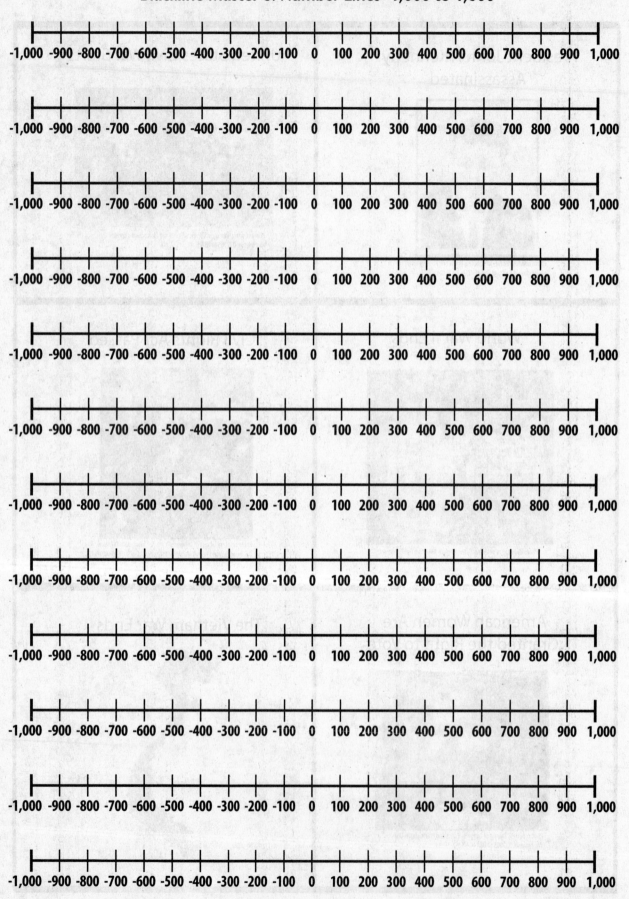

EMPower™
© 2015 TERC

Blackline Master 7: Number Lines -20 to 20

-20 -19 -18 -17 -16 -15 -14 -13 -12 -11 -10 -9 -8 -7 -6 -5 -4 -3 -2 -1 0 1 2 3 4 5 6 7 8 9 10 11 12 13 14 15 16 17 18 19 20

-20 -19 -18 -17 -16 -15 -14 -13 -12 -11 -10 -9 -8 -7 -6 -5 -4 -3 -2 -1 0 1 2 3 4 5 6 7 8 9 10 11 12 13 14 15 16 17 18 19 20

-20 -19 -18 -17 -16 -15 -14 -13 -12 -11 -10 -9 -8 -7 -6 -5 -4 -3 -2 -1 0 1 2 3 4 5 6 7 8 9 10 11 12 13 14 15 16 17 18 19 20

-20 -19 -18 -17 -16 -15 -14 -13 -12 -11 -10 -9 -8 -7 -6 -5 -4 -3 -2 -1 0 1 2 3 4 5 6 7 8 9 10 11 12 13 14 15 16 17 18 19 20

-20 -19 -18 -17 -16 -15 -14 -13 -12 -11 -10 -9 -8 -7 -6 -5 -4 -3 -2 -1 0 1 2 3 4 5 6 7 8 9 10 11 12 13 14 15 16 17 18 19 20

-20 -19 -18 -17 -16 -15 -14 -13 -12 -11 -10 -9 -8 -7 -6 -5 -4 -3 -2 -1 0 1 2 3 4 5 6 7 8 9 10 11 12 13 14 15 16 17 18 19 20

-20 -19 -18 -17 -16 -15 -14 -13 -12 -11 -10 -9 -8 -7 -6 -5 -4 -3 -2 -1 0 1 2 3 4 5 6 7 8 9 10 11 12 13 14 15 16 17 18 19 20

-20 -19 -18 -17 -16 -15 -14 -13 -12 -11 -10 -9 -8 -7 -6 -5 -4 -3 -2 -1 0 1 2 3 4 5 6 7 8 9 10 11 12 13 14 15 16 17 18 19 20

-20 -19 -18 -17 -16 -15 -14 -13 -12 -11 -10 -9 -8 -7 -6 -5 -4 -3 -2 -1 0 1 2 3 4 5 6 7 8 9 10 11 12 13 14 15 16 17 18 19 20

-20 -19 -18 -17 -16 -15 -14 -13 -12 -11 -10 -9 -8 -7 -6 -5 -4 -3 -2 -1 0 1 2 3 4 5 6 7 8 9 10 11 12 13 14 15 16 17 18 19 20

-20 -19 -18 -17 -16 -15 -14 -13 -12 -11 -10 -9 -8 -7 -6 -5 -4 -3 -2 -1 0 1 2 3 4 5 6 7 8 9 10 11 12 13 14 15 16 17 18 19 20

-20 -19 -18 -17 -16 -15 -14 -13 -12 -11 -10 -9 -8 -7 -6 -5 -4 -3 -2 -1 0 1 2 3 4 5 6 7 8 9 10 11 12 13 14 15 16 17 18 19 20

Pay your $800 rent.

Deposit a $400 IRS tax refund.

Pay the $100 electric bill.

Deposit a $650 paycheck from your day job.

Write a check for your $350 car payment.

Take out $200 from an ATM.

Deposit the $500 check from your night job.

Pay the $150 phone bill.

EMPower™
© 2015 TERC

Blackline Master 9: Balance Ups and Downs

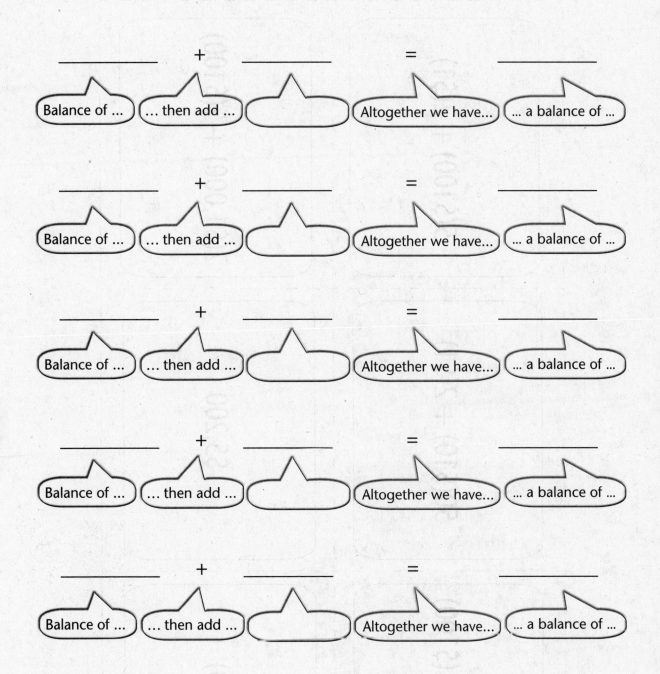

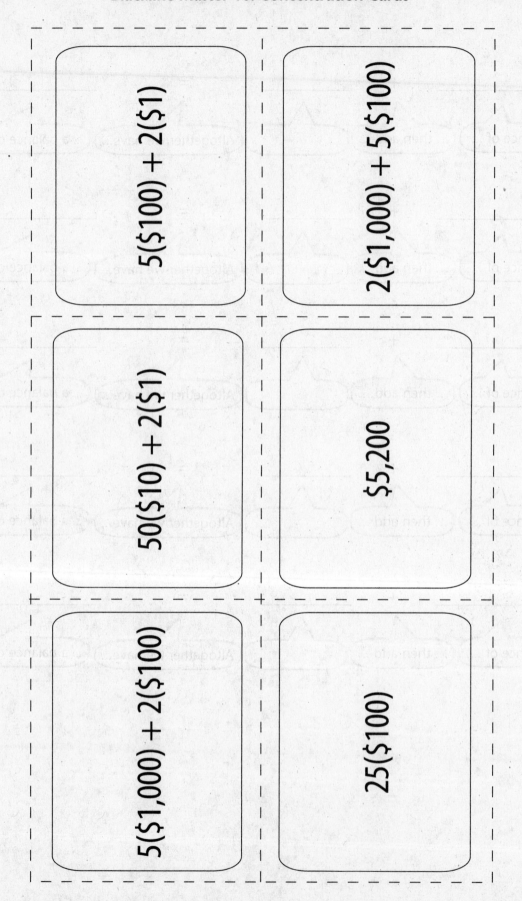

5($100) + 2($1)

2($1,000) + 5($100)

50($10) + 2($1)

$5,200

5($1,000) + 2($100)

25($100)

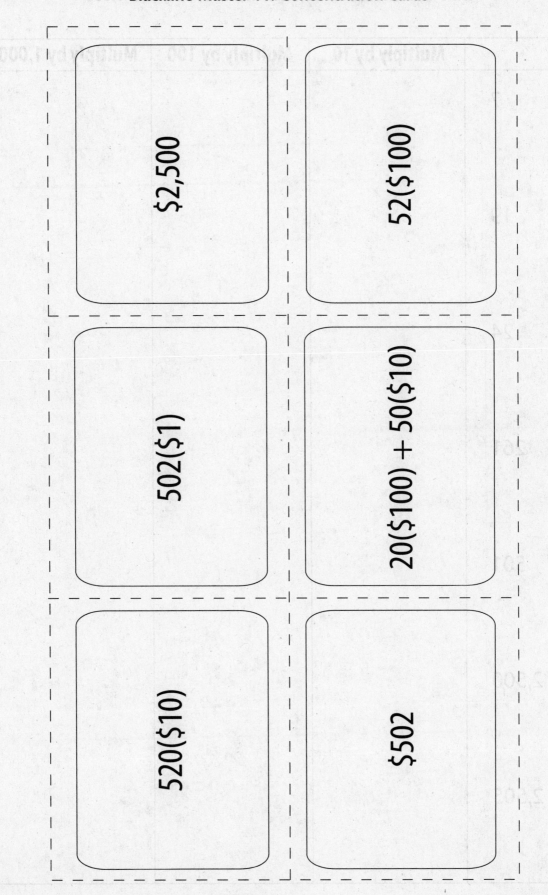

$2,500

52($100)

502($1)

20($100) + 50($10)

520($10)

$502

	Multiply by 10	Multiply by 100	Multiply by 1,000
7			
19			
24			
261			
501			
2,500			
2,505			

EMPower™
© 2015 TERC

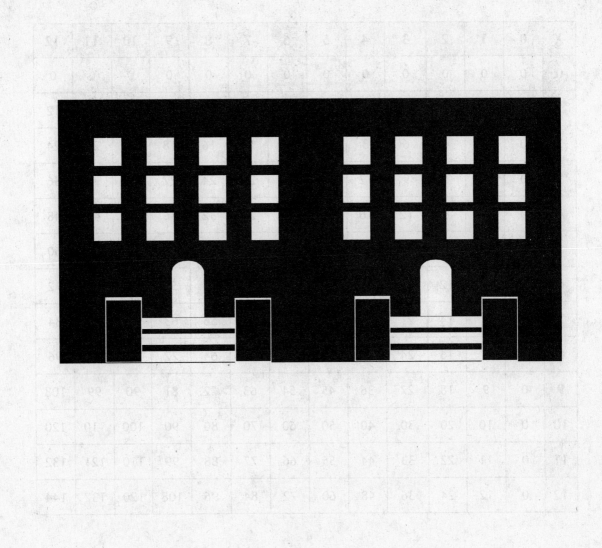

Blackline Master 14: Multiplication Table

X	0	1	2	3	4	5	6	7	8	9	10	11	12
0	0	0	0	0	0	0	0	0	0	0	0	0	0
1	0	1	2	3	4	5	6	7	8	9	10	11	12
2	0	2	4	6	8	10	12	14	16	18	20	22	24
3	0	3	6	9	12	15	18	21	24	27	30	33	36
4	0	4	8	12	16	20	24	28	32	36	40	44	48
5	0	5	10	15	20	25	30	35	40	45	50	55	60
6	0	6	12	18	24	30	36	42	48	54	60	66	72
7	0	7	14	21	28	35	42	49	56	63	70	77	84
8	0	8	16	24	32	40	48	56	64	72	80	88	96
9	0	9	18	27	36	45	54	63	72	81	90	99	108
10	0	10	20	30	40	50	60	70	80	90	100	110	120
11	0	11	22	33	44	55	66	77	88	99	110	121	132
12	0	12	24	36	48	60	72	84	96	108	120	132	144

EMPower™
© 2015 TERC

Fitness special 90 days for $39.99 Cost per day; round to the nearest penny	Annual state park pass (12 months) Total cost: $35.00 Cost per month:	10-week farm share Total cost: $89.99 Cost per week
Special 100-day membership Save on all purchases Membership: $25 Cost per day:	Yoga punch card Good for 10 classes Total cost: $59.00 Cost per class to nearest $1	10-month local gym membership Total cost: $169 Cost per month
10-month downtown gym membership Total cost: $799 Cost per month to nearest $1	Swimming lessons Good for 10 classes Total cost: $54.00 Cost per class to nearest $0.50	Schoolyear transit pass $750 for 10 months Cost per month:
10-month childcare package Total cost: $5,250 Cost per month to nearest $1	10-day car rental package Total cost: $129 Cost per day to nearest $1	Water World Summer 100-day Pass Total cost: $199 Cost per day:

E-Z Computer Mail Order Catalog

"For all of your computer needs"

Computers

(A) Desktop computer with CD-Rom Drive, 15" monitor (keyboard and mouse extra) Super Savings! **$699**

(B) Multimedia desktop computer with CD-RW Drive, 15" monitor with integrated speakers Cutting Edge Performance! **$999**

(C) Multimedia desktop computer Upgrade! Add a 17" flat panel monitor and CD burner! **$1,399**

(D) Advanced Multimedia computer with CD/DVD-Rom Drive, 15" monitor, storage capacty of up to 4GB Impressive Perfomance! **$1,800**

(E) Upgrade to a 17" flat panel monitor and CD/DVD burner! **$2,000**

(F) Laptop computer with CD-Rom Drive, 15.4" screen **$1,989**

(G) Laptop computer Upgrade! Add a 17" screen and CD/DVD burner! **$2,275**

Printers

(H) All-in-One Laser Printer Up to 25 ppm! **$1,299**

(I) Color Inkjet Printer High Quality! **$150**

(J) Color Inkjet Photo Printer, 2.5 LCD screen Connect directly to your camera! **$599**

Digital Cameras

(K) Digital Camera 5.0 Megapixel, 6x optical zoom, 2.5" LCD screen **$399**

(L) Digital Camcorder Record directly to DVD! **$1,400**

Surge Protectors

(M) Essential 6-Outlet Surge Protector **$18**

(N) 11-Outlet Surge Protector with Phone and Coaxial Protection **$40**

Keyboard/Mouse

(O) USB QWERTY Keyboard **$25**

(P) Cordless Ergonomic Keyboard **$49**

(Q) USB Mouse **$20**

(R) Optical Mouse—3 Button with scroll wheel **$50**

(S) Expert Gaming Mouse— Optical Trackball, 4 Button and scroll wheel **$50**

Ink Cartridges

(T) Laser Printer Ink Cartridges **$90/each**

(U) Black Inkjet Printer Cartridges **$24/each**

(V) Colot Inkjet Cartridges **$25/each**

Software

(W) Educational Software Package (for school practice) Single copy (for one computer) **$49** For 15 computers **$199**

(X) Game Software Package Single copy (for one computer) **$39** For 15 computers **$159**

(Y) Office Software (for creating office documents like letters, reports, etc.) Single copy **$429** Site license (110 computers) **$2,500**

Media

(Z) CD's (for storing information and documents) 25-pack **$15/pack**

(AA) DVD's (for storing digital movies) 5-pack **$10/pack**

Paper

(BB) Standard Paper—500 sheets (1 ream) **$5 per ream**

(CC) Bright White Paper—500 sheets (1 ream) **$8 per ream**

EMPower™
© 2015 TERC

Blackline Master 17: Computer Lab Scoring Rubric

Committee Members' Names:

_____

_____

Give 0–4 points for each area.

0 = not at all

1 = somewhat, but vague

2 = adequate

3 = well done

4 = exceeds expectations

_____ Selected equipment and supplies to meet the needs of the computer lab users

_____ Stayed within budget

_____ Used mental math to make reasonable cost estimates

_____ Used the calculator to arrive at exact costs

_____ Compared calculator results with estimated answers

_____ Clearly explained in words the reasoning behind the plan

_____ Clearly explained the plan with math notation and/or diagrams

_____ If an oral presentation to the class, answered questions from others fully

_____ Other _____

_____ **Total Points**

Notes

_____

_____

_____

_____

_____

1. Double $70

2. Double $45

3. Halve $38

4. Double $2,500

5. Add 65¢ and 35¢

6. $3,700 − $60 =

7. $9,770 – $400 is

8. 10 times $45 is

9. 15 x $30 =

10. 33 x $100 =

11. How many $10 make $270?

12. $480 ÷ 6 =

Yes or No?

If you have $20, do you have enough money to buy

13. Two books of stamps
   at $13.60 each?

14. Movie tickets for 4 children
   at $4.50 each?

EMPower™
© 2015 TERC

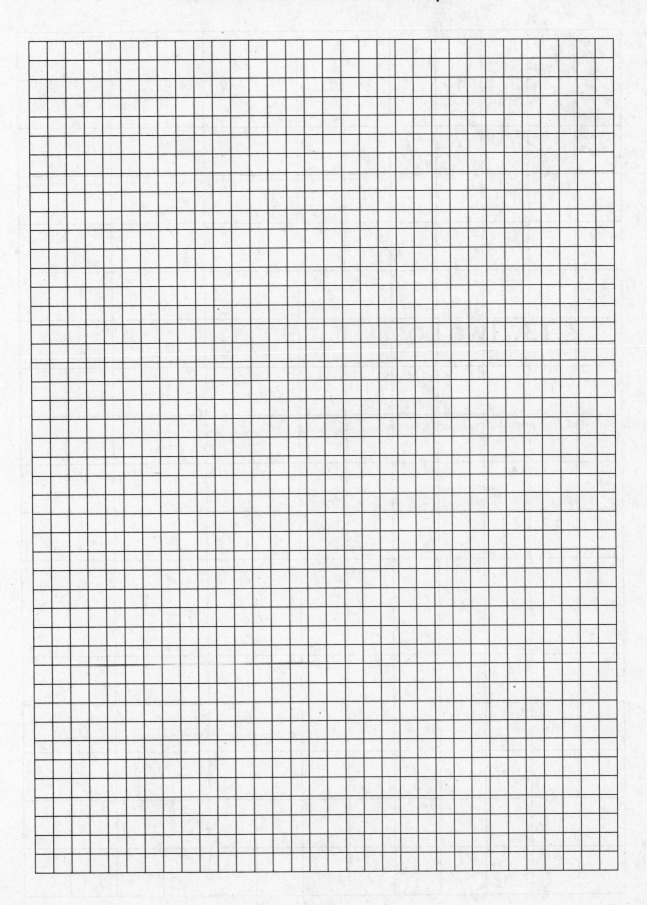

Blackline Master 22: 0.5-Inch Grid Paper

EMPower™
© 2015 TERC

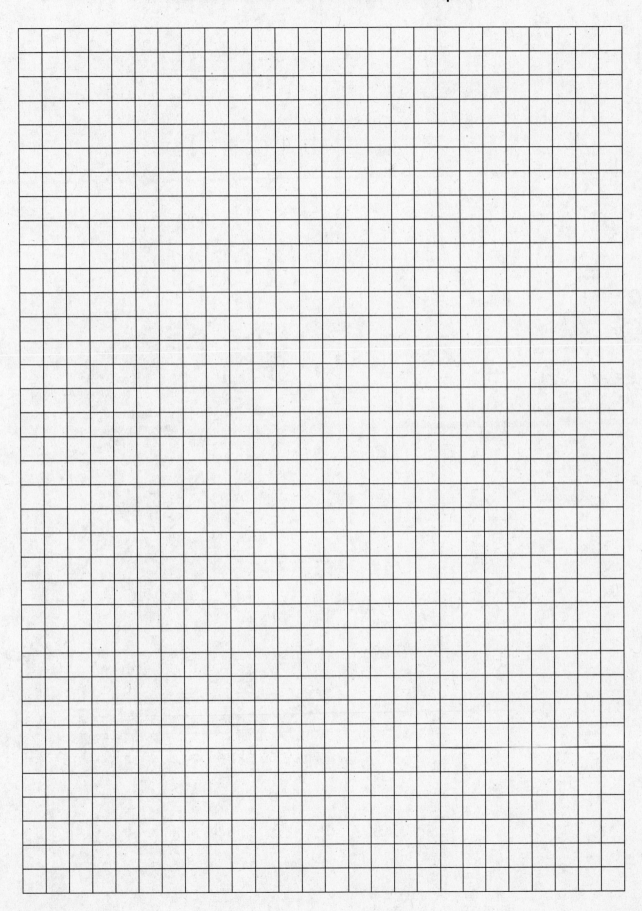

Glossary

Reminder: Students generate their own definitions for terms as they arise in class, using language that makes sense to them. However, to help you guide the discussion, we include mathematical definitions for most of the terms.

Italicized terms are *not* included in the *Student Book* but are included in the *Teacher Book* as background information. The lesson number in which the term first appears is in parentheses following the term.

10's place (2)—in a number, the location of the digit with a value of 10. For example, in the number 593, 9 is in the 10's place and has a value of nine 10's, or 90.

100's place (2)—in a number, the location of the digit with a value of 100. For example, in the number 593, 5 is in the 100's place and has a value of five 100's, or 500.

approximate (1)—*adj.* not quite exact, but only slightly more or less in number or quantity. *v.* to make an estimate of something.

array (10)—an arrangement of objects in rows and columns. The following array has four rows and four columns, and 16 objects in all.

difference (4)—the amount by which one quantity is greater or smaller than another; the result of subtraction.

equation (2)—a mathematical statement that two expressions are of the same value.

equivalent expressions (10)—mathematical statements that have the same value.

estimate (Opening)—*n.* a number close to an exact amount. *v.* to make an approximate calculation of something.

expanded notation (6)—a way to write numbers to show the value of each digit. For example, 5,342 = 5(1,000) + 3(100) + 4(10) + 2(1) = 5,000 + 300 + 40 + 2.

exponent (8)—a number placed to the upper right of a number or mathematical expression that indicates the number of times the number or expression is to be multiplied by itself. For example, in the equation $3^2=9$, 2 is the exponent.

expression (Opening)—a mathematical phrase that combines numbers and operations. More generally, a mathematical phrase that combines numbers, variables, and operations. For example, 3 + 6 2 or 500 – 75.

factor (8)—one of two or more whole numbers that can be multiplied together to give a specified number. For example, 1, 2, 3, 4, 6, and 12 are the factors of 12 because 1×12, 2×6, and $3 \times 4 = 12$.

linear measurement (*13*)—a measurement of length, width, height, or distance. Some linear measurement units are inches, feet, yards, and miles.

mathematical notation (*Opening*)—the use of numerals, operations signs, and other mathematical symbols to write expressions and relationships.

mental math (Opening)—the process of performing mathematical calculations in one's head, whether partially or totally. The use of strategies which are less dependent on paper-and-pencil algorithms or calculators.

multiples of 10, 100, and 1,000 (1)—a number that can be divided exactly by 10, 100, or 1,000 respectively.

negative numbers (6)—numbers that are less than zero.

number line (3)—a line with equally spaced tick marks named by numbers. For example:

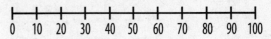

number sentences (*8*)—equations (or more generally, equations and inequalities).

order of operations (9)—rules for performing operations in mathematical expressions with more than one operation: First, do the operations within the parentheses; then, multiply or divide from left to right; then, add or subtract from left to right.

parentheses (6)—the symbols used to show which operation or operations should be done first. For example, $(20 - 4) \times 5 = 16 \times 5 = 80$.

positive numbers (6)—numbers that are greater than zero.

range (6)—the difference between the smallest and largest values in a set of data. For example, the range of the temperatures 32°F and 212°F is 180°F.

remainder (14)—the amount sometimes left over when one number is divided by another number.

rounding (1)—a type of estimation or approximation that makes it easier to work with numbers. For example, if you are counting clips and there are 148, you might round to 150, the nearest 10.

square number (10)—the number resulting from multiplying a whole number or integer by itself.

sum (1)—the total amount resulting when two or more numbers or quantities are added together.

visual models (*Opening*)—pictures, diagrams, or concrete objects that make the mathematics in a situation visible. Examples of visual models for $3 \times 4 + 2$:

and

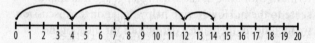

Answer Key

Opening the Unit: Everyday Numbers

Activity 1: Where is the Math in Your Life?
Answers will depend on students' experiences.

Activity 2: Number of the Day
Answers will vary.

Activity 3: Initial Assessment

Task 1: Mental Math Challenge
1. $20
2. $46
3. $28
4. $3,000
5. $1.00
6. $1,480
7. $8,365
8. $250
9. $300
10. $2,200
11. 18
12. $90
13. no
14. yes

Task 2: Picturing the Math
1. a. Answers will vary. Sample answer:

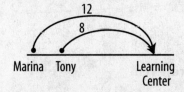

   b. Answers will vary. Sample answer:
   How far does Marina live from Tony?
   $12 - 8 = 4$.

2. a.

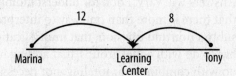

   b. Answers will vary. Sample answer based on 1a and 2a: The distance between Tony's house and Marina's house increased.

3. Answers will vary. Sample answer: $3 \times 4 = 12$

4. Picture A; explanations will vary.

5. a. Answers will vary. Sample answer:

   XX
   XX
   XX   XXXXXX

   b. Answers will vary. Sample answer:

               XX
               XX
               XX
               XX
               XX
               XX
               XX
               XX
               XX

6. a. Each sister should pay $370. Students may total all the costs for the trip and divide by 2.

   b. Rosa owes Ida $190. Using the model of subtraction where one finds the difference between two numbers, the difference between the amounts spent, $180 and $560, is $380. Divide it in two: 190. Rosa owes Ida $190.

7. Answers will vary. Possible answer:

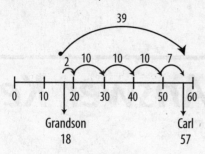

Task 3: Four Operations

1. Answers will vary. Look for understandings that there is more than one way to interpret subtraction and division, that multiplication has to do with equal groups, that adding has to do with combining or totaling, not necessarily always yielding a larger answer.

2. Answers will vary. Look for an understanding that addition and subtraction are inverse operations, as are multiplication and division. Another way to say this is that you can check your answer by doing the inverse operation. Students might point out that you can add up or subtract back to get an answer to a division problem. They may know other ways to solve multiplication problems that involve adding or rounding and subtracting.

Task 4: Is It Always True?

2. **a.** Agree

   b. Answers will vary. Examples: 5 + -5 = 0 or
   100 + -100 = 0

Task 5: Four Problems

1. 549. Possible solution:
   $(380 + 50 + 120) + 2 - 1 - 2 = 550 - 1 = 549$

2. 905. Possible solution:
   $(1,000 - 100) + 3 + 2 = 900 + 3 + 2 = 905$

3. 390. Possible solutions:
   $(70 + 8) \times 5 = (70 \times 5) + (8 \times 5) = 350 + 40 = 390$
   or
   $(80 \times 5) - (2 \times 5) = 400 - 10 = 390$

4. 53. Possible solutions:
   $(650 + 39) \div 13 = (650 \div 13) + (39 \div 13) =$
   $50 + 3 = 53$
   or
   $13 \times \underline{50} = 650, 13 \times \underline{3} = 39$, so $13 \times \underline{53} = 689$

Lesson 1: Close Enough with Mental Math

Activity 1: About How Much?

1. c. $6
2. b. $16
3. c. $46
4. b. $30
5. b. $27
6. c. $19

Activity 2: Wish List

1. Answers will vary.
2. Answers will vary.
3. Answers will vary.

Math Inspection: Agree or Disagree?

1–4. Lianne, Peter, Ana, and Chen's methods will all produce the same sum, and each of their methods will always work. Lianne, Peter, and Ana are demonstrating the commutative property of addition, which states that the sum is always the same regardless of the order of the addends. Chen's method relies on the associative property of addition, since he is grouping the addends while adding — a method that will also result in the same sum.

5. Answers will vary. Students may suggest always adding the numbers in the order given, or grouping addends that will make the arithmetic easier (such as looking for combinations that add to 10).

6. See explanation above.

Practice: Nearest Dollar

1. $11
2. $1
3. $7
4. $0
5. $44
6. $30
7. $99
8. $610
9. $1,000

Practice: Nearest Ten

1. $10
2. $80
3. $10

4. $0

5. $40

6. $40

7. $220

8. $600

9. $1,000

Practice: Closest Answer

1. b. $50

2. c. 50

3. b. 75

4. b. 100

5. c. $45

Practice: It's about . . .

1. a. 320

   b. 19 tables is about 20; $20 \times 8 = 160$;
      $160 \times 2 = 320$

   c. Above the actual amount because 19 was
      rounded up to 20.

2. a. $40

   b. $32 + $8 = $40

   c. Answers will vary. Possible answer: above
      the actual amount because both costs were
      rounded up.

Practice: Getting Close

1. b

2. c

3. d

4. f

5. c

6. e

Practice: Digital Read-out

Note: Responses may vary slightly for these
questions.

1. 15 psi

2. 35-36 psi

3. 37-38 mph

4. 460 degrees, 459-462 acceptable

5. 66-68 degrees

Mental Math Practice: How Much Money Is in the Jar?

1. a. $6

   b. $5

2. Possible answer. $0.50 + 50¢ = $1; 60¢ + $0.40
   = $1; $0.80 + $0.20 = $1; $0.75 + $0.25 = $1;
   $0.90 + $0.10 = $1

3. a. $4.50

   b. $5.00

Mental Math Practice: Bigger Jars of Money

1. a. $50

   b. $600

2. Possible answer. $6.00 + $4.00 = $10.00; $7.50 +
   $2.50 = $10.00; $1.50 + $8.50 = $10.00; $3.50 +
   $6.50 = $10.00; $3.00 + $7.00 = $10.00

3. a. $45

   b. $450

Extension: Big Bucks Estimates

1. a

2. Possible answer. $11 million + $9 million =
   $20 million + 14 million = $24 million + $2.5
   million = a little more than $35 million

3. a

4. $879,000 is about $900,000. $154,000 is about
   $150,000. $53,000 is about $50,000, and
   $627,000 is about $600,000. So, $900,000 +
   150,000 + $50,000 + $600,000 = $1,700,000.

Test Practice

1. (b)

2. (e)

3. (e)

4. (b)

5. (a)

6. $88

Lesson 2: Mental Math in the Checkout Line

Activity 1: Math in Line

1. No, but almost enough. Explanations will vary.
   Sample explanation:
   The milk is about $2 and the cheese is about
   $3 for a total of about $5. Because the estimate
   is so close to the limit of $5, an exact answer is
   needed here.

2. a. Yes. Three loaves of bread at about $3 each is about $9.

   b. Answers will vary. Sample answer: She could round up to $3 for each loaf, but that is $0.02 more. $3 \times 3 = \$9 - \$0.06$ ($\$0.02 \times 3$) = $8.94. So her change would be $10.00 − $8.94 = $1.06.

3. a. $0.82

   b. Answers will vary. Sample answer: $5 − $4 (estimate) = $1. But each box cost $0.09 more than $2.00, so the actual cost is $4.18.

4. a. No. Each shirt cost about $7. $7 \times 4 = \$28$, much more than $25.

   b. Answers will vary. Sample answer: He could round $6.95 to $7 and multiply that amount by 4 for a total of $28. Then he could subtract $0.05 four times because the estimate is $0.05 more than the actual amount. The total would be $28 − $0.20 = $27.80.

5. a. Olga had about $1.50 left in her wallet.

   b. The two books were $14, less $0.02; the two cards were $4.50. $14 + $4.50 = $18.50. $20 − $18.50 = $1.50 (and $0.02 from rounded amount for two books) for a total of $1.52.

Activity 2: Rounding and Adjusting

1.

Items	Round	Est	Adj + or −	
			+	**−**
b.	$300	$900		-5 × 3 or -$15
	Exact Amount: 3($300) − 3($5) = $900 − $15 = $885			
c.	$20	$140		-$0.50 × 7 or -$3.50
	Exact Amount: 7 ($20) − 7($0.50) =$140 − $3.50 = $136.50			
d.	$2	$12	$0.10 × 6 or $1.20	
	Exact Amount: 6($2) + 6($0.10) = $12 + $0.60 = $12.60			
e.	$7	$35		-$0.02 × 5 or -$0.10
	Exact Amount: 5($7) − 5($0.02) = $35 − $0.10 = $34.90			
f.	$5	$40		-$0.03 × 8 or -$0.24
	Exact Amount: 8($5) − 8($0.03) = $40 − $0.24 = $39.76			
g.	$10	$50	$0.25 x 5 or $1.25	
	Exact Amount: 5($10) − 5($0.25) = $50 − $1.25 = $50 − $1.25 = $48.75			

2. Answers will vary.

Math Inspection: Make It True

1. a. $12 + 3 + 6 = 1 + 10 + 10$

   b. $28 + 19 = 3 + 24 + 20$

   c. $2 + 19 + 8 = 3 + 24 + 2$

   d. $35 + 3 = 19 + 12 + 0 + 7$

   e. $32 = 16 + 8 + 4 + 2 + 1 + 1$

2. Answers will vary, but may include the strategy of looking from the left side and the right side and trying to keep the sums "close"; or adding from left to right until the value started to seem too big to be able to reach with the remaining values.

3. Answers will vary.

Math Inspection: Check Both Sides of the Equal Sign

1–2. Answers will vary. Key points are:

The expressions on each side of the equation are equal to one another, but different. One addend increases and one addend decreases by the same amount.

When two numbers are added, if you increase one addend by an amount and decrease the other addend by the same amount, the sum doesn't change. In symbols, $a + b = (a + c) + (b − c)$.

In each equation the expression on the right has values that have become easier to add because there is a multiple of 10 or 100, and these "rounded" values were created by regrouping the addends on the left hand side. For instance, $9 + 7 = 9 + (1 + 6) = (9 + 1) + 6 = 10 + 6$. This regrouping is possible based on the associative property of addition.

3. Answers will vary, but should include adding something to one addend and decreasing the other addend by the same amount. For example: $36 + 178 = 34 + 180$

4. When two numbers are added, if you increase one addend by an amount and decrease the other addend by the same amount, the sum doesn't change. In symbols, $a + b = (a + c) + (b - c)$.

5.
a. $8 + \mathbf{12} = 10 + 10$

b. $11 + \mathbf{7} = 10 + 8$

c. $\mathbf{128} + 428 = 126 + 430$

d. $239 + 722 = 240 + \mathbf{721}$

e. $852 + 209 = 851 + \mathbf{210}$

f. $\mathbf{175} + 479 = 174 + 480$

g. $183 + 549 = \mathbf{182} + 550$

h. $429 + 204 = \mathbf{430} + 203$

i. $67 + 223 = \mathbf{70} + 220$

j. $628 + \mathbf{319} = 630 + 317$

Practice: Using Math Notation

2. $4(\$11) - 4(\$0.03)$

3. $8(\$3) + 8(\$0.09)$

4. $6(\$20) - 6(\$0.07)$

5. Student examples will vary. Sample situation: A pastry chef buys 12 pounds of butter at $3.02 per pound.

6. Student examples will vary. Sample situation: A woman buys four tickets to a concert for $31.88 each.

Practice: More Adjustments

Symbols in parenthesis reflect the sub-column for Adjustment (+) or (−).

1.
b. 7 items at $1.05 each
$1
$7
$(+) 7 \times \$0.05$
$7(\$1) + 7(\$0.05) = \$7 + \$0.35 = \$7.35$

c. 2 items at $39 each
$40
$80
$(-) 2 \times \$1$
$2(\$40) - 2(\$1) = \$80 - \$2 = \$78$

d. 4 items at $2.19 each
$2
$8
$(+) 4 \times \$0.19$
$4(\$2) + 4(\$0.19) = \$8 + \$0.76 = \$8.76$

e. 5 items at $6.98 each
$7
$35
$(-) 5 \times \$0.02$
$5(\$7) - 5(\$0.02) = \$35 - \$0.10 = \$34.90$

f. 3 items at $9.97 each
$10
$30
$(-) 3 \times \$0.03$
$3(\$10) - 3(\$0.03) = \$30 - \$0.09 = \$29.91$

2. Answers will vary.

Practice: Closer to $50 or $60?

1. Answers will vary. Sample answer: Troy may have left the radio price as $15 and then added $5 (for five cups) to get $20. Rounding $27 up to $30 would give an estimate of $50. Since he rounded up, he knows it's less than $50.

2. Answers will vary.

3. Eve did not make as much as Lilli who made $55. Eve made $42. Possible answers $40 or $45.

Mental Math Practice: Fast Actions with 10 or 100

1. If you add $100 to $5<u>6</u>8, you get $<u>668</u>.

2. If you add $10 to $2<u>8</u>3, you get $<u>293</u>.

3. If you add $100 to $<u>2</u>83, you get $<u>383</u>.

4. If you add $10 to $6<u>5</u>0, you get $<u>660</u>.

5. If you add $100 to $<u>6</u>50, you get $<u>750</u>.

6. If you add $10 to $3<u>9</u>6, you get $<u>406</u>.

7. If you add $100 to $<u>3</u>96, you get $<u>496</u>.

8. If you add $10 to $9<u>6</u>9, you get $<u>979</u>.

9. If you add $100 to $<u>9</u>69, you get $<u>1,069</u>.

10. 2

11. 7

12. 428

Mental Math Practice: Fast Actions with 9 or 90

1. a. 75   b. 74

2. a. 147   b. 146

3. a. 99   b. 98

4. a. 416   b. 415

5. a. 675   b. 674

6. a. 208   b. 207

7. Answers will vary. Sample answer: To add 9 to the number, first add 10 and then subtract 1.

8. **a.** 750 **b.** 740
9. **a.** 537 **b.** 527
10. **a.** 909 **b.** 899
11. **a.** 1,016 **b.** 1,006
12. Answers will vary. Sample answer:
    To add 90 to the number, first add 100 and then subtract 10.

Extension: Weekly Totals

1. **a.** 28
   b. Answers will vary. Sample answer:
      30 minutes or more is rounded to the next hour, but less than 30 minutes is rounded down. So, 5 hr. 15 min. is about 5 hr.; 3 hr. 45 min. is about 4 hr.; 7 hr. 10 min is about 7 hr.; and 5 hr. 15 min. is about 5 hr. 5 + 7 + 4 + 7 + 5 = 28 hours

2. **a.** 21 miles
   b. Answers will vary. Sample answer:
      0.5 miles or more is rounded to the next mile, but less than 0.5 miles is rounded down. So, 3.1 mi. is about 3 mi.; 3.8 mi. is about 4 mi.; 4.1 mi. is about 4 mi.; 2.7 mi. is about 3 mi. 3 + 4 + 3 + 4 + 3 + 4 = 21 miles

Test Practice

1. (d)
2. (b)
3. (c)
4. (b)
5. (d)
6. $7.12

Lesson 3: Traveling with Numbers

Activity 1: How Many Miles to Boston?

1. 13
2. Montana will probably take the longest time to cross; Pennsylvania will probably take the shortest time.
3. Somewhere in South Dakota. Minnesota is a reasonable estimate as well.
4. **a.**

   b. 10–11 days

Activity 2: Planning Where to Stay

1. Answers will vary. Sample answer:
   Night 1—Post Falls, ID
   Night 2—Butte, MT
   Night 3—Sheridan, WY
   Night 4—Box Elder, SD
   Night 5—Hartford, SD
   Night 6—La Cross, WI
   Night 7—Chicago, IL
   Night 8—Cleveland, OH
   Night 9—Syracuse, NY
   Night 10—Boston, MA

2. Answers will vary. Sample answer based on sample answers for Problem 1:

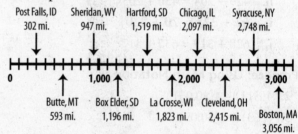

3. Answers will vary. Sample answer based on sample answer above: Yes, two nights in South Dakota (depending on cities chosen, two nights could be spent in Montana).

4. Hartford, SD (1,519 miles)

5. 10 travel days; 9 nights

6. Answers will vary.

Activity 3: Rounding Distances

1. **State/Mileage/ Mileage rounded**

   a. Washington: 300
      Idaho: 70, 100
      Montana: 560, 600
      Wyoming: 210, 200
      South Dakota: 410, 400
      Minnesota: 280, 300
      Wisconsin: 190, 200
      Illinois: 100, 100
      Indiana: 160, 200
      Ohio: 240, 200
      Pennsylvania: 50, 100
      New York: 390, 400
      Massachusetts: 160, 200
      Total 3,120; 3,300

   b. Answers will vary. Sample answer:
      If there were 5 miles or more in the 1's place, I rounded up or I thought about the 10's on the number line and to which 10 the number was closer.

2. Answers will vary. Sample answer based on sample rounding above:
(280 + 70) + (100 + 300) + (410 + 190) + (210 + 390) + (160 + 240) + 50 + 160 + 560 = 3,120

3. a. Washington: 300
Idaho: 100
Montana: 600
Wyoming: 200
South Dakota: 400
Minnesota: 300
Wisconsin: 200
Illinois: 100
Indiana: 200
Ohio: 200
Pennsylvania: 100
New York: 400
Massachusetts: 200
Total estimate of miles: 3,300

b. Answers will vary.

Practice: Trip Investigation

Answers will vary, but should be approximately:

1. 30
2. 15
3. 10
4. 7-8
5. 6
6. 5
7. 4-5
8. 3-4

Practice: High and Not So High Peaks

1. a. Mt. David—48 ft.
   b. Bradbury Mountain—485 ft.
   c. Cadillac Mountain—1,532 ft.
   d. Mt. Apo—9,692 ft.
   e. Pico Duarte –10,417 ft.
   f. Mt. Etna—10,902 ft.
   g. Mt. Cook—12,349 ft.
   h. Kilimanjaro—19,340 ft.

2. Answers will vary. Sample answer:

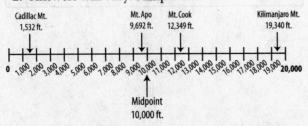

3. Mt. David would be rounded to 0 ft.
4. Answers will vary.

Practice: Checks—Say It in Words

1. a. Answers will vary, depending on how students rounded. Sample answer:
$8,000 + $3,000 + $5,000 + $10,000 + $10,000 + $10,000 = $46,000

   b. $45,615

2. a. four thousand seven hundred nine and 00/100
   b. three thousand eighty-one and 00/100
   c. ten thousand one and 00/100
   d. ten thousand ten and 00/100
   e. ten thousand one hundred and 00/100

Practice: More Check Writing

1. a. $9,653.00
   b. $2,097.00
   c. $8,008.00
   d. $5,106.00

Practice: Filing

A. 1998, 2992
B. 4107, 3002, 4080
C. 5555
D. 9777, 8989

Practice: More Filing

A. 2110, 2992
B. 4459, 5551, 4397, 5555, 3878
C. 6632
D. None

Practice: How Close Is Close Enough?

1. Answers will vary. Some responses could be:

Receipts	Rounded	Rounded	Rounded
$74.85	$75	$70	$100
$97.13	$100	$100	$100
$125.42	$125	$130	$100
$89.12	$100	$90	$100
$123.89	$125	$120	$100
Estimated total	$525	$510	$500
Purpose	Estimated to nearest $25 for a general idea	Estimated to nearest $10; need a more accurate estimate	Estimated to nearest $100—very rough idea.

© 2015 TERC

2. Answers will vary. Some responses could be:

Budget Item	Amount	Rounded	Rounded	Rounded
Rent	$775	$800	$775	$780
Transportation	$127.14	$150	$125	$130
Food	$561.50	$600	$550	$560
Utilities	$346.82	$350	$350	$350
Entertainment	$72.50	$100	$75	$70
	Estimated Total	$2,000	$1,875	$1,890
	Purpose	Estimated up to next $50 to have some "cushion" in the budget	Estimated to nearest $25 since those values are easy to add	Estimated to nearest $10 in order to be more exact, and counting by 10's is easy

Practice: Getting Close (Lesson 1 revisited)

Answers will vary slightly as these are estimates.

	1. Mountain Bike	2. Ray's tire	3. Oven dial
A	42	20	190
B	45	25	210
C	50	27	260
D	58	32	275
E	63	36	310
F	73	38 or 39	350
G	76	42	375

Mental Math Practice: Doubles

1. 0, 2, 4, 6, 8, 10, 12, 14, 16, 18, 20
2. 20, 40, 60, 80, 100, 120, 140, 160, 180, 200
3. 24, 42, 66, 88, 102, 124, 146, 168, 184, 206
4. 10, 30, 50, 70, 90, 110, 130, 150, 170, 190, 210
5. 32, 54, 76, 98, 112, 134, 156, 178, 192, 214
6. Answers will vary.

Mental Math Practice: Triples

1. 0, 3, 6, 9, 12, 15, 18, 21, 24, 27, 30
2. 30, 60, 90, 120, 150, 180, 210, 240, 270, 300
3. 36, 63, 99, 132, 153, 186, 219, 252, 276, 309
4. 15, 45, 75, 105, 135, 165, 195, 225, 255, 285, 315
5. 48, 81, 114, 147, 168, 201, 234, 267, 288, 321
6. Answers will vary.

Mental Math Practice: Rolling in Money

1.

Sunday	Monday	Tuesday	Wednesday
$1 million	$2 million	$4 million	$8 million
$2 million	$4 million	$8 million	$16 million
$3 million	$6 million	$12 million	$24 million
$5 million	$10 million	$20 million	$40 million
$10 million	$20 million	$40 million	$80 million
$20 million	$40 million	$80 million	$160 million

Thursday	Friday	Saturday
$16 million	$32 million	$64 million
$32 million	$64 million	$128 million
$48 million	$96 million	$192 million
$80 million	$160 million	$320 million
$160 million	$320 million	$640 million
$320 million	$640 million	$1,280 million or $1 billion, 280 million

a. The patterns identified will vary, but may include ways to use the first row to find other rows (for example, the second row is twice the first, and the row starting with $10 million is 10 times the first row). Students may recognize that once you have a value you have seen before (like $2 million), the amounts that follow are repeated as well. Students may also recognize the powers of 2 showing up in some of the rows.

b. One thousand millions is a billion. The investment of $20 million exceeds one billion dollars on Saturday.

2.

Sunday	Monday	Tuesday	Wednesday
$1 million	$3 million	$9 million	$27 million
$2 million	$6 million	$18 million	$54 million
$3 million	$9 million	$27 million	$81 million
$5 million	$15 million	$45 million	$135 million
$10 million	$30 million	$90 million	$270 million
$20 million	$60 million	$180 million	$540 million

Thursday	Friday	Saturday & final amount
$81 million	$243 million	$729 million
$162 million	$486 million	$1,458 million or $1 billion, 458 million
$243 million	$729 million	$2,187 million, or $2 billion, 187 million
$405 million	$1,215 million	$3,645 million, or $3 billion, 645 million
$810 million	$2,430 million	$7,290 million, or $7 billion, 290 million
$1,620 million	$4,860 million	$14,580, or $14 billion, 580 million

a. The patterns identified will again vary, but will likely be similar to those found in the doubling table. For instance, the second row is twice the first; the row beginning with $20 million can be found by adding a zero to the row starting with $2 million (multiplying by 10); some rows are multiples of other rows (like the row beginning with $5 million and the one starting with $20 million); and once you have a value that has occurred before, all the amounts following will be the same as well. Students may also recognize the powers of three occurring in some of the rows, as well as other patterns.

b. The $20 million investment exceeds a billion on Thursday. The $5 and $10 million investments exceed a billion on Friday. The $2 and $3 million investments exceed 1 billion on Saturday.

Test Practice

1. (c)

2. (c)

3. (h)

4. (b)

5. (b)

6. 373

Lesson 4: Traveling in Time

Activity 1: Birthday Numbers

1. Answers will vary. Possible strategy:

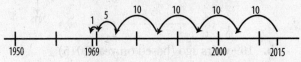

2. **a.** Answers will vary. Possible strategy:

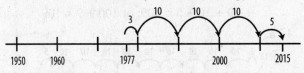

   b. Answers will vary. Sample strategy: Go down or to the left 10 more (46) and 2 more (48).

3. Answers will vary. Possible strategy:

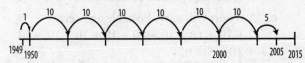

4. Answers will vary.

Activity 2: How Long Ago?

1. **a.**

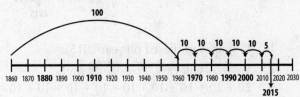

   b. 154 years ago (based on year 2015)

   c. Answers will vary. Possible answer:
   100 + 10 + 10 + 10 + 10 + 10 + 4

2. **a.**

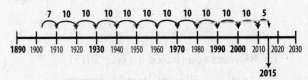

   b. 112 years ago (based on year 2015)

   c. Answers will vary. Possible answers:
   7 + 10 + 10 + 10 + 10 + 10 + 10 + 10 + 10 + 10 + 10 + 5 = 112; or 100 + 12 = 112

3. a.

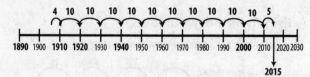

b. 109 years ago (based on year 2015)

c. Answers will vary. Possible answers:
$4 + 10 + 10 + 10 + 10 + 10 + 10 + 10 + 10 + 10 + 10 + 5 = 109$; or $100 + 9 = 109$

4. a.

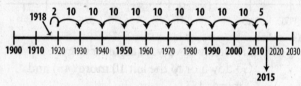

b. 97 years ago (based on year 2015)

c. Answers will vary. Possible answer:
$2 + 10 + 10 + 10 + 10 + 10 + 10 + 10 + 10 + 10 + 5 = 97$

5. a.

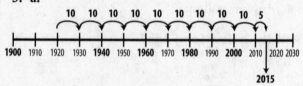

b. 95 years ago (based on year 2015)

c. Answers will vary. Possible answers:
$10 + 10 + 10 + 10 + 10 + 10 + 10 + 10 + 10 + 5 = 95$; or $90 + 5 = 95$

6. a.

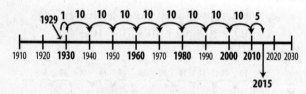

b. 86 years ago (based on year 2015)

c. Answers will vary. Possible answer:
$1 + 10 + 10 + 10 + 10 + 10 + 10 + 10 + 10 + 5 = 86$

7. a.

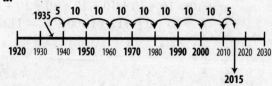

b. 80 years ago (based on year 2015)

c. Answers will vary. Possible answers:
$5 + 10 + 10 + 10 + 10 + 10 + 10 + 10 + 5 = 80$; or $5 + 70 + 5 = 80$

8. a.

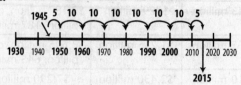

b. 70 years ago (based on year 2015)

c. Answers will vary. Possible answer:
$5 + 60 + 5 = 60$

9. a.

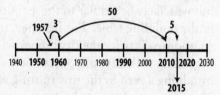

b. 58 years ago (based on year 2015)

c. Answers will vary. Possible answer:
$3 + 50 + 5 = 58$

10. a.

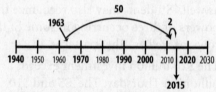

b. 52 years ago (based on year 2015)

c. Answers will vary. Possible answers:
$50 + 2 = 52$; or $7 + 40 + 5 = 52$

11. a.

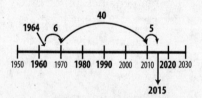

b. 51 years ago (based on year 2015)

c. Answers will vary. Possible answer:
$6 + 40 + 5 = 51$

12. a.

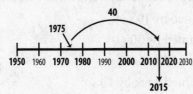

b. 40 years ago (based on year 2015)

c. Answers will vary.
Possible answers: $10 + 10 + 10 + 10 = 40$;
or $5 + 30 + 5 = 40$

Math Inspection: Make It True

1. The answers will vary, but could include these:
   a. $40 - 20 = 40 - 20$
   b. $40 + 20 = 40 + 20$
   c. $40 + 20 - 40 = 20$
   d. $40 = 20 + 40 - 20$

2. The order of the answers will vary, but in general the equations have the same two values (40 and 20) repeated in the same order.

3. Answers will vary, but some possible strategies are searching for ways to "cancel" one of the values on one side of the equation, or using the same operation to the same pair of numbers to keep the expressions equal, or trying all the possible combinations of where the plus, minus, and equal signs can go, to see which result in true equations.

4. Answers will vary, but it should work for any pair of numbers, a and b. Students may say that the first number has to be the larger — if they are limited to positive numbers.

   $a + b = a + b$ Reason: Anything is equal to itself. In mathematics, this is called the reflexive property of equality.

   $a - b = a - b$ Reason: Anything is equal to itself. In mathematics, this is called the reflexive property of equality.

   $a + b - a = b$ Reason: On the left side of the equal sign, adding a and then subtracting a results in 0, so b is left on both sides of the equation.

   $a = b + a - b$ Reason: On the right side of the equal sign, addition and then subtraction of b results in 0, so a is left on both sides of the equation.

Math Inspection: Check Both Sides of the Equal Sign

1. Answers will vary, but may include observation that in the subtraction problem on the right $(10 - 7)$, the numbers are each 1 more than the subtraction problem on the left $(9 - 6)$, but the difference is still the same (3). That is what the number line shows: the distance is the same for both, so the answer is the same. In the second equation, each number is three more. In the third, each number is 25 more. The difference remains the same as the original numbers. Another observation might be that in each case, the expression on the right side of the equation is easier to simplify since it is subtracting a multiple of 10, and that the right side can be created from the left by adding the same number to each value (for instance, adding a 1 to the 9 and to the 6 results in $10 - 7$).

2. Answers will vary, but should include on one side of the equation a set of numbers that result from the same value being added to both numbers on the other side of the equation. For instance, $48 - 13 = (48 + 2) - (13 + 2) = 50 - 15$. It would be good to also include easier (rounded) numbers.

3. Answers will vary, but the general rule demonstrated is that adding the same value to both numbers in a subtraction problem results in an equivalent expression. You can add the same amount to both numbers, and the difference will remain the same.

4. **a.** 785
   b. 1,000
   c. 68
   d. 391
   e. 210

Practice: Use Up the Space—Plan Well

1.
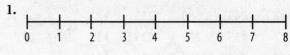

2.
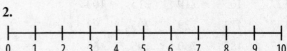

3.

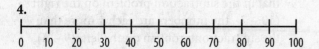

4.

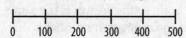

5. Answers will vary. Sample answer:

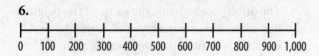

6.

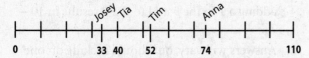

Practice: On the Number Line

1. Josey: 33; Tim: 52; Tia: 40; Anna: 74

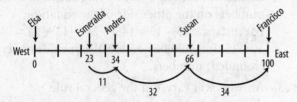

2. 34 miles between Susan's home and Francisco's.

Mental Math Practice: Count Up and Down by 10's

27	365	619	315	203
37	375	629	305	193
47	385	639	295	183
57	395	649	285	173
67	405	659	275	163
77	415	669	265	153
87	425	679	255	143
97	435	689	245	133
107	445	699	235	123
117	455	709	225	113
127	465	719	215	103
137	475	729	205	93
147	485	739	195	83
157	495	749	185	73
167	505	759	175	63

Mental Math Practice: By What Did I Count?

1. 83; counted by 10's

2. 100; counted by 30's

3. 414; counted by 100's

4. 230; counted back by 10's

5. 297; counted back by 40's

6. 996; counted back by 10's

7. 906; counted back by 100's

Extension: Life Line

1. Answers will vary.

2. Answers will vary.

3. a. Answers will vary.

b. Answers will vary.

Test Practice

1. (b)

2. (c)

3. (d)

4. (d)

5. (b)

6. 115

Lesson 5: Meanings and Methods for Subtraction

Activity 1: Ways to Think About Subtraction

1. Answers will vary, but students should notice that the total amounts for all three problems are the same. One of the known parts is $30. The missing amount is always the same $50.

2. Answers will vary, but students should notice that the first problem seems to be asking for what is missing, the second problem is asking for a comparison, and the third problem is asking how much is left.

Activity 2: How Do You See It?

Part 1

1. Answers will vary, but visual model should represent 40 – 27.

2. Answers will vary. Check to see that 2 and 3 show different ways of thinking about subtraction.

3. Answers will vary.

Part 2

1. Answers will vary, but students may tend to see this as a comparison where they can readily add up from $3,998 to $4,001.

2. Answers will vary, but students may tend to see this as a comparison where they can readily add up from $20,040 to $20,080.

3. Answers will vary, but students may tend to see this as a missing part.

4. Answers will vary, but students may tend to see this as a take-away since there is no borrowing involved.

5. Answers will vary, but students may tend to see this as a comparison of two ages.

6. Answers will vary, but students may tend to see this as a difference between what he had and what he spent. They might also see it as a missing part.

Math Inspection: Showing What the Shorthand Means

1. Step 1 $67 = 60 + 7$
   $-39 = -(30 + 9)$

   Step 2 $67 = (50 + 10) + 7$
   $-39 = -(30 + 9)$

   Step 3 $67 = 50 + (10 + 7)$
   $-39 = -(30 + 9)$

   Step 4 $67 = 50 + 17$
   $-39 = -(30 + 9)$

   Step 5 $20 + 8 = 28$

2. Step 1 $859 = 800 + 50 + 9$
   $-370 = -(300 + 70 + 0)$

   Step 2 $859 = (700 + 100) + 50 + 9$
   $-370 = -(300 + 70 + 0)$

   Step 3 $859 = 700 + (100 + 50) + 9$
   $-370 = -(300 + 70 + 0)$

   Step 4 $859 = 700 + 150 + 9$
   $-370 = -(300 + 70 + 0)$

   Step 5 $400 + 80 + 9 = 489$

3. Step 1 $672 = 600 + 70 + 2$
   $-289 = -(200 + 80 + 9)$

   Step 2 $672 = (500 + 100) + (60 + 10) + 2$
   $-289 = -(200 + 80 + 9)$

Step 3 $672 = 500 + (100 + 60) + (10 + 2)$
$-289 = -(200 + 80 + 9)$

Step 4 $672 = 500 + 160 + 12$
$-289 = -(200 + 80 + 9)$

Step 5 $300 + 80 + 3 = 383$

4. Step 1 $703 = 700 + 3$
   $-316 = -(300 + 10 + 6)$

   Step 2 $703 = (600 + 100) + 3$
   $-316 = -(300 + 10 + 6)$

   Step 3 $703 = 600 + (90 + 10) + 3$
   $-316 = -(300 + 10 + 6)$

   Step 4 $703 = 600 + 90 + (10 + 3)$
   $-316 = -(300 + 10 + 6)$

   Step 5 $703 = 600 + 90 + 13$
   $-316 = -(300 + 10 + 6)$

   Step 6 $300 + 80 + 7 = 387$

Practice: Check Both Sides of the Equal Sign—Addition

1. Answers will vary, but students may connect these equations to what is happening when "borrowing" is used and the recent work with expanded form. They should at least recognize that given an addition expression, subtracting a 10, 100, 1000, or any number from one of the addends and adding it to another addend creates an equal expression. Symbolically, $a + b = (a - c) + (b + c)$.

2. Answers will vary. For example: $5,000 + 300 + 90 + 3 = 4,000 + 1,300 + 80 + 13$

3. Answers will vary, but generally the examples show that if a number is written in standard notation so that it is clear what each digit of a number represents, an equal expression can be created by taking a power of ten away from one of the expanded addends and adding it to another. Students may not use words like "addend" or "powers of 10." Listen for descriptions of these concepts in their own words.

4. a. 14
   b. 16
   c. 180

EMPower™   Answer Key **245**
© 2015 TERC

Practice: Check Both Sides of the Equal Sign—Subtraction

1. Responses may vary, but generally, the expressions on the left hand side of the equations are the same as the right hand side expressions, and you can get the right side by adding the same value to each of the numbers that make up the subtraction problem on the left. Symbolically, $a - b = (a + c) - (b + c)$. It may also be easier to solve the right hand side of each equation by thinking about the comparison of the two values since the number that is being taken away is a multiple of 10.

2. Answers will vary. For example: $36 - 27 = 39 - 30$.

3. Given any subtraction problem, the difference remains the same if you add an amount to both the subtrahend and the minuend. Symbolically, $a - b = (a + c) - (b + c)$. Look and listen for ways that students explain this in their own words. They may also make reference to the distance remaining the same on a number line.

4. a. 75
   b. 40
   c. 49

   Comments: Students might not be ready at this point to state $a - b = (a + c) - (b + c)$, but if they are, go for it!

Practice: What's My Purpose for Estimating?

1. a. He has more than his estimate since rounding $23.45 to $25 makes it seem as if he spent more than he did, so he must have more left over.
   b. Answers will vary, but he may have calculated $40 – $25.

2. a. She has more than her estimate.
   b. Answers will vary, but she may want to underestimate what is left so she is sure not to run out of money for food at the end of the month.
   c. Answers will vary, but she has about $275 left.

3. a. She has less than her estimate.
   b. Answers will vary, but she may overestimate so she mentally prepares herself for a longer drive than she really has.
   c. Answers will vary, but she has about 470 miles to go.

Test Practice

1. (b)
2. (d)
3. (d)
4. (b)
5. (c)
6. $2,500

Lesson 6: Extending the Line

Activity 1: In the Red

1. Balance: -$75
2. Balance: $875
3. Balance: $150
4. Balance: -$300
5. Balance $500
6. No, he only had $500 in his checking account.

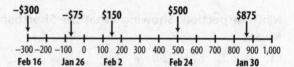

Activity 2: Record Highs, Record Lows

Part 1

1. Answers will vary. Sample answer of 58°F shown on thermometer.
2. See thermometer.
3. See thermometer.
4. Answers will vary. Sample answer of 109°F shown on thermometer.
5. Answers will vary. Sample answer of -12°F shown on thermometer.
6. Answers will vary. Sample answer based on samples above: 121°F. From 0°F to 109°F = 109°F; from 0°F to -12°F is 12°F. 109°F + 12°F = 121°F.
7. Answers will vary.

Part 2

8. 136°F
9. -129°F
10.

11. c

12. 265°F; 136°F + 129°F = 265°F

13. Answers will vary. Sample answer: The difference between 134°F (Death Valley, U.S.) and -87°F (Northrice, Greenland) is 221°F. 134°F + 87°F = 221°F

14. Answers will vary. Sample answer: When you compare temperatures below 0°F with temperatures above 0°F, you add the two temperatures. When you compare the difference between two temperatures that are either both above 0°F or below 0°F, you subtract to find the difference.

Practice: Planting Zones

1.

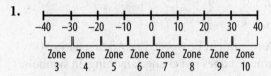

| Zone 3 | Zone 4 | Zone 5 | Zone 6 | Zone 7 | Zone 8 | Zone 9 | Zone 10 |

2. 50°F (-30°F compared to 20°F)

3. No, the temperature went down to -45°F which is below the average minimum temperature.

4. Yes, the temperature dropped down to about -5°F, which is still above the average minimum temperature.

5. Answers will vary.

Practice: What's the Range?

1. 175°F

2. 182 kWh

3. 16″

Practice: Ordering Numbers

1. Answers will vary, but each number line should include Cal at $1,000, Ollie at -$850, 0, and one other name and balance from list.

2. $1,850

3. **a.** Ollie: -$850

b. Tanya: -$490

c. Aaron: -$125

d. Sean: -$79

e. Kim: -$53

f. Zoe: -$10

g. Devon: -$5

h. Lee: $0

i. Alice: $5

j. Sue: $142

k. Tad: $269

l. Cal: $1,000

Mental Math Practice: Count Up and Down by 10's

-100	-75	-11	27	123	2,045
-90	-65	-1	17	113	2,035
-80	-55	9	7	103	2,025
-70	-45	19	-3	93	2,015
-60	-35	29	-13	83	2,005
-50	-25	39	-23	73	1,995
-40	-15	49	-33	63	1,985
-30	-5	59	-43	53	1,975
-20	5	69	-53	43	1,965
-10	15	79	-63	33	1,955
0	25	89	-73	23	1,945
10	35	99	-83	13	1,935
20	45	109	-93	3	1,925
30	55	119	-103	-7	1,915
40	65	129	-113	-17	1,905

Extension: Sorry, Account Overdrawn

Dear Sir or Madam:

It has come to our attention that your account is now overdrawn for the amount of $300. During the past weeks, you made several deposits, but also several withdrawals (reflecting checks you wrote).

You had a balance of $500 in your checking account at the start of the month. You then made four deposits, each for $100, giving you a new balance of $900. However, you wrote 6 checks for $200 each, which means you made withdrawals totaling $1,200. This left you with a net balance of -$300 (the amount you are overdrawn).

It is our duty to inform you when you have overdrawn your account and show a negative balance. We are sure you are aware of bank policy regarding overdrawn accounts: We impose a one-time charge of $50 plus $15 for each check not covered by your balance.

Therefore, because there were insufficient funds for two of your checks, we will be placing an additional total charge on your account of $80. Please note this deduction in your checkbook. We trust you will be making a deposit soon to cover these charges and the overdrawn amount.

Sincerely,

Shondra Washington, Bank President

Extension: Below Sea Level

1. 144'
2. 980'
3. 30,000'
4. 6; answers will vary

Test Practice

1. (d)
2. (c)
3. (c)
4. (b)
5. (e)
6. 221

Lesson 7: Ups and Downs with Addition

Activity 1: Bank Balance Ups and Downs

Answers will vary, but final balances should be correct.

Activity 2: Show the Bank Activity with Chips

1. Answers will vary, but final balances should be correct.
2. Answer should be yes.
3. Answers will vary.
4. Answers will vary but should include the idea that withdrawal means to subtract and deposit means to add.

Math Inspection: Check Both Sides of the Equal Sign

1. Answers will vary, but in general the three equations are adding a negative integer on the left hand side of the equation and writing equivalent expressions using subtraction of a whole number (or positive integer) on the right side.
2. Answers will vary, but the equations all have addition of a negative integer on one side and subtraction of a positive number on the other.
3. Example: $92 + (-19) = 92 - 19$
4. Answers will vary, but may include the fact that adding a negative number is the same as subtracting the positive of that number.
5. a. $120 - 42 = 78$
   b. $-320 - 180 = -500$
   c. $-1,000 - 689 = -1,689$
   d. $\$400 - \$520 = -\$120$

Practice: Number of the Day

Answers will vary, but should always total -10.

Practice: More Practice Adding Integers

1. a. -2   11   -1   -11
   b. -1   4   -6   3
   c. -1   5   -22   3
   d. -13   18   -5   -1

2. All answers are 0. A rule might be worded as: The sum of any number and its inverse results in 0. The sum of a positive amount and its negative is 0. In symbols, $a + -a = 0$ and commutatively, $-a + a = 0$. $-a$ is the additive inverse of a, and a is the additive inverse of $-a$.

3. a. -4   9   -12   4
   b. 8   -3   10   -1

   A rule might be worded as: Adding 0 to an amount does not change anything. In symbols, $a + 0 = 0 + a = 0$.
   0 is called the additive identity.

Practice: Adding Integers in Different Situations

1. a. $20 overdrawn, -20
   b. Methods and reasons will vary. Possible answer: Numbers are big for counting objects, so showed in numbers and a number line.
      $45 + (-35) = 10; 10 + (75) = 85;$
      $85 + (-105) = -20,$ or $20 overdrawn

2. a. $19 in the account
   b. Methods and reasons will vary. Possible answer: $78 + (-50) = 28; 28 + (-46) = -18;$ $-18 + 104 = 86; 86 + (-67) = 19,$ or $19 in the account

3. a. Gained workers, +5
   b. Methods and reasons will vary

4. a. +15, 2015
   b. -20, 2013
   c. Methods and reasons will vary.

5. a. $24
   b. Methods and reasons will vary. Possible answer:
      $30 + (-10) + 14 + (-5) + (-5) = 24,$ or now has $24

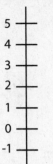

Practice: Up and Down the Elevator

1. Vertical number line from -5 to 101.

2. Number line with floors from -1 to 5 marked for the mall.

```
 5 ┼
 4 ┼
 3 ┼
 2 ┼
 1 ┼
 0 ┼
-1 ┼
```

3. Answers will vary. For example: 10 + 3 + -8 + -8 = -3. (Start at the 10th floor, go up 3 floors, stopping at the 13th, then go down 8 floors, getting off at floor 5, and finally go down another 8 floors, and get off 3 levels below 0.)

Test Practice

1. (e)
2. (d)
3. (c)
4. (c)
5. (a)
6. 23 floors

Lesson 8: Take Your Winnings

Activity 1: How Do You Take Your Winnings?

1. Andrea: three $1,000 bills, eight $100 bills, four $10 bills and three $1 bills; Barbara: 38 $100 bills, four $10 bills and three $1 bills; Carla: 384 $10 bills and three $1 bills

2. Andrea: two $1,000 dollar bills, one $100 dollar bill, and five $1 bills; Barbara: 21 $100 dollar bills and five $1 bills; Carla: 210 $10 bills and five $1 bills

3. Andrea: 11 $1,000 bills, three $10 bills and five $1 bills; Barbara: 110 $100 dollar bills, three $10 bills and five $1 bills; Carla: 1,103 $10 bills and five $1 bills

Activity 2: Concentration

Answers will vary. See *Activity 2*, p. 93, for some suggestions.

Activity 3: Mystery Numbers

1. +30
2. -300
3. +2,000
4. +100
5. +600
6. +500
7. -20
8. -2,000
9. -400
10. +600

Activity 4: How High Can You Go?

1.

Numeral	In words
10	Ten
100	One hundred
1,000	One thousand
10,000	Ten thousand
100,000	One hundred thousand
1,000,000	One million
10,000,000	Ten million
100,000,000	One hundred million
1,000,000,000	One billion

Showing the repeated multiplication	Exponent form
10	10^1
(10)(10)	10^2
(10)(10)(10)	10^3
(10)(10)(10)(10)	10^4
(10)(10)(10)(10)(10)	10^5
(10)(10)(10)(10)(10)(10)	10^6
(10)(10)(10)(10)(10)(10)(10)	10^7
(10)(10)(10)(10)(10)(10)(10)(10)	10^8
(10)(10)(10)(10)(10)(10)(10)(10)(10)	10^9

Patterns noticed will vary, but may include 1) the number of zeroes in the numeral is the same as the number used as an exponent, and 2) the number used for the exponent is the same as the number of tens written as repeated multiplication.

2.

Numeral	In words
3	Three
30	Thirty
300	Three hundred
3,000	Three thousand
30,000	Thirty thousand
300,000	Three hundred thousand
3,000,000	Three million

Showing the 10's multiplying	Exponent form
3(1)	$3(10^0)$
3(10)	$3(10^1)$
3(10)(10)	$3(10^2)$
3(10)(10)(10)	$3(10^3)$
3(10)(10)(10)(10)	$3(10^4)$
3(10)(10)(10)(10)(10)	$3(10^5)$
3(10)(10)(10)(10)(10)(10)	$3(10^6)$

Patterns noticed will vary, but may include (as in #1 above) 1) the number of zeroes in the numeral is the same as the number used for the exponent and 2) the number used for the exponent is the same as the number of tens when the value of the numeral is written as repeated multiplication, and 3) for each numeral, the number of zeroes and the exponent increase by one as the table is read from top to bottom. The number of zeroes and the exponent decrease by one from bottom to top. This rule helps explain the zero as an exponent in the first row.

Challenge: should be filled in as the first row of the chart for Problem 2: 3, three, 3(1), $3(10^0)$

3. a. $20, $100, ***$200***

   b. $8,356, ***$10,000***, $8,400

   c. $3,000,000, $6,000, ***$30,000,000***

   d. $120,000, $12,000, ***$1,000,000***

   e. $1,000,500, ***$15,000,000***, $25,000

Math Inspection: Symbols for Multiplication

1. Answers may vary, but could include:

   a. seven times seven times seven times seven times seven times seven

      7^6

      (7)(7)(7) (7)(7)(7)

      $7 \cdot 7 \cdot 7 \cdot 7 \cdot 7 \cdot 7$

   b. 5^4

      $5 \cdot 5 \cdot 5 \cdot 5$

      $5 \times 5 \times 5 \times 5$

   c. eleven times eleven times eleven

      11^3

      (11)(11)(11)

   d. twenty-seven times twenty-seven

      (27)(27)

      27^2

2. a. $3^4 = 3 \times 3 \times 3 \times 3 = 81$

   b. $6 \times 6 \times 6 = 6^3 = 216$

   c. $18^2 = (2 \times 9)^2 = 2^2 9^2 = 18 \times 18$

   d. $5^5 = 5 \times 5 \times 5 \times 5 \times 5$

3. Student-created problems will vary.

4. a. $3(1,000) + 5(100) + 4(10) + 2 = 3(10^3) + 5(10^2) + 4(10^1) + 2(10^0)$

   b. $8(10,000) + 5(1,000) + 3(10) = 8(10^4) + 5(10^3) + 3(10^1)$

   c. $4(100,000) + 7(10,000) + 6(1,000) + 4(100) + 7 = 4(10^5) + 7(10^4) + 6(10^3) + 4(10^2) + 7(10^0)$

   d. $5(10,000) + 9 = 5(10^4) + 9(10^0)$

Practice: True or False?

1. True

2. True

3. False
   Answers may vary. Possible statement: $6,503 = 6(1,000) + 5(100) + 3(1)$

4. False
   Answers may vary. Sample statement: $666 + 40 = 706$

5. False
   $5,958 - 300 = 5,658$

6. False
   Answers may vary. Sample statement: $92(10) = 9(100) + 2(10)$

7. True
8. True
9. False
   Answers may vary. Sample statement:
   $5(1,000) + 6(100) + 78(1) = 5,678$

Practice: More Mystery Numbers

1. $543 \underline{+ 1,000} = 1,543$
2. $876 \underline{- 350} = 526$
3. $1,088 \underline{+ 2,000} = 3,088$
4. $1,077 \underline{- 370} = 707$
5. $21,156 \underline{+ 4,000} = 25,156$
6. $2,006 \underline{- 300} = 1,706$
7. $4,640 \underline{- 50} = 4,590$
8. $10,065 \underline{- 5} = 10,060$
9. $9,009 \underline{- 9,000} = 9$
10. $1,750 \underline{+ 600} = 2,350$

Practice: Calculating with Money

1. $1.00   1 (or 100 if not using the decimal in front of 30 and 70)
2. $30.70   30.7
3. $3.07   3.07
4. $30.07   30.07
5. $307   307
6. $8.09   8.09
7. $80.90   80.9
8. $8.90   8.9
9. 98¢   0.98 (or 98 if not using decimal in front of 8 and 90)
10. $170   170
11. Answers will vary.
12. Answers will vary. Possible answers:
    The calculator leaves off the last 0 when it is to the right of the decimal. You have to be sure to add a decimal point when you are working with both dollars and cents.

Practice: College Registration

1. Answers will vary. Possible answer: U.S. History, Math for Nonmajors, and Civil Engineering.
2. Answers will vary. Sample answer based on course selection above: $\$100 \times 3 \times 3 + \$100(2) = 900 + 200 = \$1,100$. With fees of $3,900 that expends the $5,000 scholarship.

Practice: Number of the Day

Answers will vary, but could include:
$\$656(10^6), \$6(10^8) + \$5(10^7) + \$6(10^6); \$474(10^6), \$4(10^8) + \$7(10^7) + \$4(10^6)$

Mental Math Practice: Double Trouble

1. a. 24
   b. 19
   c. 88
   d. 59
   e. 18
   f. Answers will vary. Sample answer: The 1's digit will be a 9 because $9 + 9 = 18$, or the digit in the one's place could be 4 because $4 + 4 = 8$. There are two possible scenarios, not just one.
2. a. 174 lbs.
   b. 194 lbs.
   c. 214 lbs.
   d. 234 lbs.
   e. 254 lbs.
   f. All the digits in the 1's place are 4's.
3. a. 32
   b. 72
   c. 112
   d. Answers will vary. Sample answer: When you double 6, the number in the 1's place will be 2.
   e. (1) 46
      (2) 48
      (3) 54

Test Practice

1. (a)
2. (b)
3. (c)
4. (e)
5. (c)
6. 300

Lesson 9: Patterns and Order

Blackline Master 12: Patterns with 10, 100, and 1,000

	Multiply by 10	Multiply by 100	Multiply by 1,000
7	70	700	7,000
19	190	1,900	19,000
24	240	2,400	24,000
261	2,610	26,100	261,000
501	5,010	50,100	501,000
2,500	25,000	250,000	2,500,000
2,505	25,050	250,500	2,505,000

Activity 1: Mental Math or Calculator?

1. 900
2. 30
3. 85
4. 85,000
5. 90,000
6. 30
7. 790
8. 79
9. 90,000
10. 79
11. Answers will vary. Sample answer: If it is a whole number, all I have to do is add a zero to the right of the number.
12. Answers will vary. Sample answer: If it is a whole number that ends in a zero, all I have to do is get rid of the last zero in the 1's place.
13. Answers will vary. Sample answer: If it is a whole number, all I have to do is add two zeroes to the right of the number.
14. Answers will vary. Sample answer: If it is a whole number that ends in at least two zeroes, all I have to do is get rid of the two zeroes in the 1's and 10's place.
15. Answers will vary. Sample answer: If it is a whole number, all I have to do is add three zeroes to the right of the number.
16. Answers will vary. Sample answer: If it is a whole number that ends in at least three zeroes, all I have to do is get rid of the three zeroes in the 1's, 10's, and 100's place.

Activity 2: 3, 4, 5

Part 1

1. Answers will vary. Sample answers: $3(4) + 5 = 17$; $3 + 4(5) = 23$
2. Answers will vary.

Part 2

3. a. $1 + 9 \times 5 = 46$
      Multiply, then add
   b. $3 \times 7 + 2 = 23$
      Multiply, then add
   c. $12 \times 2 + 6 = 30$
      Multiply, then add
   d. $8 + 3 \times 4 = 20$
      Multiply, then add
   e. $10 \times 10 + 16 = 116$
      Multiply, then add
   f. $13 + 7 \times 3 = 34$
      Multiply, then add

4. If the answer indicates that multiplication happened first, even if addition was entered first, then the calculator followed order of operations. If the calculator didn't follow order of operations, you would have 50 for the first answer, not 46.

5. a. 30
   b. 3
   c. Answers will vary.

Activity 3: How Many Different Ways Can You Solve It?

Answers will vary, but could include expressions such as:

$12(\$100) + 12(\$40) + 12(\$2)$

$10(\$142) + 2 (\$142)$

$6(\$142) + 6(\$142)$

$12(\$140) + 12(\$2)$

$4(\$142) + 3(\$142) + 5(\$142)$

$12(\$32) + 12(\$50) + 12(\$60)$

Math Inspection: Who Is Right?

1. Rae is correct, because the parentheses require that $3 - 1$ happens first.
   $4(3 - 1) = 4(2) = 8$
2. Jay is correct, because the parentheses require that $7 + 3$ is added first.
   $5(7 + 3) = 5(10) = 50$

3. Joe is correct, because the parentheses happen first, followed by multiplication.

   $6(4-1) + 7 = 6(3) + 7$

4. Don is correct, because multiplication happens before addition.

   $5 + 3 \times 7 = 5 + 21 = 26$

5. Juan is correct, because division happens before subtraction.

   $10 - 8/2 = 10 - 4 = 6$

6. Mike is correct, because what is inside the parentheses happens first, and then the rest. This also uses the distributive property.

   $3(7 + 4) - 3(2 + 3) = 3(11) - 3(5) = 3(11 - 5)$

Practice: Number of the Day
Answers will vary.

Practice: Just Like the Calculator

1. $3 + 6 \times 5 =$ 33   33
2. $7 \times 7 + 2 =$ 51   51
3. $4 \times 12 + 2 =$ 50   50
4. $18 - 3 \times 4 =$ 6   6
5. $10 \times 10 + 10 =$ 110   110
6. $15 - 7 \times 2 =$ 1   1
7. Answers will vary.
8. Answers will vary.

Practice: More or Less?

1. More than 200. $50 \times 4 = 200$; 54 is more than 50, so 54×4 is more than 200.
2. Less than 800. $400 \times 2 = 800$; 370 is less than 400, so 370×2 is less than 800.
3. More than 1,000. $200 \times 5 = 1,000$; 203 is more than 200, so 203×5 is more than 1,000.
4. Less than 270. $90 \times 3 = 270$; 89 is less than 90, so 89×3 is less than 270.

Mental Math Practice: Shopping Mentally

1. Explanations will vary, but may include thinking of buying three shirts for $20, and so spending $60, and then taking off $0.02 for each of the three shirts, so subtracting $0.06, to get a cost of $59.94.
2. Explanations will vary, but may include thinking of buying twelve gallons of gas for $4, and so spending $48, and then adding $0.03 for each of twelve gallons, so adding $0.36, to get a cost of $48.36.

3. Explanations will vary, but may include thinking of buying five candy bars for $1 each, and so spending $5, and then subtracting $0.01 for each of five candy bars, so subtracting $0.05, to get a cost of $4.95.
4. Explanations will vary, but may include thinking of buying seven cans of cat food for $0.50, and so spending $3.50, and then adding $0.05 for each of the seven cans, so adding $0.35, to get a cost of $3.85 (or multiplying $0.05 times 7 and adding $0.35 to $3.50).
5. Explanations will vary, but may include thinking of buying two pairs of slacks for $40, and so spending $80, and then taking away $0.10 for each pair of pants, so subtracting $0.20, to get a cost of $79.80.
6. You had to do multiplication twice, making sure to multiply each part of the number you broke apart. If you multiplied the first number and then just added the broken off part, the answer came out wrong.

   Instead of multiplying all the numbers in place value order, you deal with a rounded chunk and then the small amounts that are left.

Mental Math Practice: Multiply and Divide with 10, 100, or 1,000

1. $25 \times 10 = 250$

   $25 \times 100 = 2,500$

   $25 \times 1,000 = 25,000$

2. $205 \times 10 = 2,050$

   $205 \times 100 = 20,500$

   $205 \times 1,000 = 205,000$

3. $30 \times 10 = 300$

   $30 \times 100 = 3,000$

   $30 \times 1,000 = 30,000$

4. $360 \times 10 = 3,600$

   $360 \times 100 = 36,000$

   $360 \times 1,000 = 360,000$

5. $6,000 \div 10 = 600$

   $6,000 \div 100 = 60$

   $6,000 \div 1,000 = 6$

6. $100,000 \div 10 = 10,000$

   $100,000 \div 100 = 1,000$

   $100,000 \div 1,000 = 100$

7. $36{,}000 \div 10 = 3{,}600$

   $36{,}000 \div 100 = 360$

   $36{,}000 \div 1{,}000 = 36$

8. $306{,}000 \div 10 = 30{,}600$

   $306{,}000 \div 100 = 3{,}060$

   $306{,}000 \div 1{,}000 = 306$

Extension: The Answer Is 24

1. Answers will vary. Sample answer: $2(4 + 8) = 24$

2. Answers will vary. Sample word problem solved with b. By first adding and then dividing: Jon counted 200 cassettes in one crate and 40 in another. He packed cassettes 10 to a box. How many boxes did he need for all the cassettes? To solve: Add $200 + 40 = 240$ and then divide by $10 = 24$.

3. Answers will vary.

Extension: Wrong Number!

1. a. $4.00

   b. Answers will vary. Sample answer: The cashier rang up 40¢ as 40 instead of $0.40.

2. a. $7.25

   b. Answers will vary. Sample answer: Anton may have hit the subtraction key (−) instead of the division key (÷).

3. a. $49.90

   b. Answers will vary. Sample answer: Jorge probably hit the addition key (+) instead of the multiplication key (×).

Test Practice

1. (b)
2. (c)
3. (e)
4. (d)
5. (b)
6. 10

Lesson 10: Picture This

Activity 1: Pictures and Numbers

Part 1

1. Answers will vary. Sample answer: There are 4 groups of 6 cans for a total of 24.

2. Answers will vary. Sample answer: There are 9 groups of five fingers for a total of 45.

3. Answers will vary. Sample answer: There are 10 rows of 10 heads for a total of 100.

4. Answers will vary. Sample answer: There are 6 rows of 3 stamps plus 2 more for a total of 20.

5. Answers will vary. Sample answer: There are 6 groups of 3 candies, plus 1 more for a total of 19.

Part 2

1. b
2. d
3. c
4. a
5. a. 143

   b. Answers will vary. Sample answer: $10 \times 13 = 130$; $1 \times 13 = 13$; $130 + 13 = 143$

6. Answers will vary. Sample answer: They all total 143.

Activity 2: Counting Smart

Part 1

1. Answers will vary. Sample answer based on the following array:

   xxx   xxx xxx

   xxx   xxx xxx

2. Answers will vary. Sample answer based on the array above: $(3 \times 2) + (3 \times 4)$.

3. Answers will vary. Sample answer based on array above:

   xxxxx   xxxxx

   xxxxx   xxx

4. Answers will vary. Sample answer based on array above: $1(10) + 8$

Part 2

1. Answers may vary. Possible answer:

   oooo   oo
   oooo
   oooo
   oooo
   oooo
   oooo
   oooo
   oooo
   oooo

2. Answers may vary. Possible answer:

    OOOOO
    ∅∅∅∅∅
    ∅∅∅∅∅
    ∅∅∅∅∅

3. Answers may vary. Possible answer:

    OOO OOO OOO OOO OOO
    OOO OOO OOO OOO OOO
    OOO OOO OOO OOO OOO
    OOO OOO OOO OOO OOO

4. Answers may vary. Possible answer:

    OO OOO
    OO OOO
    OO OOO
    OO OOO
    OO OOO
    OO OOO

5. Answers will vary.

Activity 3: Garden Pathway

1. Answers will vary. Sample answer:
    $2(12)(2) + 2(10)$

2. Answers will vary. Sample answer:
    $2(14) + 2(10)(2)$

Activity 4: Understanding the "Whys" …

1. 13 T-shirts would cost $143.

2. 32 months @ $45/month = $1,440

Math Inspection: Rectangles, Arrays, Area, and the Distributive Property

1. a. Answers will vary. The grids are the same (42 square units). Both have a side of 6 units and a side of 7 units. In the second grid, 7 is broken up into two parts, 5 and 2. Six remains the same whole amount. Each of the smaller parts of 7 can be multiplied by 6, and then the sub-products can be added to find the total of 42.

    b. $6 \times 7 = 42$ and $6(5 + 2) = 6(5) + 6(2) = 30 + 12 = 42$

2. a. Answers will vary.

    b. Answers will vary, but should include reference to one of the amounts being broken into two parts. The two parts are each multiplied and then the two products are added together. Possibilities: $8(5 + 4)$, $8(6 + 3)$, $9(5 + 3)$, $9(7 + 1)$, and so on.

    c. Answers will vary, but should be aligned with the representation drawn in 2a.

3. a. Answers will vary. Students may show either.

    b. Answers will vary, but should include reference to the two-digit amount being broken into two parts. The two parts are each multiplied and then the two products are added together. Possibilities: $5(10 + 2)$, $5(11 + 1)$, $5(4 + 8)$, among others.

    c. Answers will vary, but should be aligned with the representation drawn in 3a, e.g., $2(5 \times 6)$ or $(5 \times 10) + (5 \times 2)$

4. a. $6 \times 7 = 6 \times 4 + 6 \times \mathbf{3}$

    b. $9 \times 8 = \mathbf{5} \times 8 + 4 \times 8$

    c. $7 \times 7 = 2 \times 7 + \mathbf{5} \times 7$

    d. $6 \times 7 = 5 \times 7 + \mathbf{1} \times 7$

    e. $7 \times 6 = 5 \times 6 + \mathbf{2} \times 6$

    f. $9 \times 9 = 5 \times 9 + \mathbf{4} \times 9$

    g. $8 \times 7 = \mathbf{3} \times 7 + 5 \times 7$

Math Inspection: Connecting Arrays to Multiplication

1.

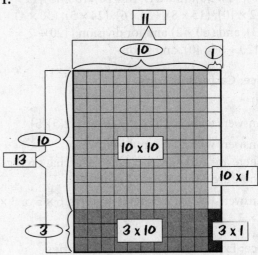

    a. Eleven is broken up into two parts as a sum: $10 + 1$. Thirteen is broken up into two parts: $10 + 3$. Four rectangles are created: (10×10), (10×1), (3×10) and (3×1). Each of these sub-products are added to find the total.

    b. $11 \times 13 = (10 + 1) \times (10 + 3)$
        $= (10 \times 10) + (10 \times 3) + (1 \times 10) + (1 \times 3)$
        $= 100 + 30 + 10 + 3 = 143$

c. Answers will vary but explanation should include reference to 11 being 10 + 1 and 13 being the same as 10 + 3. There are four sub-products: (10×10), (10×3), (1×10), and (1×3). Once you have all the sub-products, you add them together to find the total.

2. a. Array should be broken up into 30 + 2 and 40 + 5. Sub-products are: (40×30), (5×30), (40×2) and (5×2). 1,200 + 150 + 80 + 10 = 1,440.

   b. Answers will vary, but probably the easiest to see is 40×30. Answers will vary, but probably the most difficult to see is the 5×2.

   c. Answers will vary, but should include the idea that you can break amounts apart, find the sub-products of each smaller part, and then add all the sub-products together. This is an application of the distributive principle of multiplication over addition: $a(b + c) = ab + ac$.

Practice: Number of the Day

Answers will vary but examples include (2×60), (3×40), (4×30), (5×24), (6×20), (8×15), (10×12), (12×10), (15×8), (20×6), (24×5), (30×4), (40×3), and (60×2) and for division $(120 \div 2 = 60)$, $(120 \div 3 = 40)$, and so on.

Practice: Cartons of Eggs

1. 30

2. Answers will vary. Sample answer: 2(3)(5)

3. Answers will vary. Sample answer:
   There are 2 rows with 3 eggs each. That's 6 eggs. There are 5 sets of 6, so $5 \times 6 = 30$.

4. Answers will vary. Possible answers. 6×5 or $3 \times 5 \times 2$

Practice: Expressions, Arrays, and Stories

Part 1

1. $3 \times 3 + 10$

2. $3(10 + 3)$; $4 \times 7 - 3$

3. $5 \times 5 + 5 + 5 + 5$

Part 2

4. Array 3

5. Array 1

6. Array 2

Practice: How Do You See It?

1. a. Answers will vary. Sample answer:

   $2(3) + 1$

   b. Answers will vary. Sample answer:

   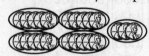

   $4(5) + 3$

   c. Answers will vary. Sample answers:

   $3(3)$

2. a. Answers will vary. Possible answer: $2(8) + 2(7)$; $2(9) + 2(6)$

   b. Answers will vary.

Practice: Stone Paths

1. a. $2(6) = 12$

   b. $1(12) = 12$

   c. $3(4) = 12$

2. a.
   XXXXXXXXXXXXXXXXXXXXXXX 1(23)

   XXXXXXXXXXXXXXXXXXXXXXXX 1(24)

   XXXXXXXXXXXX
   XXXXXXXXXXXX 2(12)

   XXXXXX
   XXXXXX
   XXXXXX 4(6)
   XXXXXX

   XXXXXXXX
   XXXXXXXX 3(8)
   XXXXXXXX

   XXXXXXXXXXXXXXXXXXXXXXXXX 1(25)

   XXXXX
   XXXXX
   XXXXX 5(5)
   XXXXX
   XXXXX

   b. One array for 23: 1(23); four arrays for 24: 1(24), 2(12), 3(8), 4(6); two arrays for 25: 1(25), 5(5)

c. Answers will vary. Sample answer: There are more ways to multiply numbers to get 24 than to get 23 or 25.

Practice: Sketch the Two Expressions

Representations will vary. Here, subtraction is indicated with graying out.

1.

2.

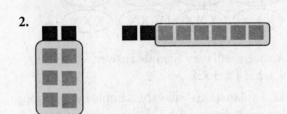

3.

4.

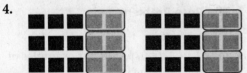

5.

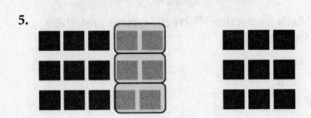

Mental Math Practice: Square Numbers

1. n^2

| 0 | 1 | 4 | 9 | 16 | 25 | 36 |

n^2

| 49 | 64 | 81 | 100 | 121 | 144 |

2. a. $6 \times 6 = 36$

b. $9 \times 9 = 81$

c. $9 = 3^2$

d. $8^2 = 64$

e. $0^2 + 1^2 + 2^2 + 3^2 = 14$

Extension: Missing Rolls of Film

1. There are 36 rolls missing.

2. Explanations will vary. Possible explanation: The rolls are stacked 3 deep. There are 2 rows that have 6 rolls each missing: $3 \times 2 \times 6 = 36$.

Extension: Seeing Squarely

1.

```
X X X X X
X X X X X
X X X X X
X X X X X
X X X X X
```

2.

```
X X X X X     X X X
X X X X X     X X X
X X X X X     X X X
X X X X X
X X X X X
```

3.

```
X X X X X O O O
X X X X X O O O
X X X X X O O O
X X X X X O O O
X X X X X O O O
O O O O O O O O
O O O O O O O O
O O O O O O O O
```

4.

```
O O O O O
O O O O O
O O O Ø Ø
O O O Ø Ø
O O O Ø Ø
```

Test Practice

1. (b)

2. (d)

3. (d)

4. (d)

5. (e)

6. 106

Lesson 11: What Is the Story?

Activity 1: What Is the Story?
Problem 1
Person A

1. All of the windows in one building. Sketches will vary. Sample sketch:

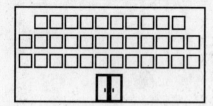

2. Answers will vary. Sample answer:
$4(12 + 12 + 10) = 4(34)$

3. 136. Explanations will vary. Sample explanation:
Person A added $12 + 12 + 10$ to get a total of 34 windows in one building. Since there are four buildings, he then multiplied 4×34.

Person B

1. All of the windows on the first floor. Sketches will vary. Sample sketch:

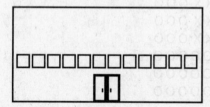

2. Answers will vary. Sample answer:
$4(12) + 4(12) + 4(10) = 48 + 48 + 40$

3. 136. Explanations will vary. Sample explanation:
Person B multiplied 4×12 to find the total number of windows on the first floor of all four buildings. She then multiplied 4×12 to find the total number of second-floor windows and 4×10 for the total number of third-floor windows.

Problem 2
Person A

1.

```
X X X X X X X X X
X X X X X X X X X
X X X X X X X X X
X X X X X X X X X
```

2. Answers will vary. Sample answer:
$4(9) \div 3 = 36 \div 3$

3. 12. Explanations will vary. Sample explanation:
Person A multiplied 9×4 to figure out the total number of children. Then he divided the total by 3 because there were 3 shirts per pack.

Person B

1.

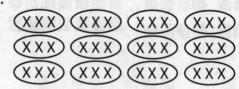

2. Answers will vary. Sample answer:
$9 \div 3 \times 4 = 3 \times 4$

3. 12. Explanations will vary. Sample explanation:
Person B divided $9 \div 3$ to figure out the total number of shirts needed for one class. Then she multiplied that amount by 4 because there were 4 classes needing shirts.

Activity 2: The Rose Problem
1. 48.
2. See *Lesson 11 in Action*, p. 140, for examples of how students solved the problem.

Math Inspection: Perfect Squares and Their Square Roots
1. a. 1
   b. 7
   c. 5 or $\sqrt{25}$
   d. 2 or $\sqrt{4}$
   e. 40
   f. 5
2. a. False. Square root of 100 is 10. Square root of 25 is 5. To make 10, you need $5 + 5$ and the square root of 75 won't give you anything like 5.
   b. False. $(3 + 4)^2 = 49$ and 49 does not equal $3(3) + 4(4)$, which is $9 + 16$ or 25.

Part 2
1. a. An array that is 3 by 3 has 9 square units.
   b. 3 on each side, 3×3, surface area = 9 tiles.
2. a. 25
   b. 5 on each side, 5×5, surface area = 25 tiles.

3. a. 4

   b. 4^2 or 4×4 or $\sqrt{16}$

4. a. 5

   b. 5^2 or 5×5 or $\sqrt{25}$

5. 10

6. a. Can't do it. Answers will vary. Possible answer: You can get a 3×4 rectangle, but that is as close as you can get to a square without cutting up squares.

   b. Possible answer: 3×4, 2×12; The square root is somewhere between 3 and 4.

7. No.

   a. 11

   b. Explanations may vary. 11 doesn't have a factor that can be multiplied by itself to get 11. There's no square shape you can make with 11 square units. The best you can do is a rectangle that is 11 x 1 with whole numbers or that is a whole number and decimal or fractional amount close to 3.

Part 3

1. 16 square units

2. 5 units

3. 2 units

4. 7 units

5. 256 square units

6. 100 units

Part 4

1. 1, 4, 9, 16, 25, 36, 49, 64, 81, 100 should be circled.

2. Explanations may vary. Possible explanation: I circled one number to go with the digits 1-9 and 10 as well. After that, if your product is larger than 100 and not on the chart. In other words, pay attention to squaring 1-10 to make sure no perfect squares were missing.

3. e. $\sqrt{16} = 4$

   f. $\sqrt{25} = 5$

   g. $\sqrt{36} = 6$

   h. $\sqrt{49} = 7$

   i. $\sqrt{64} = 8$

   j. $\sqrt{81} = 9$

   k. $\sqrt{100} = 10$

Math Inspection: What's the Rule?

1. Karen is correct. $10^3 \times 10^2 = 10 \times 10 \times 10 \times 10 \times 10 = 10^5 = 100,000$

2. a. $2^6 = 64$

   b. $10^6 = 1,000,000$

   c. $5^5 = 3,125$

   d. $7^7 = 823,543$

   e. $8^7 = 2,097,152$

   f. $9^5 = 59,049$

3. Answers will vary, but should include the fact that when multiplying numbers with equal bases, the base stays the same and the exponents are added. For example: $4^6 \times 4^2 = 4^8$

4. a. True. $(2 \times 2) \times (2 \times 2 \times 2 \times 2) = (2 \times 2 \times 2 \times 2) \times (2 \times 2) = 2 \times 2 \times 2 \times 2 \times 2 \times 2$

   b. False. $100,000 = 10 \times 10 \times 10 \times 10 \times 10 \neq 10 \times 10 + 10 \times 10 \times 10 = 1,100$

   c. False. $5 \times 5 \times 5 \times 5 \times 5 \neq 2 \times 2 \times 2 \times 2 \times 2 \times 3 \times 3 \times 3 \times 3 \times 3$

   d. False. $7 \times 7 \times 7 \neq 3 \times 3 \times 3 \times 3 \times 3 \times 3 \times 3$

   e. True. $(8 \times 8) \times (8 \times 8) = 8 \times 8 \times 8 \times 8$

   f. False. $3 \times 10 \times 10 \neq 3 \times 3 \times 10$

Practice: Drawings and Equations

1. Answers will vary. Sample answer:

Ø Ø O O O O   Ø Ø Ø O O O
Ø Ø O O O O   Ø Ø Ø O O O
Ø Ø O O O O   Ø Ø Ø O O O
Ø Ø O O O O   Ø Ø Ø O O O
Ø Ø O O O O   Ø Ø Ø O O O

$5(6 - 2) + 5(6 - 4) = 5(4) + 5(2) = 30$

2. Answers will vary. Sample answer:

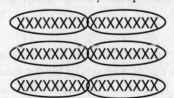

$16(3) \div 8 = 48 \div 8 = 6$

© 2015 TERC

3. Answers will vary. Sample answer:

$$X \ X \ X \ X \ X = \$9$$
$$X \ X \ X \ X \ X = \$9$$
$$X \ X \ X \ X \ X = \$9$$
$$X \ X \ X \ X \ X = \$9$$
$$X \ X \ X \ X \ X = \$9$$
$$X \ X \ X \ X \ X = \$9$$

$$30 \div 5 \times 9 = 6 \times 9 = \$54$$

4. Answers will vary. Sample answer:

C C C = $45	C C C = $32
C C C = $45	C C C = $32
C C C = $45	C C C = $32
C C C = $45	C C C = $32
C C C = $45	C C C = $32
C C C = $45	C C C = $32
C C C = $45	C C C = $32
C C C = $45	C C C = $32
C C C = $45	C C C = $32
C C C = $45	C C C = $32

$$30 \div 3 \times (45 - 32) = 10 \times 13 = \$130$$

Practice: Equations and Word Problems

1. Answers will vary. Sample answer:
   $5(14) + 2$. There are five preschool classes. The director wanted to limit the class size to 14, but when a set of twins enrolled, the director allowed them to join one of the already full classes. How many children were there altogether?

2. Answers will vary. Sample answer:
   $5(2(4) + 3(4))$. There are two rows of shelves with four crates on each row across the top and three rows of shelves with four crates on each row on the bottom. If there are a total of five such sets of shelving, how many crates are there altogether?

3. Answers will vary. Sample answer: $4(10)$. Jane is building pyramids with sets of blocks. Each pyramid uses 10 blocks with four blocks used as the base. If she builds four pyramids, how many blocks does she need in all?

Practice: The Answer Is ____

1. Answers will vary. Sample answer: 42

2. Answers will vary. Sample problem based on answer above:
   Seth earns $7 an hour. How much does he earn for working 6 hours? $7(6) = 42$

3. Answers will vary. Sample problem based on answer above:
   Tabitha has eight nickels and two pennies in her pocket. How much change does she have altogether?
   $8(\$0.05) + 2(\$0.01) = \$0.40 + \$0.02 = \$0.42$

Practice: One Day, I ...

Answers will vary.

Mental Math Practice:

There are many patterns in the multiplication tables. Some, but certainly not all, follow:

The multiples of 10 end in zero.

The multiples of five end in zero or five.

Any number mutiplied by one is itself ($a \times 1 = a$).

Any number multiplied by zero is zero ($a \times 0 = 0$).

The square numbers run along the diagonal.

There is a mirror image along the diagonal of the squares ($a \times b = b \times a$).

The multiples of six are even.

Test Practice

1. (b)
2. (b)
3. (c)
4. (c)
5. (b)
6. 90

Lesson 12: Easy Payments

Activity 1: Easy Payments

Answers for estimated payments may vary.

1. $9,600 over 4 months $2,500 $2,400
2. $9,600 over 8 months $1,250 $1,200
3. $9,600 over 12 months $1,000 $ 800
4. $9,600 over 24 months $ 300 $ 400
5. Answers will vary. Sample answer:
   I estimated by rounding $9,600 to $10,000. Then I divided by 4. To find the exact answer, I subtracted $400 \div 4 = 100$ from my estimate ($\$10,000 \div 4 = \$2,500; \$2,500 - \$100 = \$2,400$).
6. Answers will vary. Sample answer:
   I estimated by rounding $9,600 to $10,000. To find the exact answer, I subtracted $400 \div 8 = 50$ ($\$10,000 \div 8 = 1,250; \$1,250 - \$50 = \$1,200$).

7. Answers will vary. Sample answer: I estimated by rounding $9,600 to $12,000. To find the exact answer, I subtracted $2,400 ÷ 12 = $200 ($12,000 ÷ 12 = $1,000; $1,000 − $200 = $800).

8. Answers will vary. Sample answer: I estimated by rounding $9,600 to $12,000. To find the exact answer, I halved the amount for 12 months.

9. Answers will vary.

Activity 2: Payment Plans

Answers will vary.

Math Inspection: How Do You See It – Multiplication or Division?

1. a. John will use 10 gallons.
   b. Responses will vary. Both division (500 miles ÷ 50 miles per gallon = __ gallons) and multiplication (50 miles per gallon × __ gallons = 500 miles) could be used to solve this problem.
   c. Depending on response to **b**, 500 miles ÷ 50 miles per gallon = 10 gallons, or 50 miles per gallon × 10 gallons = 500 miles.

2. a. 3,000 miles ÷ 300 miles per day = __ days
   b. 45 miles/gallon × __ gallons = 180 miles
   c. 8 hours × __ miles per hour = 480 miles
   d. 384 miles ÷ 32 miles per gallon = __ gallons

3. Answers will vary, but should include the fact that multiplication and division are inverses of one another, and that finding a missing factor in a multiplication problem *is* division.

Practice: Four Ways to Write Division

$8\overline{)56}$	$56 \div 8$	$\dfrac{56}{8}$	56 divided by 8
$5\overline{)30}$	$30 \div 5$	$\dfrac{30}{5}$	30 divided by 5
$6\overline{)180}$	$180 \div 6$	$\dfrac{180}{6}$	180 divided by 6
$1\overline{)40}$	$40 \div 1$	$\dfrac{40}{1}$	40 divided by 1
$7\overline{)2}$	$2 \div 7$	$\dfrac{2}{7}$	2 divided by 7
$y\overline{)x}$	$x \div y$	$\dfrac{x}{y}$	x divided by y
$10\overline{)m}$	$m \div 10$	$\dfrac{m}{10}$	m divided by 10
$\$0.50\overline{)\$10.00}$	$\$10.00 \div \$0.50$	$\dfrac{\$10.00}{\$0.50}$	$10.00 divided by $0.50

Practice: Which Is Not the Same?

1. c
2. a
3. a
4. b

Practice: Those Monthly Payments

1. <
2. >
3. <
4. <

Practice: 10's, 100's, and 1,000's

Answers will vary.

1. $10 \times 9 = 90$. Then: $2 \times 9 = 18$; $90 + 18 = 108$
2. $21 \times 10 = 210$. Then: $21 \times 1 = 21$; $210 + 21 = 231$
3. $25 \times 10 = 250$. Then: $2 \times 250 = 500$ and $3 \times 25 = 75$; $500 + 75 = 575$
4. $100 \div 5 = 20$. Then: $30 \div 5 = 6$; $20 + 6 = 26$
5. $1,000 \div 4 = 250$. Then: $200 \div 4 = 50$ and $72 \div 4 = 18$; $250 + 50 + 18 = 318$

Mental Math Practice: Flowers by the Month

1. Join the Flower Club!
   12 months: $192.00
   10 months: $160.00
   6 months: $96.00
   2 months: $32.00
   Monthly: $16.00
2. Monthly Flower Club
   12 months: $456.00
   10 months: $380.00
   6 months: $228.00
   2 months: $76.00
   Monthly: $38.00
3. Flower Club of the Month
   12 months: $324.00
   10 months: $270.00
   6 months: $162.00
   2 months: $54.00
   Monthly: $27.00

Test Practice

1. (b)
2. (d)
3. (b)
4. (e)
5. (c)
6. $4,788

Lesson 13: String It Along

Activity 1: String It Along
Part 1

1. a. 16
   b. 12
   c. 8
2. 48 inches. Answers will vary.
   Sample answer: 3″ × 16 = 48″
3.

4. Answers will vary. Sample answers:
   3″(16) = 48″; 48″/4″ = 12; 48″/6″ = 8

Part 2

1. a. 12
   b. 8
   c. 4
2. 72 inches. Answers will vary. Sample answer:
   12 × 6″ = 72″
3.
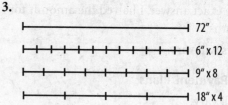
4. Answers will vary. Sample answers:
   72″/6″ = 12; 9″(8) = 72″; 18″(4) = 72″

Activity 2: Scales on Maps

1. a. 710 miles
   b. 2,840 miles
   c. 2,130 miles
2. a. 2,000 miles
   b. 1,200 miles
   c. 300 miles
   d. 1,250 miles
3. a. 0.21 inches or 1/5"; 6 cm.
   b. 0.42 inches or 3/7"; 12 cm.
   c. 10.56 inches or 10 1/2"; 300 cm.
   d. Answers will vary.
4. Answers will vary.

Math Inspection: Working with Symbols

1. a.
$$\frac{30 \times 9^2}{5 \times 3^2} = \frac{6 \times 5 \times 9 \times 9}{5 \times 9} = 6 \times 9 = 54$$

   b.
$$(2^4 \times 10^6) \div (2^3 \times 1{,}000) = \frac{2^4 \times 10^6}{2^3 \times 10^3} = 2 \times 10^3 = 2{,}000$$

   c.
$$\frac{35 \times 10^4}{7 \times 10^3} = \frac{5 \times 7 \times 10 \times 10 \times 10 \times 10}{7 \times 10 \times 10 \times 10} = 5 \times 10 = 50$$

   d.
$$(2^3 \cdot 10^5) \div (4 \cdot 10{,}000) = \frac{2^3 \cdot 10^5}{4 \cdot 10{,}000} =$$

$$\frac{2 \cdot 2 \cdot 2 \cdot 10 \cdot 10 \cdot 10 \cdot 10 \cdot 10}{2 \cdot 2 \cdot 10 \cdot 10 \cdot 10 \cdot 10} = 2 \cdot 10 = 20$$

e.

$$(8^3 \cdot 7^2) \div (4^2 \cdot 2^3) = \frac{8^3 \cdot 7^2}{4^2 \cdot 2^3} =$$

$$\frac{8 \cdot 8 \cdot 8 \cdot 7 \cdot 7}{16 \cdot 8} = \frac{8 \cdot 7 \cdot 7}{2} = 4 \cdot 7^2 = 196$$

2. **a.** 3
   b. 1
   c. 2

Math Inspection: The Commutative Property and the Four Operations

Explanations may vary, but should include the following ideas:

1. True. Finding the difference between two numbers can happen by finding how many are needed to add to the one value to get to the other.

2. True. Addition is commutative, so the order does not matter.

3. False. Subtraction has three common meanings: missing part, comparison, and take away.

4. True. Multiplication can be thought of as repeated addition.

5. False. Subtraction, unlike addition and multiplication, is not commutative, so the order matters.

6. True. Multiplication is commutative, so the order does not matter.

7. False. Adding two whole numbers will always result in a larger number, but this is not true when adding any two integers.

8. True. The long division algorithm represents the operation as repeated subtraction, but division problems can be solved using addition. For example, how many $50 payments will it take to buy the $200 TV? 50 + 50 + 50 + 50 = 200. It will take four payments.

9. False. Division is not commutative, and so the order does matter.

10. False. Division and multiplication are inverse operations, and addition and subtraction are inverse operations.

Practice: How Many Blanks in a Blank?

1. **a.** $36 \div 12 = 3$
   b.
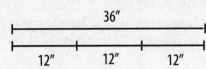
   c. 3

'2. **a.** $60/15 = 4$
   b.
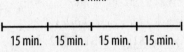
   c. 4

3. **a.** $128/16 = 8$
   b.
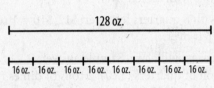
   c. 8

4. **a.** $10,000/2,000 = 5$
   b.
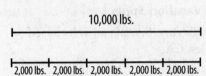
   c. 5

5. **a.** $24 \div 3 = 8$
   b.
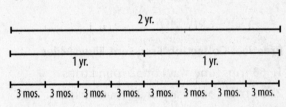
   c. 8

6. **a.** Answers will vary.
   b. Answers will vary.
   c. Answers will vary.

Practice: About How Many Times as Large?

1. 10; Explanations will vary. Sample explanation: 72 is about 70. 70/7 = 10

2. 2; Explanations will vary. Sample explanation: 68 is about 70. 140/70 = 2

3. 100; Explanations will vary. Sample explanation:
197 is about 200. 200/2 = 100

4. 2; Explanations will vary. Sample explanation:
6 feet is 72 inches. 72 inches is about 70.
70/35 = 2

Practice: Coin Rolling

1. a. 100

b. 20

c. 10

d. 4

2. 24; 50¢ × 2 = $1; 12 × $1 = $12

3. 6; $12/$2 = $6. No change left over.

4. 2 rolls of $5 with 20 dimes left over; $12/$5 = 2 rolls with $2 left over.

5. 1 with 8 quarters left over; $12/$10 = 1 roll with $2 left over.

6. Answers will vary. Sample answer:
1 roll of quarters ($10), 2 rolls of dimes ($10), 1 roll of nickels ($2), and 4 rolls of pennies ($2): $10 + $10 + $2 + $2 = $24

Practice: Vacation Spots

Answers will vary. Sample answers based on Los Angeles, CA.

1. a. 40 hours; 2,000/50 = 40

b. 26 hours and 40 minutes (26.67 hours); 2,000/75 = 26.66

c. 30 hours and about 45 minutes (30.77); 2,000/65 = 30.77

2. Answers will vary.

Practice: Collecting Frequent Flyer Miles

1. 63 trips (one-way) or 32 round trips

2. 56 trips (one-way) or 28 round trips

Mental Math Practice: Factors

1. a. 1, 2, 4, 5, 10, 20

b. 1, 23

c. 1, 2, 3, 4, 6, 8, 12, 24

d. 1, 5, 25

2. a. 20, 25

b. 24

c. 20

d. 23

e. 24

Test Practice

1. (b)

2. (b)

3. (c)

4. (c)

5. (d)

6. 3

Lesson 14: Making Do

Activity 1: Party Favors

1. E

2. CS

3. E

4. SL

5. E

6. CS

7. CS

8. CS

9. CS

10. CS

Activity 2: Making Do

Answers may vary based on personal experience.

1. Three feet of wire with 3 feet left over (or 3.75 feet each)

2. 60 feet of board

3. 67.5 feet of rope

4. About 50 screws each

5. Only three sites can have paint and one will have to do without; or 3/4 cans for each site.

6. 7.5 pounds of plaster

7. One bag each with two 40-pound bags left over

8. About 80 stones each

Activity 3: Understanding the "Why" of Methods for Division

1. a. $2,600

b. $10,600 ÷ 4 = $2,650

2. a. $2,700

b. $10,999 ÷ 4 = $2,749.75

$10,999 ~ $11,000

$11,000 ÷ 4 = 2,750 but since we went up by $1, we need to subtract $1 ÷ 4 = $0.25, so $2,750 − $0.25 = $2749.75

Math Inspection: The Four Operations

1. Answers will vary.
2. Answers will vary. See possible answers in the *Teacher Book*, p. 182

Practice: Interpreting Remainders

1. h
2. d
3. j
4. f
5. i or l
6. i or l
7. e
8. k
9. c
10. b
11. a
12. g

Practice: Pill Problems

1. On May 21 there will be only 2 strips left.
2. No. Explanations will vary. Sample explanation: 2 pills every 4 hours for 3 days is about 36 pills, leaving 64. After that she would take 8 pills a day, so the remaining 64 pills would last 8 more days. Three days + 8 days is less than a month.
3. No
4. 15 units

Practice: Meaningful Remainders

1. 6; 100/15 = 6.; She will have between $6 and $7 left, but not enough to buy another gift card.
2. 6; 175/30 = 5.8; 0.8 must become one more trip.
3. 30 inches, or 2.5 feet with no leftovers.
4. 8; 75/9 = 8.33; 0.33 feet is not enough for another jump rope.
5. 12; $25/$1.99 = 12.5; she can't buy half of a truck.
6. $370.60 each with no leftovers.
7. 1.5 feet with no leftovers.
8. Answers will vary. Sample answer: There are 29 children who are to be grouped into teams of 4 each. There would be 7 teams and 1 child who would become a helper.

Mental Math Practice: Money in My Pocket

3 or 63

Test Practice

1. (d)
2. (b)
3. (d)
4. (c)
5. (b)
6. 7.5 cookies

Closing the Unit: Computer Lab

Activity 1: Computer Lab Project

Answers will vary.

Computer Lab Warm-Up 1:
Mental Math Calculations for Paper Use

1. a. 200; Explanations will vary. Sample explanation: $20 \times 10 = 200$
   b. 1,100; Explanations will vary. Sample explanation: $20 \times 50 = 1,000$ and $20 \times 5 = 100$
   c. 2,000; Explanations will vary. Sample explanation: $20 \times 100 = 2,000$
   d. 2,400; Explanations will vary. Sample explanation: $20 \times 100 = 2,000$ and $20 \times 20 = 400$
   e. 4,000; Explanations will vary. Sample explanation: $20 \times 200 = 4,000$

2. a. 1,000; Explanations will vary. Sample explanation: $50 \times 20 = 1,000$
   b. 6,250; Explanations will vary. Sample explanation: $50 \times 100 = 5,000$, $50 \times 20 = 1,000$, and $50 \times 5 = 250$

Computer Lab Warm-Up 2:
How Much More for … ?

1. a. $286
   b. Answers will vary. Sample answer: $2,275 – $1,975 = $300; $1,989 is $14 more than $1,975, so $300 is $14 over estimate. $300 – $14 = $286.

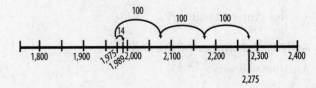

2. a. $1,576

   b. Answers will vary but may include $2,275 −
      $700 = $1,575 and $1,575 + $1 = $1,576

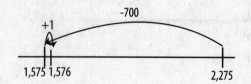

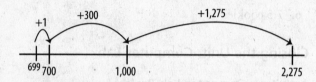

Computer Lab Warm-Up 3: Inventory Count

1. Answers will vary. Three possibilities are shown
   here:

                $4 \times 6 = 24$

                $8 \times 3 = 24$

        $2 \times 12 = 24$

2. a. $5 \times 3 \times 6 = 5 \times 18 = 90$

   b. $5 \times (4 \times 2 \times 2) - 10(2) = 80 - 20 = 60$

   c. $5 \times (4 \times 5 \times 4) - 10(3) = 400 - 30 = 370$

Computer Lab Warm-Up 4: Item Costs

1. a. 6
      $1,500 \times 2 = $3,000;
      $3,000 \times 3 = $9,000; 2 \times 3 = 6$

   b. Yes, answers for leftover $1,000 will vary.

2. a. About $3,333

   b. Answers will vary.

Activity 2: Number of the Day

Answers will vary.

Activity 3: Final Assessment

Task 1: Mental Math Challenge

1. $140

2. $90

3. $19

4. $5,000

5. $1.00

6. $3,640

7. $9,370

8. $450

9. $450

10. $3,300

11. 27

12. $80

13. No

14. Yes

Task 2: Picturing the Math

1. a. Answers will vary. Sample answer:

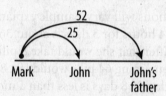

   b. Answers will vary. Sample answer: How old
      was John's father when John was born? To
      solve it, I would subtract 25 from 52.

2. a. 3 days: is approximately 1,000 miles each
      day

   b. 4 days: is approximately 775 miles each day
      (an estimate from 750 – 800 is reasonable)

   c. 5 days: is a little over 600 miles each day

   d. 8 days: is a little under 400 miles each day

   e. 10 days: is a little over 310 miles each day

   f. Answers will vary. Possible patterns are
      related to doubling the amount for 4 days
      to get the amount for 8 days. You can
      double the amount for five days to the get
      the amount for 10 days.

3. Answers will vary. Possible answers: $4 \times 4 = 16$
   or $4^2 = 16$

4. Picture A

5. a. Answers will vary. Sample answer:

    XX   XX
    XX   XX
    XX
    XX
    XX

b. Answers will vary. Sample answer:

    XX   OOOO
    XX   OOOO
    XX   OOOO
    XX   OOOO
    XX   OOOO

6. Answers will vary. Sample answer:

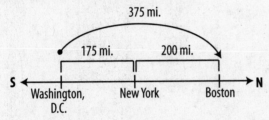

Task 3: Is It Always True?

1. a. Answers will vary. Look for the idea that addition is commutative (the oder doesn't matter), so 15 + 23 will have the same sum.

b. 23 + 15 = 15 +23 or a + b = b + a

c. Yes, because addition is commutative.

Task 4: Four Operations

1. Answers will vary. Look for understandings that there is more than one way to interpret subtraction and division, that multiplication has to do with equal groups, that adding has to do with combining or totaling, not necessarily always yielding a larger answer.

2. Answers will vary. Look for an understanding that addition and subtraction are inverse operations, as are multiplication and division. Another way to say this is that you can check your answer by doing the inverse operation. Students might point out that you can add up or subtract back to get an answer to a division problem. They may know other ways to solve multiplication problems that involve adding or rounding and subtracting.

Task 5: Four Problems

1. 646. Sample solution:
$(490 + 1) + (50 - 2) + (100 + 7) = (490 + 50 + 100) + (1 - 2 + 7) = 640 + 6 = 646$

2. 1,908. Sample solution:
$2,005 - 100 + 3 = 1,905 + 3 = 1,908$

3. 1,400. Sample solution:
$(50 + 6) \times 25 = 50(25) + 6(25) = 1,250 + 150 = 1,400$

4. 32. Sample solution:
$23 \times 10 = 230$, $23 \times 30 = 690$, $2 \times 23 = 46$, so there are <u>32</u> 23's in 736.

Sources and Resources

Mathematics Education

The National Council of Teachers of Mathematics (NCTM) publishes several excellent resources.

- *Principles to Actions - Ensuring Mathematical Success for All, 2014.*
- *Principles and Standards for School Mathematics,* 2000.
- The NCTM journals: *Mathematics Teaching in the Middle School, Mathematics Teacher, Mathematics Teacher Educator,* and *Journal for Research in Mathematics Education.*
- *Developing Number Sense in the Middle Grades, The Addenda Series, Grades 5–8,* 1991.
- *Historical Topics for the Mathematics Classroom,* 1989.

For more information on NCTM resources, visit http://www.nctm.org

Boaler, J. *What's Math Got to Do With It?* New York, NY: Penguin Books, 2015.

Boaler, J. "Memorizers Are the Lowest Achievers and Other Common Core Math Surprises." *The Hechinger Newsletter.* The Hechinger Report. 7 May 2015. <http://hechingerreport.org/memorizers-are-the-lowest-achievers-and-other-common-core-math-surprises>

Burns, M. "Introducing Multiplication of Fractions: A Lesson for Fifth and Sixth Graders." *Math Solutions Newsletter.* Math Solutions. Issue 12, Winter 2003-2004. <http://www.mathsolutions.com/documents/0-941355-64-0_L.pdf>

Cengiz, N., and M. Rathouz. "Take a Bite out of Fraction Division." *Mathematics Teaching in the Middle School* 17.3 (2011): 146-53.

Clarke, D., A. Roche, and A. Mitchell. "10 Practical Tips for Making Fractions Come Alive and Make Sense." *Mathematics Teaching in the Middle School.* 13. 7 (2008): 372-80.

Driscoll, M. *Fostering Algebraic Thinking: A Guide for Teachers,* Grades 6-10. Portsmouth, NH: Heinemann, 1999.

Driscoll, M. *The Fostering Algebraic Thinking Toolkit* Portsmouth, NH: Heinemann, 2001.

Fendel, D., D. Resek, L. Alper, & S. Fraser. *Interactive Mathematics Program.* Berkeley, CA: Key Curriculum Press, 1997.

Gregg, J., and D. Gregg. "Measurement and Fair-Sharing Models for Dividing Fractions." *Mathematics Teaching in the Middle School* 12.9 (2007): 490-96.

Ginsburg, L., M. Manly, & M. J. Schmitt. "The Components of Numeracy." *NCSALL Occasional Paper.* Boston, MA: National Center for the Study of Adult Learning and Literacy (NCSALL), 2006. Available from: <www.ncsall.net/fileadmin/resources/research/op_numeracy.pdf>.

Huinker, D. "Examining Dimensions of Fraction Operation Sense." *Making Sense of Fractions, Ratios, and Proportions, 64th Yearbook.* Eds. George Bright and Bonnie Litwiller. Reston, VA: NCTM, (2002) 72-78.

Lappan, G., J. Fey, W. Fitzgerald, S. Friel, & E. Phillips. *Connected Mathematics Series.* Parsippany, NJ: Dale Seymour Publications, Division of Pearson Education, 1998.

Markovitz, Z. and J.T. Sowder. "Students' understanding of the relationship between fractions and decimals." *Focus on Learning Problems in Mathematics* 13.1 (1991): 3–11.

Morrison, P., and P. Morrison. *Powers of Ten.* New York: Scientific American Library, 1994.

Moschkovich, J. *Mathematics, the Common Core, and Language: Recommendations for Mathematics Instruction for ELs Aligned with the Common Core.* 2012. <http://ell.stanford.edu/sites/default/files/pdf/academic-papers/02-JMoschkovich%20Math%20FINAL_bound%20with%20appendix.pdf>.

National Research Council. *Adding It Up: Helping Children Learn Mathematics.* J. Kilpatrick, J. Swafford, and B. Findell (Eds.). Mathematics Learning Study Committee, Center for Education, Division of Behavioral and Social Sciences and Education. Washington, DC: National Academy Press, 2001.

Rasmussen, S. *Key to Fractions*. Columbus, OH: McGraw-Hill Education, 1993.

Reys, B.J. "Teaching Computational Estimation: Concepts and Strategies." *Estimation & Mental Computation-1986 Yearbook*. Eds. Harold L. Schoen and Marilyn J. Zweng. Reston, VA: NCTM, 1986. 31-44.

Reys, B.J., O. Kim, and J. M. Bay. "Establishing Fraction Benchmarks." *Mathematics Teaching in the Middle School* 4.8 (1999): 530-32.

Russell, S.J., K. Economopoulos, L. Wittenberg, et al. *Investigations in Number, Data, and Space ®, Second Edition*. Glenview, IL: Pearson, 2012.

Russell, S.J., D. Schifter, and V. Bastable. *Connecting Arithmetic to Algebra: Strategies for Building Algebraic Thinking in the Elementary Grades*. Portsmouth, NH: Heinemann, 2001.

Schifter, D. "Examining the Behavior of Operations: On Noticing Early Algebraic Ideas." *Mathematics Teacher Noticing: Seeing through Teachers' Eyes*. Eds. Myriam Sherin, Vicki Jacobs and Randy Philipp. New York: Routledge, 2010. 204-20.

Seeley, C.L. *Smarter Than We Think - More Messages About Math, Teaching, and Learning in the 21st Century*. Sausalito, CA: Math Solutions, 2014.

Siegler, R., T. Carpenter, F. Fennell, D. Geary, J. Lewis, Y. Okamoto, L. Thompson, and J. Wray. *Developing Effective Fractions Instruction for Kindergarten through 8th Grade: A Practice Guide* (NCEE #2010-4039). Washington, DC: National Center for Education Evaluation and Regional Assistance, Institute of Education Sciences, U.S. Department of Education, 2010. < http://ies.ed.gov/ncee/wwc/pdf/practice_guides/fractions_pg_093010.pdf>.

Storeygard, J. *My Kids Can: Making Math Accessible to All Learners, K-5*. Portsmouth, OR: Heinemann, 2007.

Van de Walle, J., K. Karp, J. Bay-Williams. *Elementary and Middle School Mathematics: Teaching Developmentally*. 8th Edition. New York: Pearson, 2012.

Mathematics and Numeracy Education for Adults

Burns, M. *Math, Facing an American Phobia*. White Plains, NY: Math Solutions Publications, 1998.

Curry, D., M.J. Schmitt, and S. Waldron. *A Framework for Adult Numeracy Standards: The Mathematical Skills and Abilities Adults Need to Be Equipped for the Future*. Boston: World Education, 1996. < http://shell04.theworld.com/std/anpn/framewk.html>. (This framework was developed by members of the Adult Numeracy Network.) <http://shell04.the world.com/std/anpn>.

Givvin, K. B., J. W. Stigler, and B. J. Thompson. "What Community College Developmental Mathematics Students Understand About Mathematics, Part 2: The Interviews." *MathAMATYC Educator 2.3* (2011): 4-18.

Massachusetts Department of Education, Adult and Community Learning Services. *Massachusetts Adult Basic Education Curriculum Frameworks for Mathematics and Numeracy*. Malden, MA: Massachusetts Department of Education, 2005. <http://www.doe.mass.edu/acls/frameworks/mathnum.pdf>.

National Center on Education and the Economy. *What Does It Really Mean to Be College and Work Ready?* Washington, DC: 2013. <http://www.ncee.org/wp-content/uploads/2013/05/NCEE_ExecutiveSummary_May2013.pdf>.

Northcote, M., and M. McIntosh. What Mathematics Do Adults Really Do in Everyday Life? *Australian Primary Mathematics Classroom*, 4(1), 1999.

Stein, S. *Equipped for the Future Content Standards: What Adults Need to Know and Be Able to Do in the Twenty-First Century*. ED Pubs document EX0099P. Washington, DC: National Institute for Literacy, 2000.

Stigler, J. W., K. B. Givvin, and B. J. Thompson. "What Community College Developmental Mathematics Students Understand About Mathematics." *MathAMATYC Educator 1.3* (2010): 4-16.

Tobias, S. *Overcoming Math Anxiety: Revised and Expanded*. New York: W.W. Norton & Company, 1994.

Zaslavsky, C. *Fear of Math: How to Get over It and Get on with Your Life*. Piscataway, NJ: Rutgers University Press, 1996.

Web Sites

http://www.funbrain.com/fract/

http://www.kidsolr.com/math/fractions.html

http://www.mcwdn.org/FRACTIONS/Equivalents.html

http://math.rice.edu/~lanius/Patterns/